STARS AND STELLAR SYSTEMS

Compendium of Astronomy and Astrophysics

(IN NINE VOLUMES)

GERARD P. KUIPER, *General Editor*

BARBARA M. MIDDLEHURST, *Associate General Editor*

CONTRIBUTORS

W. W. BAUSTIAN

JOHN G. BOLTON

IRA S. BOWEN

ANDRÉ DANJON

F. D. DRAKE

GEOFFREY KELLER

GERARD P. KUIPER

R. R. McMATH

WILLIAM MARKOWITZ

A. B. MEINEL

BARBARA M. MIDDLEHURST

O. C. MOHLER

JURGEN STOCK

C. B. WATTS

TELESCOPES

Edited by

GERARD P. KUIPER

and

BARBARA M. MIDDLEHURST

THE UNIVERSITY OF CHICAGO PRESS

CHICAGO & LONDON

Library of Congress Catalog Card Number: 60-14356

THE UNIVERSITY OF CHICAGO PRESS, CHICAGO 60637
The University of Chicago Press, Ltd., London W.C. 1

Preface to the Series

THE series "Stars and Stellar Systems, Compendium of Astronomy," comprising nine volumes, was organized in consultation with senior astronomers in the United States and abroad early in 1955. It was intended as an extension of the four-volume "Solar System" series to cover astrophysics and stellar astronomy. In contrast to the "Solar System" series, separate editors have been appointed for each volume. The volume editors, together with the general editors, form the editorial board that is responsible for the over-all planning of the series.

The aim of the series is to present stellar astronomy and astrophysics as basically empirical sciences, co-ordinated and illuminated by the application of theory. To this end the series opens with a description of representative telescopes, both optical and radio (Vol. 1), and of accessories, techniques, and methods of reduction (Vol. 2). The chief classes of observational data are described in Volume 3, with additional material being referred to in succeeding volumes, as the topics may require. The systematic treatment of astronomical problems starts with Volume 4, as is apparent from the volume titles. Theoretical chapters are added where needed, on dynamical problems in Volumes 4, 5, and 9, and on astrophysical problems in Volumes 6, 7, and 8. In order that the chapters may retain a greater degree of permanence, the more speculative parts of astronomy have been de-emphasized. The level of the chapters will make them suitable for graduate students as well as for professional astronomers and also for the increasing number of scientists in other fields requiring astronomical information.

The undersigned wish to thank both the authors and the volume editors for their readiness to collaborate on this series, which it is hoped will stimulate the further growth of astronomy.

The editors wish to acknowledge the support by the National Science Foundation both in defraying part of the costs of the editorial offices and in providing a publication subsidy.

GERARD P. KUIPER
BARBARA M. MIDDLEHURST

Preface to Volume 1

A_T A time when the results of astronomical research are of interest to an increasingly wide audience, it is regarded as proper to include in a review series on astronomy a rather full description of the principal research tools. These—the telescopes and their accessories—often require years of construction and development, and they have in large measure directed and shaped the progress of the science.

Astronomical telescopes are of three kinds, according to their uses, and a fourth type is under rapid development. Reflectors and, to a lesser extent, refractors are used to record and analyze astronomical phenomena at optical wave lengths. Radio telescopes, of a wide variety of design and aperture, do the same at radio frequencies. Position-measuring devices obtain the basic data for a geometric and dynamic description of the universe. Each of these three classes is described in this volume in two or more chapters. Space telescopes have at present not yet attained the full development that would justify their inclusion in this reference work.

The performances and productivity of a large optical telescope are significantly affected by its location, a fact that has not always been sufficiently appreciated. Two chapters are devoted to the subject of atmospheric seeing and scintillation and other factors affecting the quality of an observatory site. The volume is concluded by a list of the major optical telescopes in current use for research. The major radio telescopes are listed and described in chapter 11.

As the title *Stars and Stellar Systems* implies, the emphasis throughout the series is on the study of objects outside the solar system. Solar telescopes, both radio and optical, which are fully treated in *The Sun*, Volume I of *The Solar System*, are therefore outside the scope of the present volume.

The editors wish to acknowledge the courtesy and patience of the authors who have collaborated on this volume. Thanks are due also for the assistance given by Dr. Leo Randić and the careful typographic work done by Mrs. M. Richmond, Mrs. N. Stephan, Miss L. Schott, and Miss G. Moeller.

GERARD P. KUIPER

BARBARA M. MIDDLEHURST

Table of Contents

12. RADIO-ASTRONOMY RADIOMETERS AND THEIR CALIBRATION 210

F. D. Drake

CHAPTER 1

The 200-Inch Hale Telescope

I. S. BOWEN

Director, Mount Wilson and Palomar Observatories
Carnegie Institution of Washington, California Institute of Technology

INTRODUCTION

THE funds for the construction of the 200-inch Hale telescope and the other equipment of the Palomar Observatory were promised in 1928 by the International Education Board. Later, part of this commitment was assumed by the General Education Board. After World War II the original grant of $6,000,000 was supplemented by the Rockefeller Foundation with additional grants totaling $550,000 to cover increased costs of construction.

After delays of several years caused by the war, the construction of the telescope and dome and the figuring of the mirror had reached a stage when the mirror could be moved to the mountain on November 19, 1947. After aluminizing, the mirror was placed in the telescope, and the first visual tests were made on December 21 and the first Hartmann tests on the next night. A long series of tests, adjustments, and minor modifications, including a small amount of refiguring, followed. While a few direct plates had been taken in the spring of 1949, the first regularly scheduled use of the telescope started on November 12, 1949. Systematic spectroscopic observations began in November, 1950, although cameras for all dispersions were not available until 1952.

A very large number of astronomers, engineers, and consultants participated in the design and construction of the instrument. As chairmen of the Observatory Council, Dr. George E. Hale and later Dr. Max Mason were in general charge of the project. The executive officer, Dr. J. A. Anderson, supervised construction and was in immediate charge of all optical work. Major contributions to detailed design and construction were made by Dr. Francis G. Pease, Dr. Sinclair Smith, Dr. John Strong, Captain Clyde McDowell, Russell Porter, Mark Serrurier, Bruce Rule, Byron Hill, and Edward Poitras. Substantial assistance was also given by a host of consultants, including engineers at companies such as the Corning Glass Works and the Westinghouse Electric and Manufacturing Company, which supplied major parts of the telescope.

1. OPTICS

The main mirror has a diameter of 200 inches and has a 40-inch hole in the center. It is ground and polished in the form of a paraboloid of 660-inch focal length; thus the focal ratio is $F3.3$. Practically all direct photographs are taken at the prime focus. Since, however, the diameter of the field of good definition of a paraboloid of this focal ratio is less than $\frac{1}{2}$ inch, a corrector lens is normally introduced in front of the plate to extend this field. By introducing a small telephoto effect into such a lens, it is also possible to change the effective focal length of the system. Several of these lenses have been designed by Dr. F. E. Ross. The two most commonly used give focal ratios of $F3.6$ and $F4.7$ and provide a well-corrected field about 3 inches in diameter.

Three hyperboloid mirrors are permanently mounted in the cage below the prime focus, where they can be quickly moved into the optical beam. One of these yields a focal length of 3200 inches or a focal ratio of $F16$. The light from this mirror passes through the hole in the center of the main mirror and forms an image about 5 feet back of the front surface of this mirror. It can also be reflected along the declination axis by a plane mirror to form an image in the east side arm of the yoke. The other two hyperboloids give a focal length of about 6000 inches and a focal ratio of $F30$ and are both used to form an image at the coudé focus on the polar axis just below the south polar bearing. One of these is used for objects lying south of declination $+43°$, for which one reflection by a plane mirror placed at the intersection of the polar axis and the optic axis of the main mirror is sufficient to direct the light down the polar axis. The other hyperboloid is used for objects located north of declination $+43°$, in which case three flat mirrors are required to reflect the light around the primary mirror and on down the polar axis.

The flat at the intersection of the optic and polar axes is mounted on a tube 36-inches in diameter extending up through the hole in the main mirror. When not in use, the mirror can be picked up by a special crane and moved to a covered housing at the side of the telescope tube. The second flat is mounted on an arch that can be turned out to intercept the light from the first flat. The third small flat is mounted on the polar axis near the upper end of the hollow south polar bearing, where it reflects the light from the second flat down the polar axis. It can be quickly moved off the axis when the single flat arrangement is used. These mirrors are shown in Plate I.

All mirrors have a ribbed structure and are cast in flame Pyrex, which has a coefficient of thermal expansion of $0.0000023/°$ C. Plate II shows this structure in the 200-inch disk. The front face and all ribs have a thickness of 3–5 inches. This provides a much lighter structure, as well as increasing manyfold the rate at which the mirror comes to thermal equilibrium with its surroundings. The main mirror has an over-all thickness of 24 inches at the edge and a finished weight of 29,000 pounds.

At best, a mirror of this size is very flexible, and an elaborate support system is required to prevent flexure under its own weight. The mirror is mounted on thirty-six support mechanisms of the type shown in Plate III, one being inserted in each of the thirty-six holes shown in Plate II. The support band, B, which makes contact with the mirror, is placed in a plane normal to the optic axis through the center of gravity of the mirror. As the telescope is turned away from the zenith, the lower end of the support system, including the weights, W, attempts to swing about the gimbals, G_1, and thereby exerts a force on the band B through the gimbals G_2 in a direction normal to the optic axis. The weights and lever arms are so adjusted that the force exerted just balances the component in the opposite direction of the pull of gravity on the section of the mirror assigned to this support. Likewise, the weights W pivot about bearings, P, in such a way as to exert a force along the rod, R, which is transmitted to the ring, S, by the gimbals G_2. These weights and lever arms are likewise adjusted so that the force exerted balances the component parallel to the optic axis of the pull of gravity on this same section of the mirror. The mirror is therefore floating on these support systems, and no forces are transmitted across the mirror.

To define the orientation of the optic axis of the mirror and the position of the mirror for translation parallel to the optic axis, three of the weights located at 120° intervals in the outer ring of supports are locked in a fixed position. For translation perpendicular to the optic axis, the mirror is defined by four pins which are mounted on the tube which extends up through the central hole in the mirror to support the coudé flat. These pins bear on the inside of the 40-inch hole in the mirror. They are constructed of materials to compensate for differences in the thermal expansion of Pyrex and steel and operate through ball bearings to eliminate the transmission of forces parallel to the axis.

The mirror was cast at the Corning Glass Works. After it arrived in Pasadena, the holes for the support systems were roughed out to the proper size. The mirror was then mounted on the support systems, and further work, including all optical tests, was carried out with the mirror mounted on the final supports. All the optical work to the point of obtaining a preliminary figure was done in a carefully thermostated optical shop in Pasadena by Marcus Brown and his assistants.

Optical tests in Pasadena were made with a Hartmann screen, and a knife-edge and illuminated pinhole placed near the center of curvature. Pinhole and knife-edge were moved together along the axis until the simultaneous cutoff of two holes of the Hartmann screen, placed symmetrically with respect to the optic axis, indicated the position of the center of curvature for the zone defined by the two holes. Just prior to moving the mirror to the mountain, these results were checked photographically by a modification of a method developed by Gaviola. By this procedure a fixed pinhole is placed on the axis at the center of curvature for central rays. Before each exposure the photographic plate is moved backward by an accurately known amount to the point on the caustic where the rays from the pair of holes to be studied are in focus. The relative separations between the pairs of images obtained from the successive exposures give an accurate definition of the surface.

In the course of the laboratory tests, all of which were, of necessity, done with the optic axis nearly horizontal, a persistent astigmatism developed, in which the shorter radius of curvature always remained vertical even when the mirror was rotated about its optic axis. A careful analysis showed that this was caused by the application of the supporting force, normal to the optic axis, to the center of the top of each glass ring in which the support is inserted. This tends to deform the ring into an ellipse with its long axis vertical. Since the stiffening members of the rear of the mirror are attached to these glass rings, this in turn tends to bend the mirror in such a way as to give the observed astigmatism.

This astigmatism was corrected by the addition of twelve "squeeze" levers placed at 30° intervals about the edge of the mirror. Each of these lever systems consists of a weight mounted on a double-acting lever so designed that it squeezes the rear edge of the mirror with a force proportional to the sine of the angle that the normal to the surface of the edge of the mirror at the squeeze lever makes with the horizontal.

As soon as the mirror was placed in the telescope, a very extensive series of Hartmann tests was carried out, using a full-size Hartmann screen mounted on the upper end of the telescope. All tests were made under average or above-average seeing conditions with a star as the source. Stars were selected to permit exposures in the 20–80-second range, as exposures of this length average out any effect of seeing on the position of the Hartmann images but are short enough that guiding is not required. For the earlier tests a Hartmann screen having one hundred and twenty 3-inch holes arranged at 6 inches between centers along six diameters was used. Later, for detailed studies during local figuring, four hundred holes on twenty diameters were used.

This detailed study of the behavior of the mirror at various zenith angles and in some cases with the deliberate introduction of small deforming forces showed that the mirror was more flexible than had been anticipated. Quantitatively, the flexure of the mirror under its own weight was found to be the equivalent of a 200-inch solid mirror between 14 and 15 inches thick. This flexibility of the mirror apparently arises because the stiffening ribs are interrupted by the circles in which the support systems are mounted. In general, such circles are much less rigid against forces of compression or tension than a continuous bar would be. This weakness was further aggravated because, in order to mount the support systems properly, it was found necessary to grind out the holes to a larger diameter than originally planned. This left the walls of the circles with a thickness of 3 inches instead of the 4 inches called for in the original design.

Simple calculations soon showed that if the deformation of the mirror was to be held within permissible limits, the component of the force parallel to the optic axis, i.e., normal to the mirror surface, must be correct to an accuracy of 0.1–0.2 per cent of the total force applied by the support system. On the other hand, measurements showed that the friction of the support system was over 1 per cent of the force applied. However, a redesign and rebuilding of the lower part of the support system in the summer of 1948 in which the simple lever of Plate III was replaced with a compound lever system with greatly lengthened lever arms reduced the friction to about 0.1 per cent. After the modification of the support system, further Hartmann tests showed that the mirror retained its shape in all positions within satisfactory limits.

The final tests in Pasadena had shown that the outer 10–20 inches of the mirror were high by amounts ranging up to one wave length. However, these tests were all made with the optic axis horizontal, and, since the mirror edge extends by 10–20 inches beyond the outer ring of supports, it was feared that this outer edge might droop by nearly this amount when the optic axis became vertical. This high edge was therefore not removed until after tests on the mountain.

By the spring of 1949 these tests had shown that the edge remained high in all orientations of the telescope. Furthermore, the more elaborate tests possible on the mountain revealed certain other small irregularities on the surface. Preparations were therefore made to refigure the surface of the mirror on the basis of tests made in the telescope. These included Hartmann photographs using the Hartmann screen with the full four hundred holes on twenty diameters plus knife-edge photographs for interpolation between diameters. Knife-edge patterns were photographed with a Leica camera with a 2-inch-focus lens placed immediately behind the knife-edge using exposures in the 20–80-second range. In general, a series of thirty-two photographs was taken for each test. Four photographs were obtained for each direction of approach of the knife-edge with increasing amounts of cutoff of the image. Eight directions of approach of the knife-edge were photographed, spaced at intervals of 45°. Figuring was carried out by Don Hendrix with a small polishing machine. This was mounted on a carriage which was pivoted at the center of the mirror and whose outer end rode on the edge of the mirror.

After the final figuring was completed, a further series of Hartmann tests was run to evaluate under actual operating conditions the performance of the mirror as finally figured. Table 1 lists the results of all tests except for a few in which the mirror was deliberately subjected to thermal shock in order to test the effect of the mirror insulation. The second column lists the usual Hartmann constant for the mirror. The last three columns list, what is probably more significant, the fraction of the light concentrated within images of various diameters expressed in microns on the plate and in seconds of arc. From this an estimate can be made of the amount of light lost from the image under various seeing conditions.

During the fall of 1949 and winter of 1950 extensive studies were made of the effect of sudden temperature changes on the figure of the mirror. In general, with any large mirror, if a sudden change in the ambient temperature occurs, a period of many hours must elapse before all parts of the mirror reach the new temperature. Furthermore, because of the low thermal conductivity of glass, large temperature differences must exist in the glass during this period. This causes a distortion of the mirror, which may result in poor images. If the temperature of the mirror is a function of the depth behind the front surface only, the main effect is a change in focus without deterioration of image. On the other hand, if there is also a variation in temperature with distance from the optic axis, a more complicated situation arises, and serious deterioration of the image occurs.

TABLE 1

FINAL OPTICAL TESTS OF THE 200-INCH MIRROR

DATE	HARTMANN CONSTANT	PERCENTAGE OF LIGHT WITHIN CIRCLE OF DIAMETER		
		25 μ 0ʺ3	50 μ 0ʺ6	100 μ 1ʺ2
Dec. 28, 1949.........	0.18	53	83	99
Dec. 30, 1949.........	.17	57	87	100
Jan. 26, 1950.........	.34	27	49	88
Jan. 27, 1950.........	.19	46	80	99
Feb. 23, 1950.........	.21	50	74	98
Feb. 24, 1950.........	0.19	53	82	96

These general conclusions were confirmed by the tests. Thus, following a sudden drop in temperature, a section of the mirror around its outer edge always turned down. Since, as originally installed, air could circulate freely about the outer edge of the mirror, the outer band of glass cooled off much faster than did the center part of the mirror. As this outer band is a continuous band, it is very rigid. Furthermore, as explained earlier, the rear part of the mirror is relatively weak compared with the solid front surface. Consequently, when this outer band contracts, it is able to compress the rear part much more than the front, thereby pulling down the outer edge. The experiment was then tried of insulating the outer and rear surfaces of this glass band around the outside of the mirror with several layers of aluminum foil inclosed in envelopes of heavy waterproof paper. This resulted in the elimination of most of the distortion of the outer band during thermal changes.

Other distortions due to thermal effects arise from the difference in exposure of the front and rear faces of the mirror, with a resultant difference in the rate of reaching equilibrium with the new ambient temperature. Thus the front surface is always exposed to ambient air during operation; on the other hand, the rear surface is separated by only about an inch from the heavy front plate of the steel structure, weighing over 15 tons, on which the mirror support systems are mounted. This steel structure itself requires many hours to reach a new ambient temperature. During this period the rear surface is exposed not to ambient temperature but to temperature which is slowly changing from the original to the new one. The rate of heat flow from the front and rear surfaces is further complicated by the fact that, since the front surface is aluminized, heat transfer can take place by convection only, while both convection and radiation play nearly equal roles in the flow of heat from the rear surface.

Experiments showed, however, that the figure of the mirror, following large temperature changes, could be materially improved by bringing the temperature of the steel structure behind the mirror about halfway to the new ambient temperature as rapidly as possible. This roughly equalizes the rate of heat flow from the front and rear surfaces of the mirror. The cooling of the supporting steel structure is accomplished by twelve fans which are mounted to circulate large volumes of air through the cell structure. The operating procedure is to run these fans for from 1 to 2 hours as soon as the dome is opened on all occasions in which a major temperature change has occurred since the preceding night.

2. TELESCOPE TUBE

As discussed under "Optics," it is necessary to combine a Ross correcting lens with the main mirror in order to obtain a large field of good definition. For proper functioning of this lens, precise collimation must be maintained between the axis of the main mirror and that of the corrector lens. Since the mirror and corrector lens are located at opposite ends of the 55-foot-long telescope tube, this in turn imposes very stringent conditions on the permissible flexure of the tube as it moves into all possible orientations.

Preliminary calculations showed that it would be impractical to hold the absolute amount of flexure below the permissible tolerances. However, the adoption of the parallelogram-type of design for the tube shown in Plate I insured that no rotation of either the mirror or the cage, in which the corrector lens is mounted, occurs with respect to the axis of the tube. Furthermore, by careful balancing of the deflection of the cage and mirror ends of the tube, the two ends of the tube always move by the same amount, thereby maintaining in all telescope positions the proper relationships of corrector lens to mirror. Tests made after the mirror was installed in the telescope showed that in no orientation of the telescope does the intersection of the optic axis of the 200-inch mirror with the corrector lens depart from its mean intersection point by more than 0.01 inch. This is well within the permissible limits for satisfactory operation of the corrector lens.

The mirror-support systems described earlier are mounted on a heavy structure which completely closes the lower end of the telescope tube. This is a welded-steel structure consisting of two circular 1-inch steel plates somewhat larger than the mirror, separated by 24 inches and strengthened by a series of perpendicular ribs between them, as well as by circular rings at the center hole and around the outer edge. The upper plate is solid except for the thirty-six holes through which the support systems pass. The lower plate has a series of large access holes through which the support systems can be adjusted and serviced (Pl. IV).

When the mirror is aluminized, the mirror, its support systems, and this plate on which the support systems are mounted are all removed from the telescope together and placed in the aluminizing tank. While in the tank, a neoprene sheet bears on the outside of the mirror and seals off grease vapors from the support systems from reaching the upper part of the tank where the actual aluminizing process takes place.

When not in use, the mirror is protected by the cover shown in Plate IV. This is of very heavy construction designed to give protection even though a heavy object should accidentally fall on it. The cover may be stopped in partially opened positions and then serves as an iris diaphragm, permitting the use of apertures between 80 and 200 inches.

3. OBSERVER'S CAGE

The Hale telescope is the first telescope that is so large that a cage for the observer may be placed directly at the prime focus without intercepting appreciably more light from the incoming beam than would be cut off by a Newtonian mirror.

As constructed, the cage is 72 inches in diameter and is centered on the optic axis. It consists of two parts which are supported independently by separate sets of radial knife-edges from the telescope tube (see Pl. V). The lower part carries all optical parts, including the secondary mirrors for the coudé and Cassegrain foci, while the upper part is the working space for the observer.

The prime focus is located about 30 inches above the floor of the upper section of the cage. Around it is a pedestal which is supported on the lower part of the cage and which provides for the mounting of plateholders, photometers, small spectrographs, and guide eyepieces. The whole pedestal may be focused manually by the observer or by the motorized equipment for focusing the secondary mirrors. The observer's seat revolves about the optic axis and also about an axis perpendicular to this through the prime focus. For the greatest comfort in observing, the seat is normally maintained underneath the prime focus (see Pl. VI). The observer may reach the cage in any position of the telescope by riding up on the prime-focus elevator. This elevator follows a curved track, so that it passes the cage at a distance of about 10 inches in all positions of the telescope. When the prime focus is in use, all secondary mirrors are carried near the side of the cage. When other foci are required, the appropriate mirror is tipped forward to the operating position by remote motorized control (see Pl. VII). At the same time, the telescope counterweights are automatically shifted to maintain the telescope balance.

LIGHT PATH TO PRIME FOCUS $f\,3.3$
CASSEGRAIN $f\,16$
COUDÉ $f\,30$

APPROXIMATE SCALE

R. W. PORTER

PLATE I.—The telescope

PLATE II.—The mirror

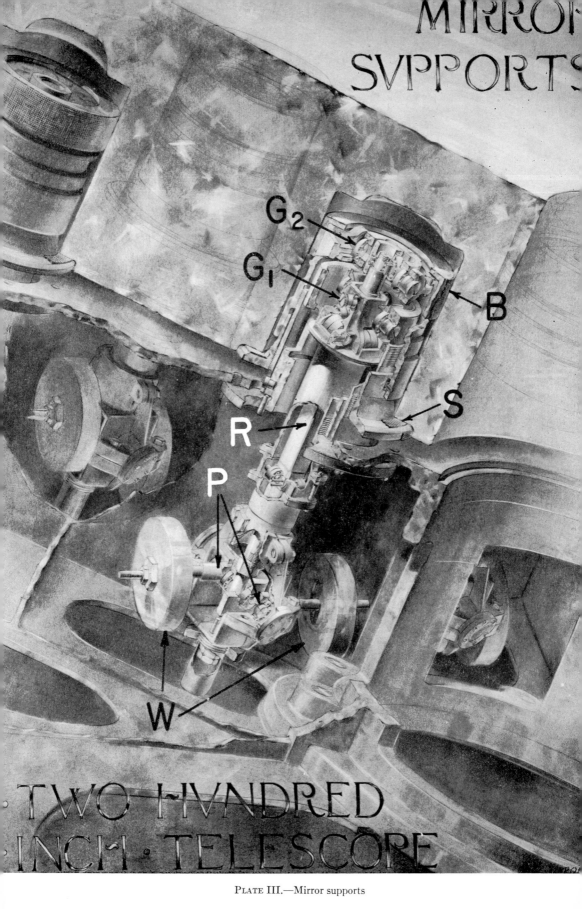

PLATE III.—Mirror supports

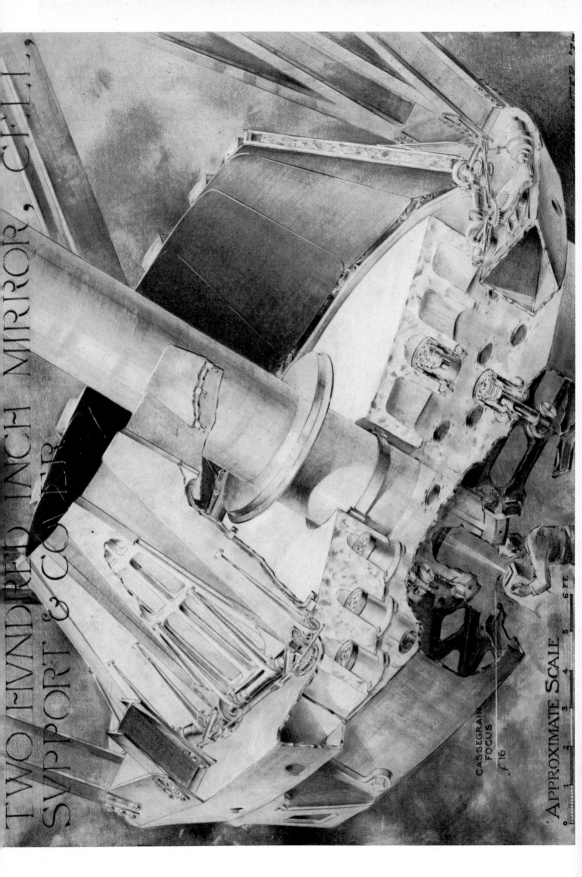

TWO HUNDRED INCH MIRROR, CELL,
SUPPORT & COVER

CASSEGRAIN
FOCUS
f 16

APPROXIMATE SCALE

0   1   2   3   4   5   6 FT

· THE · PRIME · FOCVS ·

PLATE V.—The prime focus

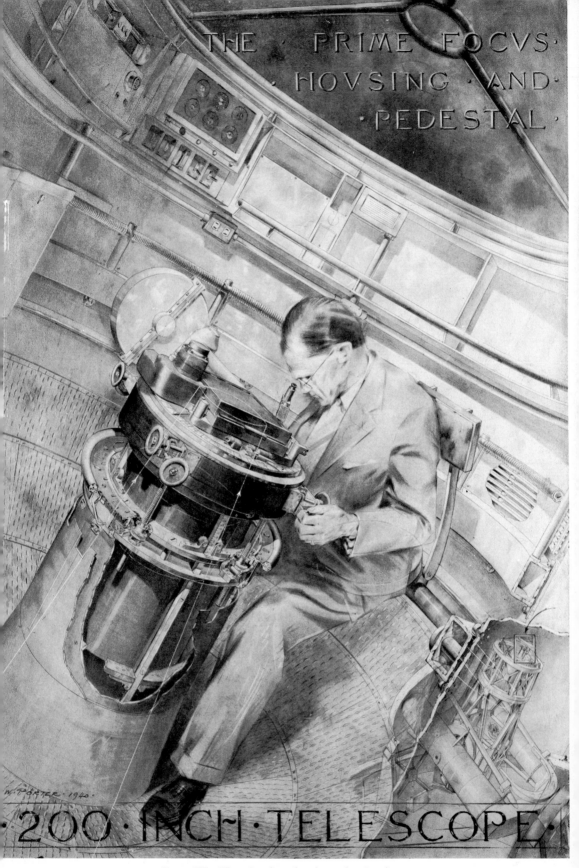

PLATE VI.—The prime-focus housing and pedestal

PLATE VII.—The prime focus, Cassegrain and coudé mirrors

PLATE VIII.—The telescope, looking northwest

PLATE IX.—North polar axis, bearing, horseshoe, and oil pads

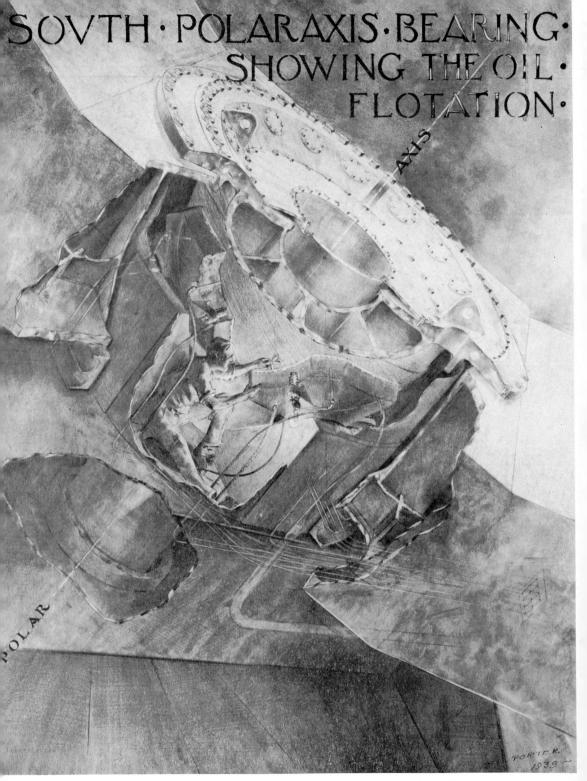

PLATE X.—South polar-axis bearing, showing the oil flotation

CUTAWAY DRAWING OF DECLINATION TRUNNION, 200 INCH TELESCOPE.

Plate XI.—Cutaway drawing of declination trunnion

PLATE XII.—Right-ascension drive and computer

PLATE XIII.—Main control desk

4. YOKE

The diameter and weight of the tube (140 tons) are so great as to render many of the conventional methods of mounting impracticable. Thus the reduction of flexure in a fork mounting requires a mass that would not be feasible. Likewise, the size of the counterbalances and the flexure introduced in the tube itself by the non-symmetrical support rule out an off-axis English mount. Furthermore, all concerned were very loath to sacrifice access to the region around the pole required by a mount similar to the Mount Wilson 100-inch.

The mount finally adopted retained the two polar bearings, one south and the other north of the tube of the 100-inch. The north bearing is of horseshoe shape and is so large (46 feet in diameter) that the telescope can be turned down into it to reach the pole (see Pls. I and VIII). This solution, however, raised other problems. One of these was the reduction of friction to a reasonable value in a bearing of such a large diameter. The total mass carried on the polar axis is about 530 tons, and it was estimated that a total torque of 22,000 pound-feet would have been required had roller bearings been adopted. Not only would this have caused serious problems in providing the necessary power at precisely controlled frequencies, but any fluctuations in the friction would have caused positional errors because of variation in the elastic distortion of the drive mechanism. The final solution was obtained through the use of oil pads. Both the cylindrical north bearing and the spherical south bearing are carefully machined and rest on pads which are accurately machined to match. Into the space between, oil is pumped at a pressure of about 300 pounds per square inch. This raises the moving part of the bearing about 0.003 inch and leaves it floating on a thin film of oil. The measured torque required to turn the telescope when tracking at the sidereal rate is 50 pound-feet.

One other problem was raised by the use of oil pads, namely, the necessity of maintaining an accurate fit between the fixed oil pad and the moving bearing in all positions. This was rendered difficult by the rather large distortion of the horseshoe at large hour angles. A solution was found by deforming the horseshoe during the machining of the outer bearing surface. On relieving the deforming forces, the outer surface was no longer a true circular cylinder. However, the amount of this deformation was so adjusted that when the telescope is far east or west, the horseshoe distorts into a circular cylinder. Plate IX shows two of the four oil pads for the north polar bearing, while Plate X shows the hemispherical south bearing with its oil pads.

In practice, the extremely low friction of the oil pads has caused certain difficulties. Thus the yoke is connected to the right-ascension drive gear by a torque tube 13 feet long and 3 feet in diameter. The natural period of vibration of the telescope and yoke due to the elasticity of this tube is about 1.4 seconds. A sudden motion of the observer in the cage or a gust of wind striking the tube may start the telescope in vibration with this period with an amplitude of up to about 1 second of arc. Because of the extremely low friction of the bearings, the vibration takes about 1 minute to damp to half-amplitude. This difficulty was corrected by introducing additional fluid friction by providing a $1\frac{1}{2}$-inch rubber-covered roller which bears on the outer surface of the horseshoe and which drives eleven disks 24 inches in diameter which are interspersed between twelve fixed disks, the whole being immersed in oil. This reduced the period required for damping to half-value to about 3 seconds. This additional friction is automatically disconnected when slewing the telescope.

The declination axis turns on ball bearings which are mounted on a flexible, bicycle-spoke type of support which prevents binding that otherwise might be caused by flexure of either telescope tube or yoke (see Pl. XI).

The fixed parts of both north and south oil-pad bearings are mounted on a single very heavy structure of steel girders which extends to ground level and maintains the bearings in their proper relationship. The footings of this structure are equipped with jack screws which can be adjusted to bring the polar axis of the telescope into alignment with the earth's axis (see Pl. I).

5. DRIVE AND CONTROL

The setting of the telescope is through the usual worm and worm-wheel drives on the declination and polar axes. On the polar axis two identical worms and worm wheels are provided. One is used for tracking at sidereal rate and the other for slewing the telescope from one object to another. This avoids excessive wear on the precision tracking worm and worm wheel. All worm wheels have 720 teeth and a diameter of 173 inches (see Pl. XII).

The co-ordinates of the position of the telescope are indicated on dials to which the information is transmitted through synchros. The use of synchros permits the combination of the hour-angle reading of the telescope with the sidereal time from a precision clock to provide dials reading right ascension directly, as well as the usual hour angle and declination. The main control desk and the prime and coudé observing positions are provided with dials reading declination and right ascension. In addition, the coudé position has dials reading hour angle. Three dials are required for each co-ordinate, the fine declination dial being graduated to 10 seconds of arc and the right-ascension and hour-angle dials to 1 second of time.

The sidereal-rate tracking mechanism was constructed to meet the specification that the accumulated error should not exceed 1 second of arc per hour and that local errors should not exceed 0.1 second of arc per 5 seconds. It was also specified that, within 45° of the zenith, setting errors should not exceed 5 seconds of arc in either declination or right ascension.

The mounting permits motion of the telescope in hour angle from 7h E. to 7h W. and in declination from −57° to +90°. Automatic stops cut off the power to the slewing motor when the telescope approaches within 5° of the horizon. Final limits are at 2° above the horizon. Three speeds are available for moving the telescope, namely, slewing at 45° per minute, setting at 40 seconds of arc per second, and guiding at 0.45 second of arc per second.

The primary time standard which gives the tracking rate is a Warren Telechron vibrating-string clock. The 60-cycle alternating current from this clock is amplified by a vacuum-tube power circuit to drive a $\frac{1}{12}$-horsepower synchronous motor which is geared to the polar-axis worm. In the Warren clock the basic tension in the string is provided by a large weight. This weight contains a permanent magnet, below which is mounted a solenoid. By sending a current through this solenoid, the tension and therefore the frequency may be varied by small amounts. Rheostats which control this current and meters which read the current, in terms of the rate change introduced in seconds of arc per hour, are located on the main control desk. Rates of drive departing from the sidereal rate by from $+30$ to -2700 seconds of arc per hour may be introduced in this manner. Provision is also made for driving the telescope in declination at rates of from 0 to 1000 seconds of arc per hour; control and indication of rate are at the main control desk. These provisions for driving the telescope with respect to a fixed object such as a star make it possible to correct for atmospheric refraction, to drift the image uniformly along a spectrograph slit in order to widen the spectrum, and to track differentially moving objects such as the moon or planets. The time standard which provides the sidereal time to be combined with the hour angle to give right ascension is also a Warren telechron vibrating-string clock operated at a fixed sidereal rate and is constant to 0.1 second per day. An automatic drive is provided for the coudé flat mirror which maintains its normal either midway between the optic axis of the main mirror and the polar axis or between the optic axis and the line to the second flat.

The main control desk is shown in Plate XIII. The upper sets of dials on the lower part of the desk are the three right-ascension and three declination dials which show the position of the telescope at all times. One procedure for setting the telescope is to hold down the appropriate slew and then set buttons until these dials read the desired position. Another procedure is to crank up the desired position on the lower set of dials and then push the "Execute" button. The telescope then automatically moves until the upper set of dials matches the lower set. In addition to the dials already mentioned, other dials read the aperture of the iris-diaphragm cover of the mirror, the positions of the motorized focus mechanism of the lower cage, the zenith angle of the telescope, etc.

Various additional safety features are provided to protect the telescope and operating personnel. Thus the thrust bearings of the telescope-drive worms are all friction-held. If the thrust exceeds a predetermined value, the bearing slips and, in so doing, cuts off the drive power and sounds a warning bell. Likewise, if the thickness of the oil in the oil pads drops below a certain minimum, a microswitch is tripped, and the power is cut off. Many telescope operations are interlocked in such a way that dangerous combinations cannot occur.

6. THE DOME

The dome has a diameter of 137 feet and a height of 135 feet. The outer skin of the dome is made up of butt-welded bumped steel plates $\frac{3}{8}$ inch thick and is stiffened by two main arches and an internal steel frame. Four feet inside this outer skin is an insulating layer consisting of 4-inch-thick steel and aluminum boxes filled with crumpled aluminum foil. The space between these two layers is vented at the top and bottom of the dome, thereby permitting air circulation to take away much of the heat absorbed by the outer skin when exposed to sunlight. This combination of air circulation and insulation reduces the inflow of heat during the day to so low a rate that at mirror level the rise above the temperature of the preceding night rarely exceeds 1° or 2° C.

The dome, which weighs 1000 tons, rotates on thirty-two four-wheel trucks rolling on two accurately ground circular tracks. It is driven by four five-horse-power motors through rubber-tired wheels bearing on a steel band near the bottom edge of the rotating part of the dome. The two dome shutters, 116 feet long, open to a width of 33 feet and are operated by three electrically synchronized motors on each side.

In addition to manual control, the dome rotation may also be operated by a mechanism which automatically holds the shutter opening in front of the telescope. This device involves a small "phantom" telescope which is held parallel to the main telescope at all times by synchros (see P, Pl. XII). Likewise, a dummy dome rotates over it and carries two long contacts which are held in positions parallel to the sides of the shutter opening. When the upper end of the phantom telescope touches one of these contacts, the proper circuits are activated to move the side of the shutter opening away from the telescope. The phantom telescope also provides the safety mechanism for de-energizing power circuits when the telescope comes within 5° of the horizon. By making contacts with a rheostat whose resistance varies with the zenith distance, the phantom telescope also provides a current which, when sent through appropriate meters on the main control desk, yields a direct reading of the zenith angle. This also provides an automatic control for holding the wind screen just below the telescope.

A 60-ton and a 5-ton crane are mounted within the dome for handling heavy parts.

7. AUXILIARY EQUIPMENT

Most of the direct photographs are taken at the prime focus, and plateholders and guide eyepieces, as well as Ross corrector lenses giving several effective focal ratios, are provided for this purpose. Equipment for photoelectric photometry is also normally mounted at this focus. This includes various photomultiplier tubes and their mounts and the necessary guide eyepieces, including offset equipment for setting on objects too faint to be seen visually. Much of the circuitry, including photon-counting equipment and current recorders, is at floor level.

A very fast spectrograph providing dispersions in the range from 85 to 750 A/mm is available for operation at the prime focus. The spectrograph for higher dispersions (2.3–38 A/mm) is located at the coudé focus. The optical details of these spectrographs are listed in chapter 10 of Volume 2.

The drawings used to illustrate this article were made by the late Russell W. Porter from the machine drawings prior to the construction of the telescope.

BIBLIOGRAPHY*

HALE, G. E.	1928	"The Possibilities of Large Telescopes," *Harper's Magazine*, **156**, 639.
ANON.	1928	"The Astrophysical Observatory of the California Institute of Technology," *Pub. A.S.P.*, **40**, 363.
HALE, G. E.	1929	"Building the 200-Inch Telescope," *Harper's Magazine*, **159**, 720.
ADAMS, W. S.	1929	"A Great Telescope and Its Possibilities," *Science*, **69**, 1.
HALE, G. E.	1934	"Deeper into Space," *Atlantic Monthly*, **153**, 463.
McCAULEY, G. V.	1934	"Making the Glass Disk for a 200-Inch Reflecting Telescope," *Scient. Monthly*, **39**, 79.
HALE, G. E.	1935	"The Astrophysical Observatory of the California Institute of Technology," *Ap. J.*, **82**, 111.
McCAULEY, G. V.	1935	"The 200-Inch Telescope Disc," *Trans. Soc. Glass Technol.*, **19**, 156.
	1935	"Some Engineering Problems Encountered in Making a 200-Inch Telescope Disc," *Bull. Amer. Ceramic Soc.*, **14**, 300.
HALE, GEORGE E.	1936	"The Astrophysical Observatory of the California Institute of Technology, The 200-Inch Reflector," *Nature* (London), **137**, 221.
	1936	"The 200-Inch Telescope," *Scient. American*, **154**, 236.
McDOWELL, CAPT. C. S., U.S.N.	1936	"The 200-Inch Telescope," *Mech. Engineering*, **58**, 345.
	1936	"As the 200-Inch Telescope Develops," *Scient. American*, **155**, 252.
McCAULEY, GEORGE V.	1936	"Cooling a 200-Inch Telescope Disc," *Elec. World*, **106**, 40 (No. 27).
ORMONDROYD, J.	1936	"Oil Pad Bearings Prove Effective for Massive Equipment," *Machine Design*, **8**, 37 (No. 12).

* Arranged chronologically.

STRONG, JOHN   1936   "The Evaporation Process and Its Application to
                                    the Aluminizing of Large Telescope Mirrors,"
                                    Ap. J., **83**, 401.

MCDOWELL, CAPT. C. S.,
   U.S.N.   1937   "Building the 200-Inch Telescope," *J. Franklin
                                    Inst.*, **224**, 675.

KARELITZ, M. B.   1938   "Oil-Pad Bearings and Driving Gears of 200-Inch
                                    Telescope," *Mech. Engineering*, **60**, 541.

SERRURIER, M.   1938   "Structural Features of 200-Inch Telescope for
                                    Mount Palomar Observatory," *Civil Engineer-
                                    ing*, **8**, 524.

MCDOWELL, CAPT. C. S.,
   U.S.N.   1938   "The 200-Inch Telescope," *Scient. American*,
                                    159, 68.

KROON, R. P.   1939   "Elastic Hinge Principle Utilized in Telescope
                                    Design," *Machine Design*, **11**, 34 (No. 1).

ADAMS, W. S.   1939   "200-Inch Telescope," *Nature*, **143**, 317.

ANDERSON, JOHN   1939   "The 200-Inch Telescope," *Pub. A.S.P.*, **51**, 24.

FREDERICKS, F., and
   Mochel, H. L.   1939   "Mounting of 200-Inch Telescope—Welded
                                    Structures," *Metals and Alloys*, **10**, 334 and 363.

WOODBURY, D. O.   1939   *The Glass Giant of Palomar*. With drawings by
                                    R. W. PORTER. New York: Dodd, Mead & Co.

ANDERSON, J. A., and
   PORTER, R. W.   1940   "The 200-Inch Telescope," *Telescope*, **7**, 29.

WARREN, H. E.   1940   "A New Time Standard," *A.I.E.E. Trans.*, **59**,
                                    137.

POITRAS, E. J., and
   ZWICKY, F.   1941   "Automatic Drive for Schmidt Telescope on Palo-
                                    mar Mountain," *Scient. Monthly*, **52**, 286.

ANDERSON, J. A.   1942   "Optical Work on the 200-Inch Telescope,"
                                    Scient. American, **166**, 46 and 106.

RULE, BRUCE R.   1942   "Electrical Features of the 200-Inch Telescope,"
                                    Elec. Engineering, **61**, 67 (No. 2).

ANDERSON, J. A.   1942   "Astrophysical Observatory of the California In-
                                    stitute of Technology," *J.R.A.S. Canada*, **36**,
                                    177.

FULLER, D. D.   1947   "Hydrostatic Lubrication. I. Oil Pad Bearings,"
                                    Machine Design, **19**, 110.

RICHARDSON, R. S.   1947   "The 200-Inch Mirror Goes to Palomar," *Pub.
                                    A.S.P.*, **59**, 310.

ANDERSON, JOHN A.   1948   "Optics of the 200-Inch Hale Telescope," *Pub.
                                    A.S.P.*, **60**, 221.

RULE, BRUCE R.   1948   "Engineering Aspects of the 200-Inch Hale Tele-
                                    scope," *Pub. A.S.P.*, **60**, 225.

Bowen, I. S. 1950 "Final Adjustment and Tests of the Hale Telescope," *Pub. A.S.P.*, **62**, 91.

1951 "The Palomar Observatory," *Scient. Monthly*, **73**, 141.

1952 "The Spectrographic Equipment of the 200-Inch Hale Telescope," *Ap. J.*, **116**, 1.

1952 "Optical Problems at the Palomar Observatory," *J. Opt. Soc. America*, **42**, 795.

1952 "Some New Tools of the Astronomers," *Observatory*, **72**, 129.

Wright, Helen 1952 *Palomar, the World's Largest Telescope*. New York: Macmillan Co.

Carnegie Institution of Washington Year Book, **48**, 3, 1949; **49**, 3, 1950; **50**, 22, 1951; **52**, 28, 1953; **55**, 53, 1956.

CHAPTER 2

The Lick Observatory 120-Inch Telescope

W. W. BAUSTIAN*

Chief Engineer, Kitt Peak National Observatory

THE Lick 120-inch telescope and the Kitt Peak 84-inch telescope represent two designs based on concepts slightly different from that of the 200-inch Hale telescope described in chapter 1. The Lick telescope, shown in Plate I,[1] is designed about an $f/5$ paraboloid mirror to be used mainly at the prime and coudé foci. Its design is the largest yet attempted with a fork mounting.

1. OPTICS AND TUBE

An f/ratio of 5.0 was selected to yield a satisfactorily large field of high definition at the prime focus to enable utilization of that focal position without correctors. A Ross corrector is provided, however, to widen the field of view for direct photography.

The f/ratio of 5.0 made it possible to use the 120-inch ribbed disk constructed earlier for tests of the 200-inch mirror. This disk, originally cast as a flat, had a total depth of 16 inches, with a top plate thickness of 4 inches and 4-inch-thick ribs. Although the $1\frac{1}{2}$-inch sagitta decreased the plate thickness to $2\frac{1}{2}$ inches at the center, it still has a relative plate stiffness comparable with that of the 200-inch mirror. Its rib structure is computed to be some eight times the relative stiffness of that of the 200-inch rib structure.

The long tube of the 120-inch telescope presented problems in deciding the location of the declination axis. A balance point at one-third would result either in a very long fork or no working room between the mirror cell and the fork. Since future usage of the Cassegrain was desired, the declination axis was placed at the one-quarter point. In order to achieve this balance, 10,000 pounds of

* Former Senior Engineer for 120-Inch Telescope Project.
[1] Plates I–IX and Fig. 1 by J. E. Chappell; Pl. X by R. E. Watson.

16

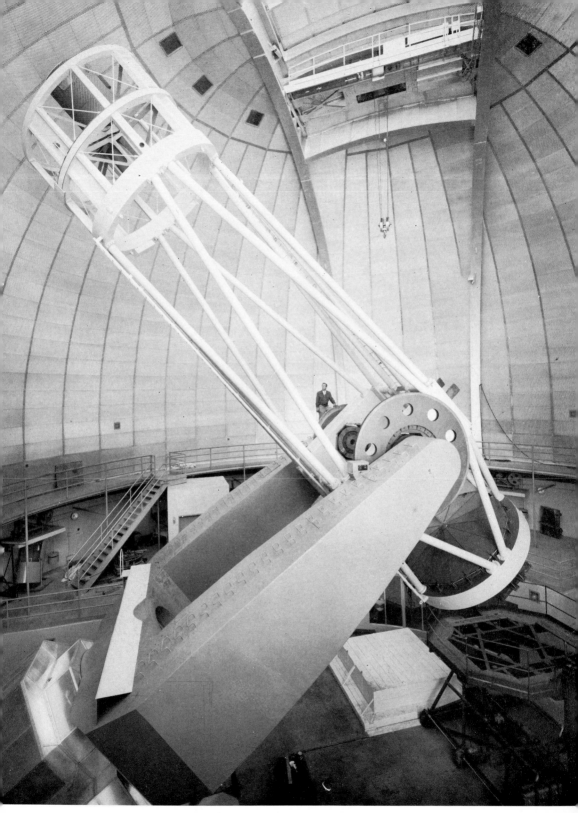

Plate I.—General view of 120″ telescope

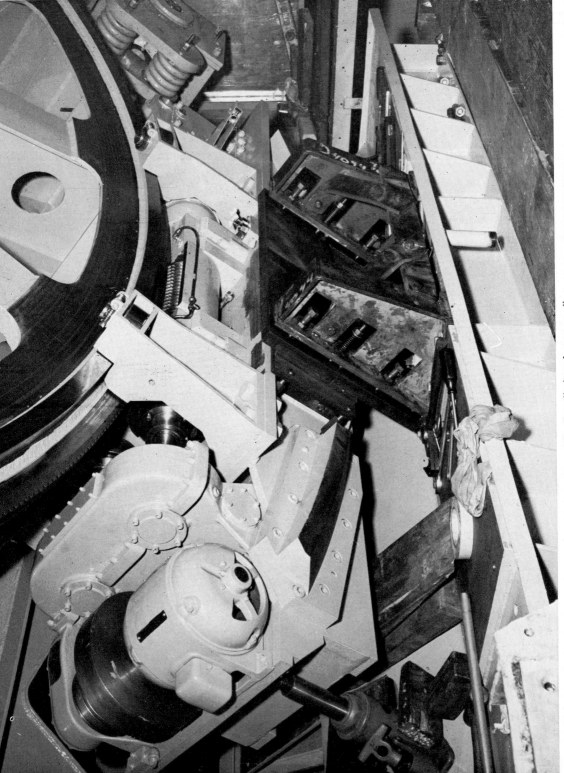

PLATE II. Installation of worm cradle

PLATE III.—Primary mirror shown on grinding machine

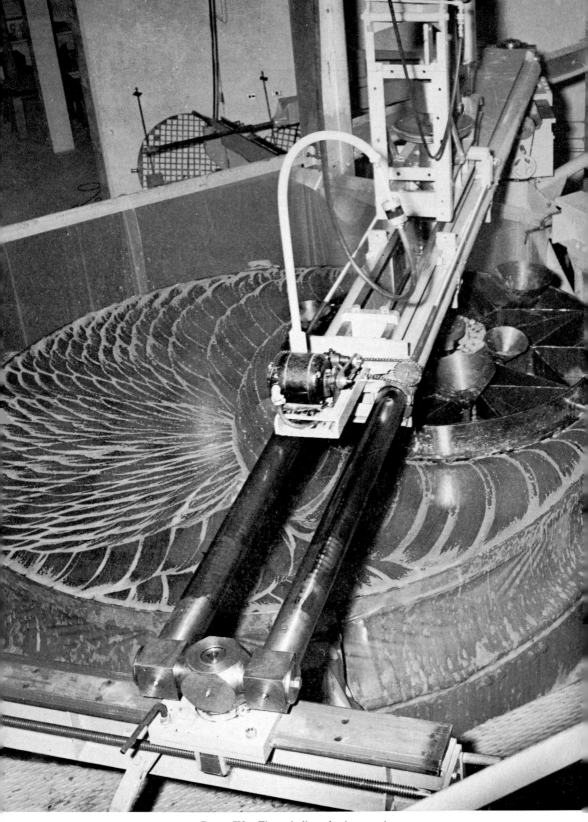

PLATE IV.—Fine grinding of primary mirror

PLATE V.—One of the eighteen support units, primary mirror

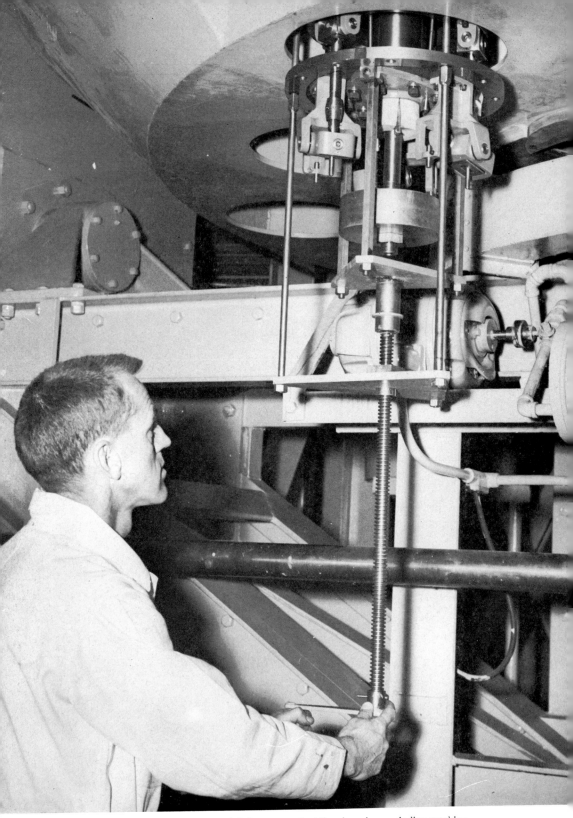

PLATE VI.—Support unit being removed while mirror is on grinding machine

PLATE VII.—Prime-focus cage

PLATE VIII.—Control panel

PLATE IX.—Mirror-handling carriage under mirror cell

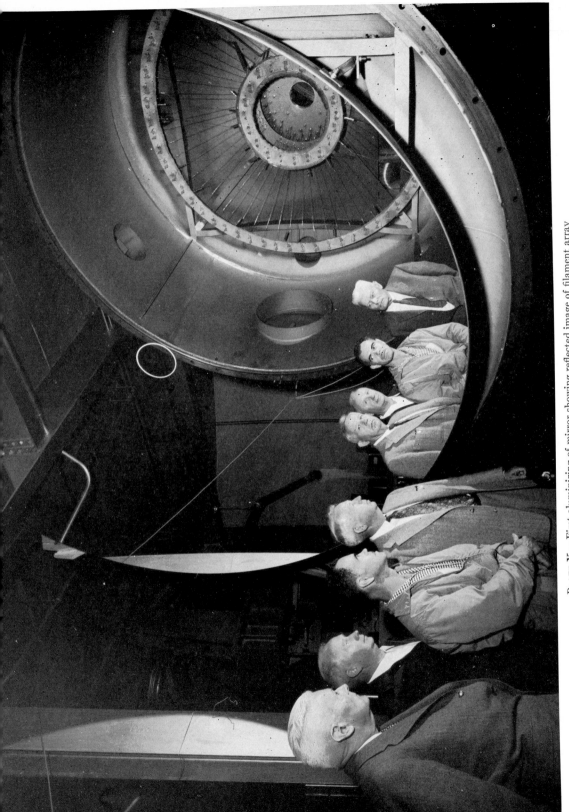

PLATE X.—First aluminizing of mirror showing reflected image of filament array

counterweight were added to the mirror cell. With this value it was possible to design a fork of sufficient length to give access to a Cassegrain position while retaining satisfactory rigidity to the fork. The distance from the throat of the fork to the declination axis is 24 feet.

The use of a one-fourth-point balance position was possible through the design of an unequal-armed Serrurier parallelogram truss for the tube. In the 200-inch telescope the observer's cell and mirror cell are equidistant from the declination axis; hence, for equal weights, they translate under the force of gravity by equal amounts. In the 120-inch telescope these distances are unequal, and the equality of deflection is accomplished by adjusting the rigidity of the supporting trusses. For the Kitt Peak 84-inch telescope the ratio of lengths is even greater, but compensation can still be achieved.

The smaller aperture of the 120-inch telescope compared to the 200-inch places several restrictions upon the prime-focus cell. In the 120-inch the ob-

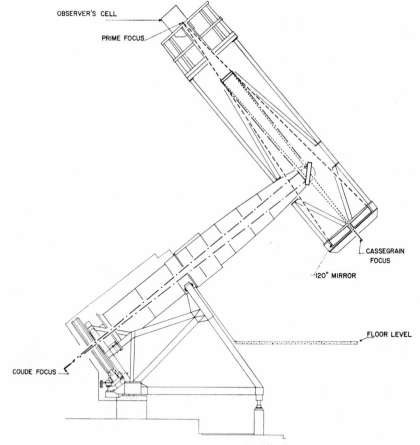

Fig. 1.—Focal arrangements of 120″ telescope

server's cell is elliptical, 32 inches wide and 48 inches long, with one focus of the ellipse on the optical axis of the telescope. The space is minimal to contain the observer and auxiliary equipment. The observer can orient the cell in any position angle determined by convenience for the observation at hand. The use of slip rings enables the cell to be rotated at will without compromise on the electrical system. Furthermore, very small electrical noise levels can be achieved in modern slip-ring systems.

The coudé optical system for the 120-inch uses moving coudé flat mirrors. The slenderness of the $f/5$ tube permits a three-mirror arrangement to be used up to approximately $+55°$ declination. To permit this range, the box section of the tube in the region of the declination axis is split to pass the coudé beam. Structural strength is preserved by two thin steel tension struts across the gap and inclined to cause a minimum interference with the coudé beam. For high declinations a five-mirror coudé system is introduced.

Figure 1 shows the focal arrangements which may be used with this telescope. Present plans include only the use of the prime focus and the coudé focus. The prime focus will be used for direct photography and for work with spectrographs and photoelectric photometers. In the spectrograph for use at the coudé focus it is planned to use a beam ranging from 6 to 12 inches in diameter and to equip it with four cameras, ranging in focal length from 20 to 160 inches. The mirror for the largest camera will be 50 inches in diameter.

2. TELESCOPE DRIVE AND SUPPORT

The drive of the 120-inch telescope uses a double worm-wheel system. One wheel operates for slewing the telescope and the second for tracking, setting, and guiding. The worm assembly is mounted on a floating support base or cradle. This cradle is fitted with axial and radial defining rolls which guide the rim of the worm wheel so that the worm is maintained in constant contact and with uniform tooth clearance by means of a system of counterweighted support levers, thus contributing to a long-lifetime accuracy of the tracking worm gear. While the system performs perfectly, its complications are such that it is not recommended where it is possible to obtain adequate service from a single worm wheel.

The polar axis of the 120-inch telescope is supported on oil pads. Two pads are located at the north end near the fork yoke for radial loads. Two more oil pads are located on top of the axis at the south end, to take upward radial loads. The southward thrust is taken on one pad located at the underside of the south end of the axis. The telescope is protected against failure of the oil supply by microswitches which monitor the thickness of the oil film. The entire polar-axis and worm-wheel system is inclosed in a dust-tight air housing, which is kept under slight pressure with electrostatically filtered air. The oil is further protected by a system of filters to assure freedom from suspended particles.

The telescope tube, weighing approximately 50 tons, is supported on pre-loaded angular-contact ball bearings. These declination bearings are gimbal-mounted to accommodate the small torsional deflections developed during rotation about the polar axis. The tube is moved in declination by means of a 10-foot-diameter spur gear and pinion. The pinion is mounted on the output shaft of the self-locking worm-gear reducer of the fast-motion or slewing drive. The complete slewing-drive assembly, including the $\frac{3}{4}$-horsepower motor, is mounted on the slow-motion tangent arm. Thus slow motions are transmitted through this locked-gear unit to the spur gear without rotation of the pinion. Since tangential preload is provided about the declination axis, the spur gear need not be of the high precision required for the right-ascension worm gear. The range of the tangent-arm travel is 4°, with controls incorporated in the system to center the tangent arm automatically whenever the slewing motion is used. The entire declination-drive system, exclusive of the spur gear and pinion, is installed inside the east-fork arm.

As stated, the polar axis is supported on an oil-pad bearing system, similar to that developed for the 200-inch telescope. A rotating weight of some 145 tons total is carried on these bearings. The average operating pressure of the oil is 800–850 pounds per square inch. The oil, specially compounded for this purpose, has a high viscosity index, that is, a relatively constant viscosity over the normal range of operating temperatures. Under average conditions the flow of oil is about 1 gallon per minute per pad. Duplicate pumping and filtering systems are provided with 3-horsepower variable-speed drives used on each pump. Each pad consists of a cylindrical surface, matching the journal surface with a central recessed cavity whose diameter is approximately half that of the pad. The high-pressure oil is introduced into this cavity and allowed to flow out to the collection channel around the rim of the pad. The oil-film thickness between the journal and the mating surface of the pad ranges from 0.002 to 0.005 inch, depending on the flow of oil metered to it. The load carried by the pad is then the area of the cavity *times* the full unit pressure *plus* the annular area *times* the pressure, integrated from full pressure to zero pressure at the collection channel.

The right-ascension worm gear, 12 feet in diameter with 720 teeth, is driven by a worm of $4\frac{1}{2}$-inch pitch diameter. The worm-gear tooth accuracy as machined was within the maximum allowable tooth-to-tooth error of 0.0002 inch. This accuracy and the tooth finish were further improved by lapping with a series of cast-iron worm laps. Plate II shows the worm cradle being installed. The $1\frac{1}{2}$-horsepower slewing motor is seen in the left foreground, directly in front of the twin secondary worm-gear reduction unit which drives both the primary worms. Both worms are driven and in mesh simultaneously, however, by means of a selective pin clutch located beyond the worms; only the driving worm has its thrust or axial motion restrained with respect to the cradle frame. The cradle frame, in turn, is secured to the base frame through a bar held in the spring-loaded clamp, visible in the right background. The clamp pressure is adjusted so that, in case of emergency overload, the cradle, supported on rollers mounted on the ends of the cradle counterweight levers, is allowed to travel with the gear a few inches. These counterweight arms are not shown, but one of the curved roller tracks may be seen in the foreground in front of and below the secondary worm-gear case. The cradle is returned to center position by means of a hydraulic jacking cylinder, which is also the hydraulic snubber for the cradle slip motion. Two of the four roller units bearing on the gear rim are visible in the central foreground. The dark unpainted plate and bracket structure located below these rollers is for cradle installation purposes only. The slow-motion drive assembly is located behind the base frame bulkhead, visible in the left background. The right-ascension drive motor is powered with current supplied by a Lombard vibrating-string standard and power amplifier.

3. BUILDING AND FACILITIES

The telescope is installed in a building 100 feet in diameter and 100 feet high. The 270-ton steel dome revolves on a stationary substructure of light-weight concrete with a wall height of 40 feet. This dome is driven by three $1\frac{1}{2}$-horse-power drive units which revolve the dome at a peripheral speed of 55 feet per minute or one revolution in 5 minutes. The dome has in its top a crane with a 15-ton normal capacity, which may be double-reaved to give a 30-ton capacity; thus it is capable of handling any of the major components of the mountings.

One important use of this crane is to transfer the mirror during aluminizing operations from the mirror-handling carriage, which removes the mirror and cell from the tube, to the vacuum chamber used for aluminizing. This is a routine maintenance operation which will be repeated every 2–5 years.

The 8500-pound ribbed primary mirror is shown in Plate III, mounted on the grinding machine purchased from the California Institute of Technology. The rib structure of the mirror is clearly visible through the top surface, which has been wet to produce transparency. The grinding machine, originally built at the California Institute of Technology and designed to produce various grinding motions by the combination of the two co-ordinate components obtained by the bridge travel and the cross-travel of the bridge traveler, was modified to a Draper-type machine.

The bridge and traveler are visible in the background of Plate III, while in the foreground the light-colored beam and tube assembly are the Pitman arm for the Draper motion. A portion of the crank is visible at the extreme left-hand edge. Rough grinding of the mirror was completed in 80 hours, by means of a 400-pound cast-iron ring tool which revolved at a rate of 80 revolutions per minute, with a Pitman arm travel of some 12–20 cycles per minute. In place of a counterweight, the tool spindle was attached to a pneumatic-cylinder-actuated lever arm which allowed the weight of pressure on the tool to be increased or decreased at will. Mirror-table-rotation speed, crank speed, tool pressure, and stroke length were all controllable from the panel mounted on the bridge of the grinding machine. The position of the spindle on the Pitman arm could also be changed or shifted from this same control panel.

Plate IV shows the fine grinding in progress, using a half-size tool of welded aluminum construction. For the grinding operation, both the full-size and the half-size welded aluminum tools were faced with 4-inch-square unglazed tile, $\frac{3}{4}$ inch thick. In the grinding process, carborundum was used in successive degrees of fineness, followed by garnet powder in successive grades. For the polishing operation, the tile was removed, and a grooved pitch surface was applied to the face of the tool. Rouge was used for the polishing operation, with tools as small as 2 inches in diameter being used in the final hand-figuring operations for local corrections. As demonstrated by the Hartmann tests, the support system performs perfectly (Mayall and Vasilevskis 1960, Astron. J. **65**, 300).

4. MIRROR SUPPORT

The principal requirement for support systems for ribbed mirrors is that they have a minimum friction in their leverage systems. In the case of the 120-inch support systems, the total friction is kept below 0.2 per cent; thus the mirror is supported with a minimum restraint at all times. The axial systems support the entire weight when the mirror is in the horizontal position, and the radial systems support the mirror when it is in the vertical position. During a shift of the mirror from a horizontal to a vertical position, or vice versa, these systems then transfer their proportional loads to each other to conform to the varying conditions. If the support systems have excessive friction, astigmatism will be developed in the mirror figure.

The 120-inch mirror is supported on its cell by eighteen support units, one of which is shown on Plate V, mounted on a test stand in a horizontal position. These units, which extend up into the cylindrical cavities from the back of the mirror, support both the axial and the radial components of the mirror weight. The radial components are transmitted through the ball-bearing head, located at the upper end of the unit, and are carried by a central lever arm whose disk-shaped counterweight is visible at the left end of the unit. The axial component of the mirror weight is supported on the flange located at the central section, with the load being transmitted through three push rods to their individual counterweight levers, located below the mounting flange of the support unit. The cylindrical counterweight of one of these levers is visible in the central foreground. The rectangular counterweights are auxiliary balance weights to neutralize the weight of the flange bearing the axial load so as to neutralize its tendency to shift the center of gravity of the mirror. A nineteenth unit, carrying only an axial component, is located at the center of the mirror, thus providing for the passage of a future Cassegrain light-beam.

Plate VI shows one of these support units being removed from the back or lower side of the mirror cell while it is on the grinding machine, by means of a special fixture designed for this purpose. This allows the unit to be removed at any time for inspection or repair, without having to remove the mirror from the cell.

5. OBSERVER'S CAGE

To work at the prime focus, the observer enters the observer's cell from a platform spanning the shutter opening of the dome and traveling on tracks mounted on the shutter arches. The platform is cable-operated by a hoist mounted on the ring girder of the dome. Since the elevator travels in an arc, the platform is maintained level by means of a gear system which transmits motion from a curved gear rack fastened to shutter arches to a small gear quadrant fastened to the platform. The gear reduction is proportional to the ratio of the radii of the curved rack and the quadrant.

The upper end of the tube assembly is removable. This element, called the *prime-focus cage* and shown in Plate VII, contains the observer's cell supported on the upper set of tension webs. The tube carrying the optical or instrument components is independently supported on the lower set of tension webs. The observer's cell, as mentioned previously, is motor-driven about the optical axis to suit; also the observer's chair is adjusted to a convenient position by a motorized drive. These motions are not automatic but are at the control of the observer.

6. THE COUDÉ FOCUS

When the telescope is to be used at the coudé focus, the prime-focus cage is removed by means of the crane and replaced with a heavy ring-girder unit carrying the convex coudé secondary mirror. The weight of this unit is such that the tube balance is maintained. The secondary mirror is supported in a cell mounted on the lower end of a tube assembly, which in turn is web-supported from the ring girder similar to the support of the prime-focus optical assembly. Motorized axial motion of the secondary cell is provided in the tube assembly for remotely controlled focusing.

The coudé flat mirror located at the declination axis is web-supported from the center section of the tube and is fitted with an accurate drive which rotates the mirror about the declination axis at half the declination angle. For some time the telescope will be used with the three-mirror coudé system. Provision is made for the later addition of the fourth and fifth flat mirrors. The fourth mirror is to be mounted on a yoke, pivot-mounted on the upper surface of the fork just above the fork yoke, and the fifth will be located on the polar axis just inside the fork yoke. These mirrors will be shifted into fixed positions when the five-mirror system is required. The coudé focus is located approximately 6 feet below the south end of the polar axis at the outer wall of the building.

The coudé slit mechanism and attendant auxiliaries are mounted on a supporting panel mounted in a 6-foot-square wall opening centered on the polar axis. The coudé spectrograph is located outside the building proper, housed in an addition to this building. The inclined concrete floor of this room goes to a depth of 12 feet below ground level. Room is provided to accommodate a light-beam up to 12 inches in diameter, which would place the collimating mirror some 38 feet from the slit when the five-mirror coudé system is used, the latter having a slightly longer focal length than the three-mirror system. The main overhead support frame for the spectrograph is essentially a simple triangle made of heavy structural I-beams. The 50-inch-diameter mirror for the 160-inch camera is rigidly suspended from this frame. The 80-inch, 40-inch, and 20-inch cameras are suspended from the support frame on transport mechanisms which allow these units to be swung into operating positions or storage positions as desired. A turret mounting for three gratings is also mounted under this base frame, with a sweep or scanning drive incorporated in the basic unit. At present, only two gratings will be installed, one with a ruling of 22,500 lines per inch and the other with 15,000 lines per inch. The range of dispersions covered by the four cameras will be from 32.8 to 0.85 A/mm.

7. CONTROLS AND AUXILIARY EQUIPMENT

All motions of the telescope and dome are controlled from the console located on the working floor along the west side of the polar-axis housing. Plate VIII shows the general arrangement of controls and indicator dials. All position indications are transmitted by synchros, with the exception of the hour-angle and right-ascension dials, which are directly connected to the right-ascension drive unit located inside the polar-axis housing behind the console. All dials are translucent and back-lighted, with controlled-intensity lamps. A phantom telescope computer similar to the one used on the 200-inch telescope is located in the base of the console. This enables the dome and wind screen to be placed on automatic control. In addition to other automatic-control functions, it also computes zenith distance, which is indicated on one of the console dials.

To remove the primary mirror from the tube, the mirror-handling carriage is centered under the mirror cell, as shown in Plate IX. The octagonal platform is then raised up to the cell on motor-driven jack screws, located in the two vertical side columns. After the mirror cell is bolted to the handling-carriage platform, it is unbolted from the telescope tube. The cell assembly is then lowered and the carriage moved out from beneath the tube. To remove the mirror from the cell, edge-support brackets are bolted to the mounting face of the cell. Three built-in jacks in the cell are brought up to take the weight of the mirror, after which the mirror-support units are lowered and locked in a retracted position in the cell, clear of the mirror. The cell and mirror are now ready to be tilted into a vertical position by means of a power-driven jack screw, attached to a pivot point under one side of the handling platform. The lower end of this jack screw with its drive is pivoted on the base frame of the carriage. The mirror is then lifted with a crane in a stainless-steel band-sling, extending from a spreader bar down around the edge of the mirror. The upper ends of this sling are fitted with hooks for suspension in the aluminizing chamber, still in a vertical position. After installation of the mirror in the chamber, the spreader bar is removed from the sling.

The aluminizing chamber is 12 feet in diameter, with a 6-foot-long cylindrical section between two elliptical heads. The mirror is suspended in the head to which the two 24-inch oil-diffusion vacuum pumps and roughing pump are attached. The mirror is placed with its back toward the vacuum pumps. To place the mirror in the tank, the cylindrical section and its head are moved as a unit away from the pump end head. A coating of aluminum is applied from a single ring of filaments, located approximately a half-mirror diameter from the mirror face. The diameter of the filament ring is slightly less than that of the mirror. Spare filaments are included on this array for use in case any of the primary set of filaments fails to function. A second, smaller array of filaments is also built in for use in coating smaller mirrors.

Plate X, photographed by a camera placed inside the retracted portion of the chamber, shows the first coating made on the 120-inch mirror. This coating was very satisfactory. The mirror, still supported in its sling on the support brackets in the pumping head of the chamber, shows a reflected image of the filament array and the general arrangement of fittings in the interior.

CHAPTER 3

Design of Reflecting Telescopes

ADEN B. MEINEL

Kitt Peak National Observatory

1. REFLECTING TELESCOPES

1.1. INTRODUCTION

Wɪᴛʜ the completion of the 36- and 40-inch refractors toward the end of the nineteenth century, one era of telescope construction came to its end. All major telescopes constructed since that time have been reflectors. While the objective of a refractor must be supported on its rim and is therefore perforce limited in size, the reflector can be supported at suitably located points anywhere on its back surface; thus no limit on the size is imposed other than dictated by the production of a large disk whose front surface can be given the desired shape. As is well known, reflecting telescopes can be used at (1) the prime focus (no secondary mirror used); (2) the Newtonian focus (a flat mirror reflects the primary beam at 90° toward the side of the telescope tube); (3) the Cassegrain focus (a hyperbolic secondary mirror reflects the beam back into the tube and forms an image below the primary mirror through a centrally located hole); (4) the coudé focus, yielding a stationary focal point, usually desired in connection with a large (stationary) spectrograph installation.

1.11. *f-Ratio.*—Perhaps the first characteristic to be fixed in a new telescope design is the *f*-ratio of the primary. The traditional *f*/5 primary for a large telescope has gradually given way in favor of smaller values. The Palomar 200-inch telescope is *f*/3.3, and the McDonald 82-inch telescope is *f*/4. The Lick 120-inch telescope is *f*/5, but the *f*-ratio in this case was limited by the thinness of the 120-inch disk, which was originally the blank for the test flat for the 200-inch telescope.

The chief factor in favor of the smallest feasible *f*-ratio is the lower cost of the completed facility. It is true that the shortness of the telescope tube does not affect the cost of the telescope directly, since the expensive parts are not affected; but indirectly the shortness contributes to lower costs through a less massive telescope, shorter fork spans, and, in particular, the cost of the dome.

The decision as to the minimum practicable f-ratio is affected by the proposed operation. If a prime-focus position is desired, then small f-ratio systems require the use of a coma-corrector. Successful spherical-element systems have been devised by Ross (1935) for the Mount Wilson and Palomar reflectors and by Maksutov (1944). Baker (1954) and Meinel (1953) have proposed coma-correctors utilizing aspheric elements. The coma-correctors for prime focus, however, have shown distortion and variation of scale with color. This distortion causes inconvenience in astrometric programs and introduces the possibility of errors in offset work at the prime focus.

The price of the elimination of the prime focus is not so high as one might at first fear. The operation of instruments adapted to accept a wide angular beam can be accomplished only at the expense of additional mirror reflections or lens elements. It is often necessary, moreover, to operate the instrument with a corrector in the beam ahead of the prime focus. As a consequence, the supposed efficiency of the prime-focus position is not realized. On the basis of the optics alone, we find that the over-all efficiency of a telescope is maximized at the Cassegrain focus. In this case the f-ratio can be such that simple optical arrangements are possible.

The 84-inch of the Kitt Peak National Observatory is the first telescope to be designed around these modified concepts. It has a primary f-ratio of 2.75 and Cassegrain f-ratios of $f/8$ and $f/12$. No use is planned for the prime focus. The fastest Cassegrain f-ratio, $f/8$, is designed to allow direct photography of moderate fields without correctors and to yield limiting-magnitude exposures in 2 hours.

The decision to make a primary paraboloid as fast as $f/2.75$ was made to gain experience beyond the 200-inch mirror of $f/3.3$. The large amplification factor of the Cassegrain secondary does not require a primary mirror of higher quality than is conventional. Since the depth of the asphericity required for a paraboloid increases according to the inverse cube of the f-ratio, the problems of the optician increase rapidly in order to achieve a final surface good to a fraction of a wave length. The expected gains from the short f-ratio, however, justify a special effort in the polishing procedures.

It is not usually appreciated that the collimation of a telescope becomes increasingly difficult as the f-ratio decreases and the secondary magnification increases, though the net optical performance depends principally upon the Cassegrain f-ratio. The coma of an $f/8$ Cassegrain for the same field angle is precisely the same as for an $f/8$ primary used at prime focus. The astigmatism is that of an equivalent prime-focus paraboloid multiplied by the magnification of the Cassegrain secondary mirror. As a consequence, the optical performance of a Cassegrain is essentially independent of the primary f-ratio.

At first sight, the sensitivity to collimation errors of a Cassegrain system with a small f-ratio primary appears to be a disadvantage. The error in the Cassegrain focal plane is given by

$$\epsilon = \frac{\Delta}{F^2}$$

if Δ is the collimation error. However, Δ itself depends on F. If we assume that the telescope is mechanically perfect, we still have decollimation due to gravitational flexure. If the weight of the secondary is small, the tube of the telescope will deflect according to

$$\epsilon = lF^3 \, ,$$

while if the secondary is an appreciable fraction of the mass, the telescope will deflect according to

$$\epsilon = lF^4 \, .$$

The net effect to decollimation by flexure is

$$\epsilon = lF \qquad \text{to} \qquad \epsilon = lF^2 \, .$$

Thus the most accurately defined optical system is obtained with a primary of *small f*-ratio. The ideal astrometric telescope may therefore be a compact instrument of small primary f-ratio.

1.12. *Mounting.*—The telescope mounting is a structure to hold the optics and maintain the direction of the optical axis with high accuracy in space. The number of ways that this basic function can be performed is so large that it is safe to say that no two research telescopes have been built alike. There are several conflicting considerations, so that the weighting of each depends on the interests of the staff making the decisions. The problem of supporting and defining the optical system is very important and is discussed separately below.

The family of telescope mountings can be divided into two main classes: the fork and yoke types of "symmetrical class" and the cross-axis of the "asymmetrical class." For modern reflectors, especially those of small f-ratio, the main difference between the two classes is the radius of the focus sweep and the accessibility at the pole for Cassegrain instruments. The focus sweep is defined as the radius from the intersection of the declination and polar axes to the focus. The radius of the focus sweep defines the vertical travel that the observer needs, to reach the focus at both the zenith and the horizon. This distance is much smaller for a symmetrical-class telescope than for the asymmetrical class. On the other hand, interference from the fork near the focus limits the usefulness of the symmetrical class unless the telescope is large.

For telescopes of large size (diameter $>100''$) the symmetrical class offers the advantage of a *minimum-mass telescope*. For telescopes of small and intermediate size ($<100''$) the asymmetrical class offers the advantage of greatest accessibility for all-sky coverage. The initial two telescopes for the Kitt Peak National Observatory—the 36-inch and the 84-inch—employ the most recent design considerations of these two classes. The 84-inch is below the size at which the symmetrical class best shows its advantages, but its design well illustrates the class.

1.2. Asymmetrical Class

1.21. *The Kitt Peak National Observatory 36-inch telescope.*—The 36-inch telescope design, by Meinel and Baustian, is shown in cross-section in Figure 1. The basic aim was to give maximum work space to the astronomer and to accommodate Cassegrain instruments up to 74 inches in length for any position in the sky. While the focus sweep is large, a moving floor provides ready access. The telescope does not need to be reversed in operation, and the floor is designed for optimum work efficiency on the east side of the polar axis.

The polar axis contains the chief innovations of this design. The polar-axis sheath has three concentric tubes. The innermost tube is the live polar axis and connects the worm with the declination-axis housing. The intermediate tube is fixed to the base and carries the upper polar-axis bearing. The flexure of this tube, therefore, does not change, and its droop can be corrected by a simple adjustment of the base. The location of the north-polar-axis bearing is optimum, close to the declination axis. The outer tube is a torque tube to carry the counterweight, which is placed at the position where it causes a minimum of interference with the observing space. The relative position of the counterweight and the north-polar-axis bearing is such that the center of gravity of the tube-counterweight system is close to the bearing. This arrangement places a minimum bending moment in the live polar-axis shaft.

Two smaller telescopes of 16-inch aperture have been constructed with the same design. These telescopes have been used on the site survey for the National Observatory and have confirmed that this design is very convenient for small telescopes. One of these telescopes is shown in Plate I.

1.22. *The McDonald 82-inch telescope.*—The 82-inch McDonald telescope shown in Plate II is one of the more recent examples of the asymmetrical class in a large size; it uses the full English or cross-axis mounting. In this case the counterweight is placed adjacent to the north-polar-axis pier. The entire working area at the Cassegrain focus is consequently completely free from interference by the counterweight. The focal sweep is again large, but a pair of hydraulic observing platforms renders work at the focus both convenient and easy.

For telescopes of large size, as in the case of the McDonald 82-inch, the use of a coudé focus is facilitated by this type of mounting. The coudé system requires two auxiliary flat mirrors, making a total of four mirror reflections. All the mirrors in this system are fixed; consequently, the problems of driving and setting moving coudé mirrors do not occur. The chief limitation of the coudé beam on the asymmetrical designs is in the length of the span between the declination-axis bearings. This is usually compensated for by increasing the diameter of the bearing nearest to the telescope tube, approaching the condition of a "plate bearing."

1.23. *Other modern telescopes, asymmetrical class.*—Other examples of recent

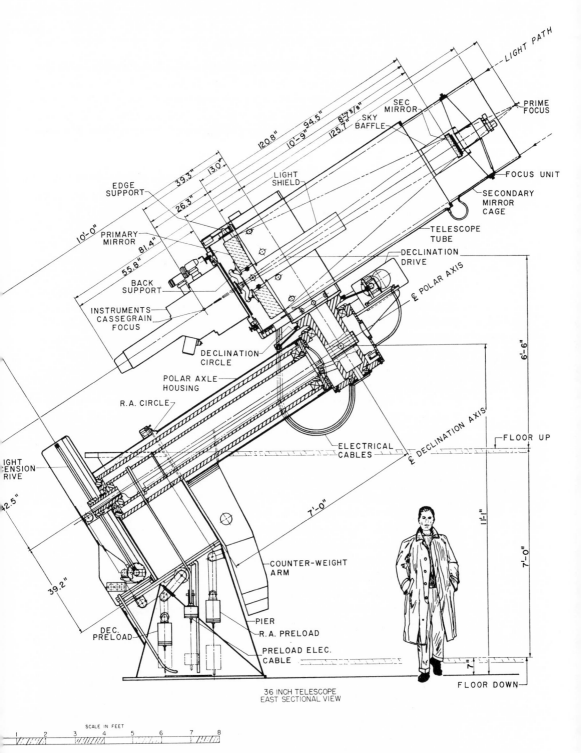

LIGHT PATH

120.8"

10'-9" 94.5"

81'-73/8"

125.7"

EDGE
SUPPORT

39.3"

13.0"

LIGHT
SHIELD

26.3"

10'-0"

PRIMARY
MIRROR

81.4"

55.8"

BACK
SUPPORT

INSTRUMENTS
CASSEGRAIN
FOCUS

SEC
MIRROR

SKY
BAFFLE

PRIME
FOCUS

FOCUS UNIT

SECONDARY
MIRROR
CAGE

TELESCOPE
TUBE

DECLINATION
DRIVE

₵ POLAR AXIS

DECLINATION
CIRCLE

POLAR AXLE
HOUSING

R.A. CIRCLE

IGHT
ENSION
RIVE

2.5"

39.2"

ELECTRICAL
CABLES

₵ DECLINATION AXIS

FLOOR UP

6'-6"

11'-1"

7'-0"

COUNTER-WEIGHT
ARM

DEC.
PRELOAD

PIER

R.A. PRELOAD

PRELOAD ELEC.
CABLE

7'-0"

FLOOR DOWN

7"

36 INCH TELESCOPE
EAST SECTIONAL VIEW

SCALE IN FEET

1   2   3   4   5   6   7   8

FIG. 1.—Cross-section drawing of the 36-inch Cassegrain telescope for the Kitt Peak National Observatory, Tucson, Arizona. Access to the focus position is by means of a hydraulic platform.

telescopes in this class are the Baker reflector-corrector 20-inch telescope of the Dyer Observatory, shown in Plates III and IV; the Carnegie 20-inch astrograph of Lick Observatory, shown in Plate V; the 24–36-inch Schmidt of the Warner and Swasey Observatory at Case Institute of Technology, shown in Plate VI; the 24–36-inch Schmidt of the University of Michigan, shown in Plate VII; and the 72-inch Dominion Astrophysical Observatory reflector, shown in Plate VIII.

1.3. Symmetrical Class

1.31. *The Kitt Peak National Observatory 84-inch telescope.*—The 84-inch telescope of the National Observatory, shown in Figure 2 and Plate IX, is an attempt to arrive at the optimum design configuration for a symmetrical Cassegrain without resorting to new departures. Two important members of this class—the Palomar 200-inch Hale telescope and the Lick 120-inch telescope—are described in chapters 1 and 2, respectively.

The 84-inch telescope is designed to have the mirror figured to a high degree of precision at least out to 80 inches. The large asphericity of the $f/2.75$ parabolic primary will make it difficult for the optician to control the figure to the full diameter. It is expected, however, that the telescope will be used at full aperture except for observations where the most exacting resolution is required.

The tolerances that have been specified for the 84-inch mirror are as follows: Out to 80 inches aperture the image shall have 75 per cent of its energy within $0''.3$, 90 per cent within $0''.6$, and 100 per cent within $1''.2$. Out to 84 inches aperture, the image shall have 100 per cent within $1''.2$. For comparison, the 200-inch mirror has 50 per cent within $0''.3$, 80 per cent within $0''.7$, and 100 per cent within $1''.5$.

The 84-inch telescope uses a conventional fork mounting. In this design the length of the fork arms is determined by two factors: (1) the clearance required for the Cassegrain instruments and (2) the minimum declination desired on the meridian. The second requirement is the more restrictive for small f-ratio systems, and the first for conventional f-ratio systems. If the telescope must reach the southern horizon, the fork rapidly becomes longer as the latitude of the observatory decreases. At 45° latitude there is no problem from tube clearance. At 30° it becomes serious. At the latitude of Kitt Peak (31°57′), clearance at the horizon requires a longer fork than is needed for the attachments themselves.

The design of the telescope tube must be such that it supports and defines the secondary or Cassegrain mirror accurately with respect to the primary mirror. Traditionally, this function is accomplished by a structure weighing many times that of the mirror. Several new approaches to this problem have been proposed, but all existing telescopes use a massive structure. As the f-ratio of the primary mirror becomes smaller, the new techniques become of practical importance. At $f/2$ the teepee-design class, outlined by Rule, is of interest. The teepee design is, in fact, an extension of the design that went into the upper end of the 82-inch McDonald telescope.

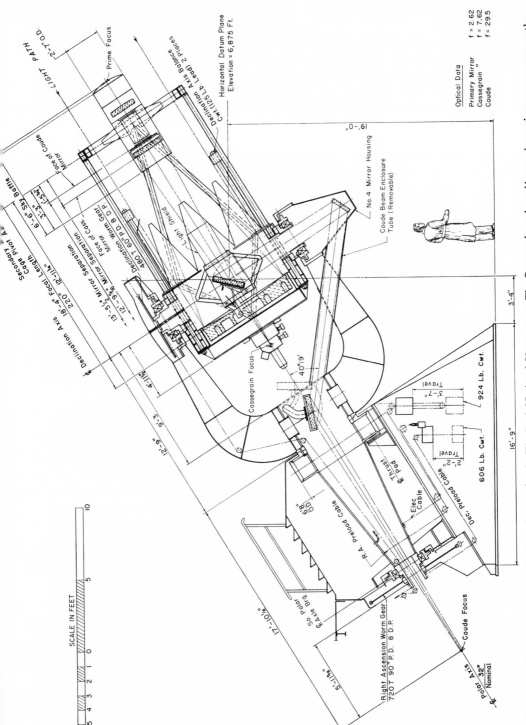

FIG. 2.—Section of the 84-inch reflecting telescope for the Kitt Peak National Observatory. The Cassegrain and coudé secondary mirrors are permanently mounted in a reversible assembly at the top of the tube.

The teepee design has one consequence that must be borne in mind. It requires support structures that are wider than the conventional support vanes. The consequence of this is an increased intensity of the diffraction rays about bright stars. The length of the ray decreases, but the intensity near the star increases. Most research applications are not particularly concerned with this fact; however, some are hampered, such as planetary observations and photoelectric work near bright extended objects, e.g., globular clusters. Diffraction from the teepee struts could be avoided by providing a mask with curved-edge elements or a series of holes, i.e., six equal apertures around the secondary.

The final 84-inch design retains the basic compensated-truss structure. The small distance from the mirror cell to the declination axis makes it necessary to adopt an internal truss to allow the mirror cell to deflect under gravity by the same amount as the secondary ring. While the mirror cell is apparently attached directly to the declination-box frame, it is actually connected to a parallelogram truss attached to the front flange inside the declination box near the junction of the truss from the secondary ring.

One important feature of the 84-inch telescope is the ability to change from the Cassegrain to the coudé focus without the addition or removal of optical components. The two secondaries are mounted back to back, and the focusing and collimating parts are located between the mirrors. The secondary assembly is mounted in a ring that is gimbal-mounted on a second ring attached to the front truss. In locked position the two rings are held rigidly at four points, to transfer stresses uniformly into the front truss.

To change from Cassegrain to coudé, the telescope operator places the telescope tube in a horizontal position, unlocks two pins, and reverses the gimbal. The change is completed by moving the coudé flat located on the optical axis at the declination axis into the beam. The entire changeover is accomplished by one person in a few minutes.

The proximity of the Cassegrain focal point to the intersection of the declination and polar axes results in a small focal sweep, typical of the symmetrical class. The travel of the hydraulic floor is equal only to that required for the observatory's 36-inch telescope of the asymmetrical class. The one disadvantage of this design is that the focus position becomes awkward to reach near the pole, especially at large hour angles. The instrument is too small to enable the observer to stand inside the span of the fork. Therefore, we consider that the fork telescope reaches its optimum only when the aperture is larger than 100 inches.

The 84-inch telescope incorporates a coudé system that has the advantages found in the asymmetrical class (i.e., McDonald 82-inch), in that fixed mirrors are used. Fixed mirrors, in fact, offer the only practical coudé system for the fork-mounted telescope of small f-ratio. The main reason is that the primary mirror is so close to the declination axis that the range of the "three-mirror" moving coudé system is quite limited. Most of the sky would require a "five-mirror" auxiliary path. A fixed system for a fork, however, requires a fifth mirror at the base of the fork to redirect the light-beam down the polar axis.

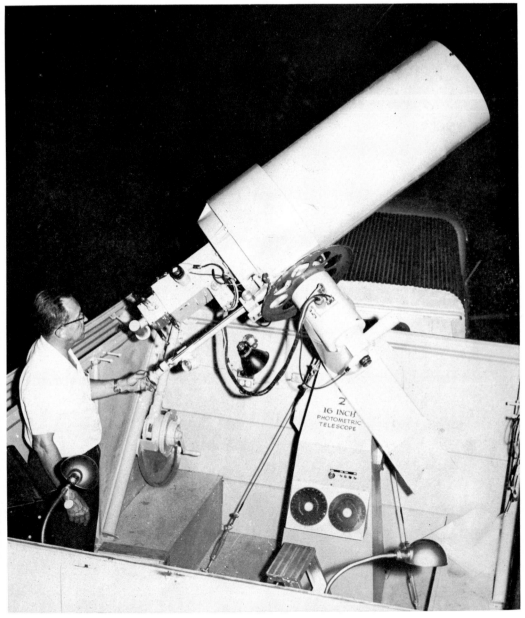

PLATE I.—Photograph of the 16-inch Cassegrain telescope for the Kitt Peak National Observatory, Tucson, Arizona, used primarily for photoelectric photometry.

PLATE II.—Photograph of the 82-inch telescope of the McDonald Observatory, Fort Davis, Texas. This telescope can be used either at the prime, Cassegrain, or coudé focus.

PLATE III.—Photograph of the 20-inch Baker reflector-corrector telescope of the Dyer Observatory, Vanderbilt University, Nashville, Tennessee.

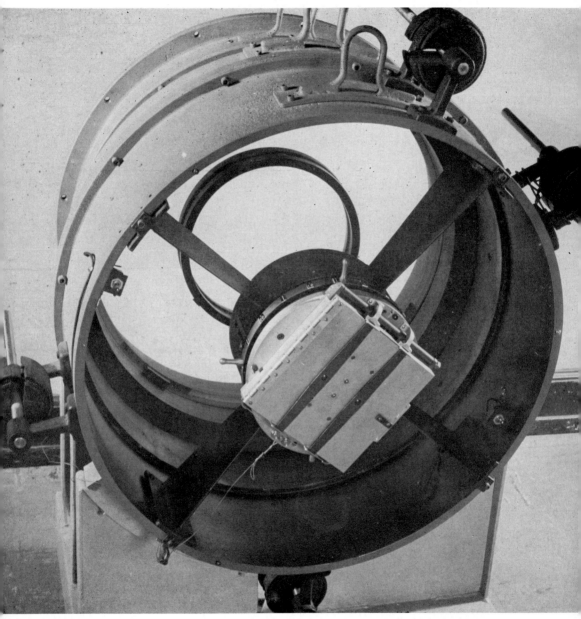

PLATE IV.—Photograph of the corrector cell and prime-focus plateholder of the 20-inch Baker reflector-corrector. The corrector includes an aspheric plate (exterior annulus) and a spherical corrector in front of focus (center) to yield a large field of critical definition.

PLATE V.—Photograph of the 20-inch Carnegie Astrograph of the Lick Observatory, Mount Hamilton, California. This telescope uses a "third motion" to facilitate guiding near the north celestial pole.

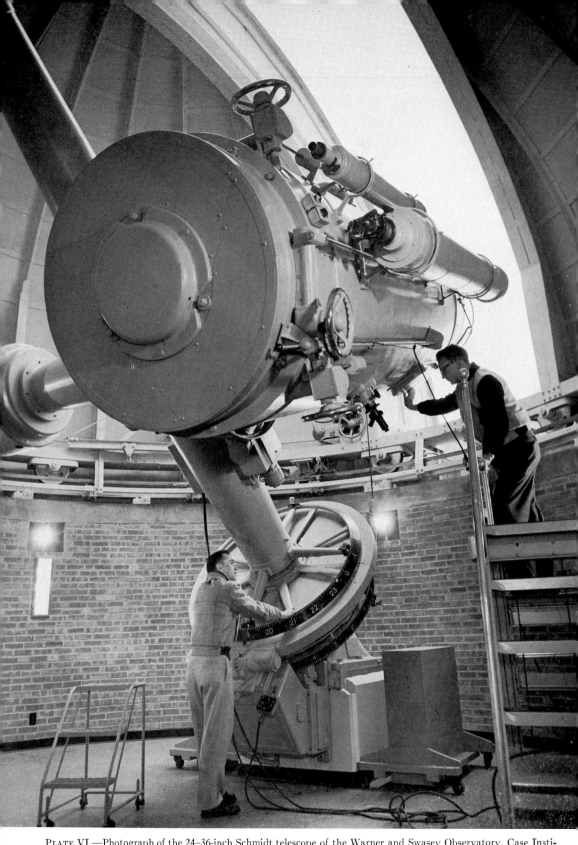

PLATE VI.—Photograph of the 24–36-inch Schmidt telescope of the Warner and Swasey Observatory, Case Institute of Technology, Cleveland, Ohio. This type of design is also shown in Pl. VII.

PLATE VII.—Photograph of the 24–36-inch Schmidt telescope of the Observatory of the University of Michigan at Portage Lake, Michigan.

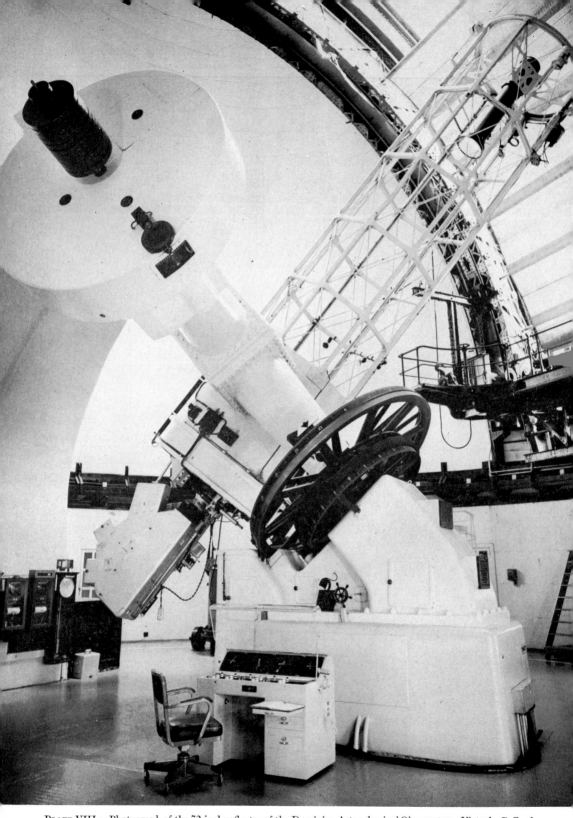

PLATE VIII.—Photograph of the 72-inch reflector of the Dominion Astrophysical Observatory, Victoria, B.C., showing the new Cassegrain spectrograph.

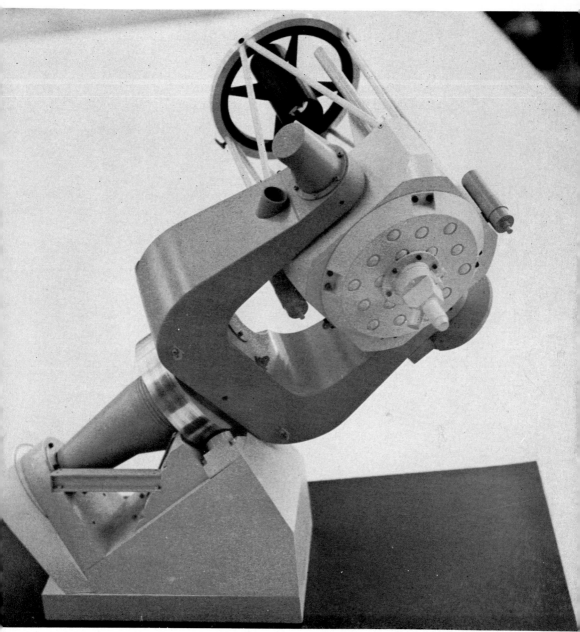

PLATE IX.—Photograph of a model of the 84-inch reflecting telescope for the Kitt Peak National Observatory

PLATE X.—Photograph of the 48–72-inch Schmidt telescope of the Palomar Observatory

PLATE XI.—Photograph of the 32–48-inch Schmidt telescope of the Hamburg Observatory

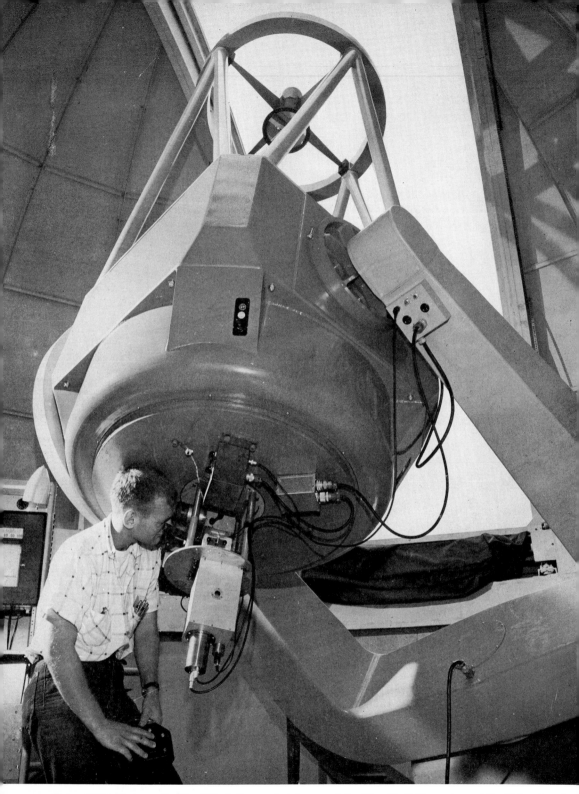

PLATE XII.—Photograph of the 36-inch Cassegrain telescope of the Pine Bluff Observatory of the University of Wisconsin.

The 84-inch telescope will have the third mirror (the first flat) permanently installed in the sky baffle, where it can be removed from the Cassegrain optical path for rapid changeover to the coudé by pivoting about its lower end.

The polar-axis bearings for the 84-inch are both oil-pad and standard ball bearings. The north-polar-axis bearing is large enough for an oil pad to be used to advantage. The south-polar-axis bearing is small, and the radius of friction is small enough for ordinary bearings to be used. The transition point between oil-pad and standard bearings is approximately 24 inches in diameter at the race.

The right-ascension drive for the 84-inch consists of a single worm wheel, used for both slewing and tracking. The size of the telescope is approaching that at which a double worm wheel can be considered. The decision depends on the cost of a single versus a double wheel, taking account of the additional loading placed upon a single wheel in slewing. The double-wheel system is very expensive, since the worm assembly must rock slightly so as to engage in contact the particular wheel for either slewing or tracking. The maintenance of close tolerances causes an expensive assembly.

The use of a single wheel results in the acceleration load of slewing being placed directly upon the tracking worm. The small dimensions of the 84-inch result in a lower moment of inertia, but the decision to use a single wheel was based on the expectation that proper lubrication of the worm will give the wheel a satisfactory lifetime.

The adopted engineering specifications and tolerances for the 84-inch are as follows:

Slew rate	120°/min
Set rate	60″/min
Guide rate	0″.5/sec
Dome rotation	180°/min
Shutter travel	45 ft/min
Pointing accuracy	1′ over sky
Deflection drift	60″ in 3 hours
Tracking accuracy	0″.5 in 1 revolution of worm (2 min)
Right-ascension worm wheel.	90″ P.D. 720 teeth
Declination worm	60″ P.D. 480 teeth, 3″ in 1 worm revolution

1.32. *The Mount Wilson–Palomar symmetrical telescopes.*—The famous instruments at these observatories span the types of the symmetrical group. The 60-inch reflector and the 18-inch and the 48-inch Schmidt telescopes have the fork design. The 48-inch Schmidt, shown in Plate X, is a fine example of a modern fork design. It in turn laid the groundwork for the design of the Lick 120-inch telescope. The 100-inch telescope mounting is a yoke in which the north-polar region is inaccessible. When the 100-inch telescope was designed, the yoke afforded the only practicable way to support the large mass of the telescope; the fork design was not yet possible. The introduction of oil-flotation supports on the 200-inch project enabled the Lick 120-inch to use the more useful fork design. The 200-inch used a yoke design modified by a horseshoe north-polar-axis bearing to allow access to the circumpolar regions. The combination of the fork and yoke design using an oversized north-polar-axis bearing still appears to be the best for very large telescopes.

1.33. *Other modern telescopes, symmetrical class.*—Other telescopes of modern design in the symmetrical group are illustrated by several recently constructed telescopes. The Hamburg-Bergedorf Schmidt telescope, shown in Plate XI, is an exceptionally clean design. The high latitude of this observatory makes it convenient to utilize a section of a sphere supported on oil pads for the north-polar-axis bearing.

Two identical telescopes utilizing a symmetrical mounting for small telescopes have recently been constructed, one for McDonald Observatory and the other, shown in Plate XII, for the Pine Bluff observing station of the Washburn Observatory. These telescopes are rapid-slewing photometric instruments. The small-focus travel arc of these telescopes makes them easy to use for most work; however, access to the focus and the maximum length of instruments is limited at high declinations.

2. MIRROR MATERIALS

2.1. DIELECTRIC MIRROR MATERIALS

2.11. *Pyrex.* Pyrex was introduced as a mirror material with the 200-inch project. The success of this telescope is, in fact, due largely to the technological breakthrough made possible by mass-produced low-expansion glass. Since this time, the use of Pyrex mirrors for large optical mirrors has become general. Several relatively low-coefficient glasses have subsequently become commercially available. The chief alternative to Pyrex is a borosilicate glass produced by Pilkington Brothers, Ltd.; the expansion coefficient of the Pilkington glass is $30\text{–}35 \times 10^{-7}$ per ° C, while for Pyrex type 7160 it is $25\text{–}30 \times 10^{-7}$ per ° C. Several other manufacturers cover the range from 35 to 50×10^{-7} per ° C.

The low-coefficient glasses vary considerably in appearance and other physical properties. Pyrex in bulk is pale greenish-orange in color and shows many striae. The glass is quite resistant to chemical attack, but the presence of certain trace ions in the solution caustics can cause stains. Pilkington glass is pale blue-green with a slight milky or fluorescent appearance. The color is apparently due to the fact that the composition of the glass is near a phase-separation point; however, the glass is stable but more sensitive to chemical attack and can be stained by the polishing tool or even finger marks. The chief agent responsible is believed to be the SO_4 ion. If water is properly buffered, these stain problems will not be encountered. For a low-coefficient glass, the Pilkington glass is relatively free from striae.

2.12. *Fused quartz or silica.*—Fused quartz or fused silica has long been regarded as the ultimate material for optics. Its coefficient of expansion of only 6×10^{-7} per ° C makes it ideal for optical working and for uses in fluctuating-temperature environments. Until about 1940, Thermal Syndicate in England

and General Electric in the United States were the chief sources of optical quartz. The intensive development program in 1930 on the 200-inch project did much to forward the production of fused quartz. The Thermal Syndicate quartz disks are clear quartz on an opaque quartz sponge, a direct result of the 200-inch research. Commercial General Electric quartz is produced by heating chunks of quartz packed in a mold until the mass melts. Stirring is not feasible in the highly viscid mass, and, as a consequence, the General Electric quartz disks show areas of residual polarization from the original crystal cullet.

The advances made in producing fused quartz of optical quality during the period from 1940 to 1945 made this material available for general use. Herraeus pioneered refinements in the blow-torch method and produced quartz of exceedingly high optical quality. Other processes involving gaseous phases of silicon, such as are used by Corning, have also made optical silica available. The available sizes of high-quality optical fused silica are limited to diameters of thin plate of 10 inches or total masses to less than 10 kg. In the field of non-optical fused silica, mirror disks up to 20 inches in diameter are stock items, and disks up to 80 inches diameter can now be obtained.

2.13. *Pyroceram.*—Up to late 1957 the only optical materials with properties suitable for large telescope mirrors were the Pyrex types of glass. The introduction of a new class of materials by Corning Glass Works called "Pyroceram" makes it necessary to reconsider the question of glasses for large telescopes. Pyroceram is basically a glass but is rendered crystalline during the annealing stage by the action of nucleating agents in the glass mix. The process is a trade secret, but the information available indicates that Pyroceram is a product of devitrification under controlled and ultimately stable processes. Pyroceram is usually opaque white, but clear varieties can be produced. The chief advantage of Pyroceram is that a zero-expansion glass can be produced. In fact, Pyroceram types having coefficients in the range of -7 to $+50 \times 10^{-7}$ are possible. Other physical parameters are related to this range, but Pyroceram exhibits mechanical strength and thermal conductivity mostly in excess of traditional glasses.

Pyroceram has been tested for suitability for optical mirrors. The material is very hard compared with glasses or quartz. The grinding rate is about half that of Pyrex, while the polishing rate is about equal to that of Pyrex. The material polishes well and can be figured without difficulty. The polished surface shows no scattering, indicating that the microcrystalline size is well below a fraction of a wave length, although the domain size is large enough to render the material opaque white. Occasional bubbles are noticed, but of the same size and frequency as those encountered in Pyrex disks.

Scattering by the Pyroceram surface has been overcome by depositing silicon monoxide on the surface by evaporation. If the layer is sufficiently thick, the coating can be polished and figured to optical accuracy. The final surface will then show no trace of the scattering attributed to the crystalline nature of Pyroceram.

The low coefficient of expansion of Pyroceram makes it of particular value for large telescopes. During the optical process, tests can be made without delay after polishing ceases. In large disks no warping of the surface of a cellular mirror under heating from the polishing tool will occur. As a consequence, it should be possible to bring a Pyroceram mirror to a better figure in less time than is needed with Pyrex. Pyroceram should prove of great value in astronomical usage because the mirror will retain its figure even under thermal shock. In existing large telescopes, some hours are required for the Pyrex mirror to reach equilibrium after the telescope is open for use. The cost of Pyroceram is about double that of Pyrex and consequently well below the cheapest fused-quartz disks.

2.2. Metal-Mirror Materials

The use of speculum and stellite for mirrors is well covered in earlier literature, and there is no need to review these facts here. Stellite is still of importance for reflecting slit jaws, although stainless steels are acceptable substitutes. The chief reasons for abolishing the use of speculum and stellite are the difficulties in casting and figuring. The material must be hard enough to make it amenable to optical polishing and stable enough to allow optical precision to be obtained and maintained.

Metal mirrors offer one outstanding advantage, namely, the large heat conductivity. In stellar telescopes this conductivity is not important, and it allows the mirror to reach equilibrium with the surrounding air quickly. In solar telescopes the conductivity becomes very important because of the absorption of some of the solar energy by the reflecting surfaces. For a metal film evaporated on glass, the conductivity is low, and the film will reach a temperature significantly above air temperature. This temperature difference will give rise to convection currents in the air that ruin the optical definition of the telescope. If the heat could be rapidly conducted through the mirror, the temperature rise could be kept small and the seeing maintained. The search for new metal materials has been vigorously pursued with some success during the last few years.

The basic requirements of hardness and stability rule out many metals and alloys. Metallurgists believe that single-element metals offer the best intrinsic stability, but most of them are soft. A wide range of steel alloys has desirable hardness, but the complex structure of steels makes predictions of optical stability hazardous.

2.21. *Beryllium.*—Beryllium offers us a fine selection of physical parameters, and large disks are now available at a cost of about $100 per pound. The metal, however, is extremely toxic—more so than arsenic. Great care and special procedures must be used in handling beryllium in the optical shop.

Beryllium is light weight, $\rho = 1.9$ (Pyrex glass, $\rho = 2.8$), and is as hard as speculum. It has high reflectivity and can be readily aluminized if needed. Polishing is slow, and figuring is as slow as speculum. The 12-inch disk tested by the National Observatory showed granularity and scattering not worse than steel. This disk was produced by vacuum powder-metallurgy, and pieces so forged show anisotropic mechanical properties aligned with the press axis. In this case the press axis was normal to the disk, so that the mechanical properties should have been optimum. No age-figure tests have been made because work was terminated because of the toxic nature of the material and the emergence of other materials. The extremely light weight of beryllium is attractive, and where weight is of paramount importance, beryllium may be of use.

2.22. *Titanium.*—Titanium is another exotic metal made common by current usage. Being a pure metal and having low density ($\rho = 4.7$) and high mechanical strength and hardness, it was considered in a recent study by the National Observatory. Titanium, moreover, has, for a metal, a low coefficient of expansion, which, combined with high heat conductivity, offered promise.

A 12-inch sintered disk of pure titanium was forged by the Rem-Cru Titanium Company for test. Grinding is very slow, and polishing is slow. The polish shows low reflectivity and trouble from sleeks. It appeared that fragments of of the metal were torn from the body of the material and picked up by the polisher. The polished surface showed much scattered light, and it was concluded that the base metal was too porous to offer high-quality mirror surface unless coated with other metals.

2.23. *Aluminum alloys.*—Both aluminum and copper are elements possessing high stability; however, they are too soft and ductile to be of practicable use. The wide range of aluminum alloys with their more satisfactory hardness now available has offered a new source of mirror materials. Ultra-stable fine-grained aluminum castings are currently in use commercially. Type 345 aluminum alloy was recommended to us as a base material. Tests are not yet complete, but this and similar alloys appear promising from the standpoint of dimensional stability.

Polishing of even hard-aluminum alloys is very difficult. A solution applied with success is to anodize the aluminum surface to Al_2O_3. The extremely hard oxide coating can be polished with diamond powders and yields a satisfactory mirror surface. The light weight of mirror aluminum castings and their high heat conductivity and abrasion-free polished oxide faces offer a desirable combination. The chief disadvantages are the scattering caused by porosity in the anodized coating and the difficulty of polishing the oxide (sapphire) surface.

2.24. *Kanogen.*—This material, developed by General Transportation Company of Chicago, is an amorphous metal coating of nickel-nickel-phosphorus composition that at low temperature can be applied to a wide range of base materials. Three properties make it important for metal mirrors: it is amorphous, hard, and chemically very stable. The hardness enables it to take a good polish and the amorphous structure results in low scattering on a polished surface. The reflectivity is good, 50–60 per cent, so that low-scattering usage is possible without coating the mirror with aluminum.

Tests using Kanogen 0.003 inch thick on pure copper and aluminum disks show that even soft metals can be used as a base if a Kanogen coating is applied. Since Kanogen adheres with great tenacity and is chemically stable when cleaned, it has promise in future metal-mirror applications.

3. MIRROR-SUPPORT SYSTEMS

The most important part of a telescope mounting is the primary mirror cell, though it must be admitted that the mirror cells for the secondaries are frequently not given the attention that they also require. A large telescope may have secondary mirrors larger than the primaries of smaller telescopes.

Basically, a mirror must be defined within close limits, yet be free to move. The mirror must be collimated and defined by only three back-support points, regardless of how many supports are used to carry the weight.

A schematic support pad is shown in Figure 3. The mirror pad, A, transmits the mirror's weight in the vicinity of A to a point-contact rolling surface. The counterweights, W, provide the balancing force. If the support is a defining support, then the arm carrying W will be constrained by micrometer stops. If it is a floating support, then W is free to move but usually has safety stops that limit the range of motion. The pad A is free to adjust in angle about the ball to align it against the mirror. It is also free to move parallel to the mirror back, to allow for differential thermal expansion between the glass and metallic supporting cell. This motion, however, must be constrained by a restoring force, to prevent the pad from dropping under its own weight when the mirror is on edge. This restoring force is also desirable to allow the pad to recenter itself merely by lifting up on the weight W.

The edge supports for a solid mirror are schematically arranged as in Figure 3. The rolling-ball contact, however, is not so satisfactory because the two surfaces contacting the ball must be parallel to avoid binding the required motion of A. The edge pads (A) are bound to the mirrors with strong nylon cords on the 48-inch Schmidt mirror (72 inches in diameter), the 82-inch McDonald reflector, and the 36-inch McDonald reflector. It is tedious to accomplish this alignment because the pads must be attached to the mirror before it is lowered into the cell.

A system that avoids the problem of the rolling ball and relieves the entire alignment problem was designed by Baustian and is shown in Figure 4. It uses a closed hydraulic system to transmit the loads. A sylphon bellows couples the pad A to the counterweight. The bellows has a natural spring action to provide the restoring force to recenter A. This system has, further, the advantage that the counterweight W and the transmitter bellows can be located at a distance from the pad bellows. A system of this type is already in use for edge supports in the new mirror cell for the 61-inch Harvard reflector. A similar system is being incorporated for the 36-inch reflector at Kitt Peak.

Gravity works in the proper direction to allow the primary mirror to be supported simply from the rear. Cassegrain and coudé *secondary* mirrors, on the other hand, have gravity operating in an inconvenient direction. In this case the most practical method of support is by drilling insert sockets in the rear and counterweighting through a thin tension-wire connector. Usually the secondary mirrors are edge-supported and defined. This support can then be a single centrally located socket, or more, depending on the diameter of the mirror. The 120-inch Lick reflector uses three support sockets drilled into the back of the secondary mirrors, each carrying 20 per cent of the mirror weight.

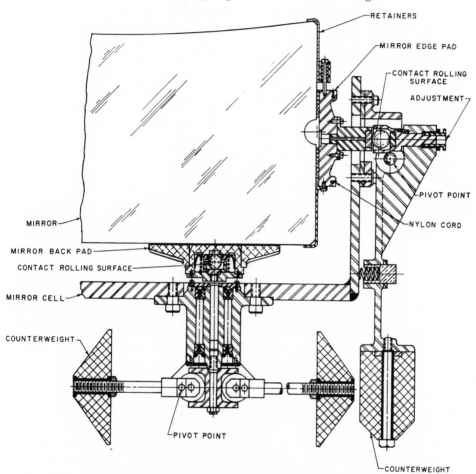

82 Inch TELESCOPE
MIRROR SUPPORT SYSTEM

SCALE IN INCHES

FIG. 3.—Cross-section of the mirror-support system for a large solid mirror, as used for the McDonald 82-inch telescope.

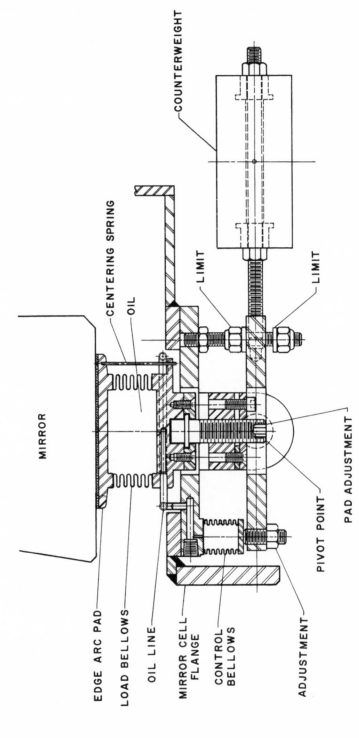

MIRROR

COUNTERWEIGHT

CENTERING SPRING

OIL

LIMIT

LIMIT

EDGE ARC PAD

LOAD BELLOWS

OIL LINE

MIRROR CELL
FLANGE

CONTROL
BELLOWS

ADJUSTMENT

PIVOT POINT

PAD ADJUSTMENT

FIG. 4.—Cross-section of a hydraulic edge support for solid mirrors, as used for the Kitt Peak 36-inch telescope

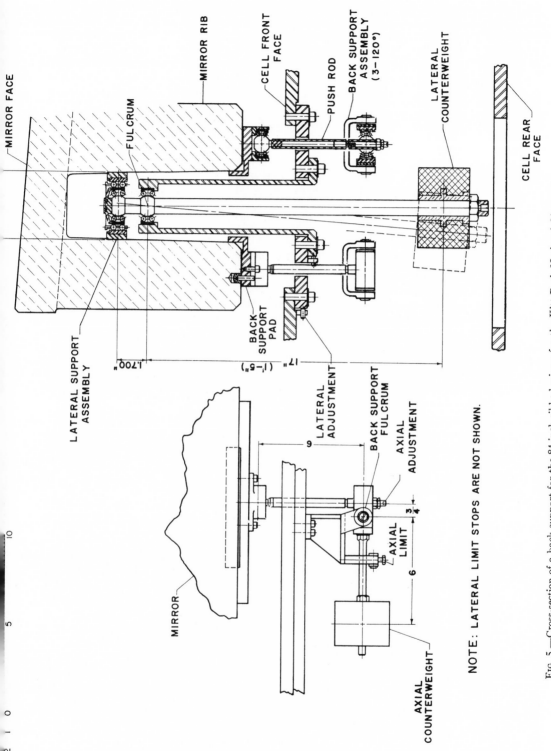

MIRROR FACE

MIRROR RIB

CELL FRONT FACE

PUSH ROD

BACK SUPPORT ASSEMBLY (3-120°)

LATERAL COUNTERWEIGHT

CELL REAR FACE

FULCRUM

LATERAL SUPPORT ASSEMBLY

1.700"

BACK SUPPORT PAD

17" (1'-5")

LATERAL ADJUSTMENT

BACK SUPPORT FULCRUM

AXIAL ADJUSTMENT

AXIAL LIMIT

9

MIRROR

3/4

6

AXIAL COUNTERWEIGHT

NOTE: LATERAL LIMIT STOPS ARE NOT SHOWN.

Fig. 5.—Cross-section of a back support for the 84-inch ribbed mirror for the Kitt Peak National Observatory

The *radial defining* of a mirror presents a more complicated problem than is encountered in defining the axial and angular alignment. Defining a large mirror (>30 inches) by the periphery is difficult because of the differential thermal expansion between mirror and cell. Either complicated compensated stops are required, or the mirror must be defined near the center. The large modern mirrors are all radially defined by adjustable pads located in the central hole of the mirror. Again the defining pad must be free in all directions except radially, in order to avoid binding when for some reason the mirror is slightly moved. A freedom of 0.030 inch takes care of motion that could be caused by maintenance on other parts of the support system.

3.1. CELLULAR DESIGNS

In the case of cellular mirrors the principles of support are the same except that the internal support offers a better load distribution than is possible with a solid disk. The 200-inch Palomar telescope combines the edge- and back-support functions in one elegant system. While the two support functions are theoretically independent, there is sufficient interaction between them to complicate adjustment operations. This experience has led to support functions for the 120-inch Lick telescope which are separate, though they use the same sockets.

In planning for future large telescopes, the design of cellular mirrors was examined. For the 84-inch telescope the basic mirror design used for the 200- and 120-inch mirrors was adopted (cf. Fig. 5). A study was made of various alternate ribbed structures, but the 200-inch type was selected as having the best thermal properties. The chief change is that the support socket has been reinforced to reduce its circular spring action, as otherwise it would materially reduce the strength of the mirror.

The subject of mirror design deserves more study. The 200-inch design is adequate for smaller mirrors, but for larger mirrors the entire question should be re-examined. The analysis involved is tedious, and actual experiments with moderate-size disks will be needed to evaluate proposed designs.

REFERENCES*

BAKER, J. G.	1954	*Sky and Telescope*, **13**, 73.
KING, H. C.	1955	*History of the Telescope* (Cambridge, Mass.: Sky Pub. Corp.)
MAKSUTOV, D. D.	1944	*J. Opt. Soc. America*, **34**, 270 (No. 5).
MEINEL, A. B.	1953	*Ap. J.*, **118**, 335.
ROSS, F. E.	1935	*Ap. J.*, **81**, 156.
SEYFERT, C.	1954	*Sky and Telescope*, **13**, 72.

* Properties of metals are given in the *International Critical Tables* (1926) and also in current company brochures.

CHAPTER 4

Schmidt Cameras

I. S. BOWEN

Director, Mount Wilson and Palomar Observatories
Carnegie Institution of Washington, California Institute of Technology

In the year 1932 Bernhard Schmidt published a short note entitled "Ein lichtstarkes komafreies Spiegelsystem" which described the optical system since known as the "Schmidt camera." The basic principle of this camera is that a single concave spherical mirror with a stop at its center of curvature has no unique axis and therefore yields equally good images at all points of its field. The field is curved, with a radius equal to the focal length. If small focal ratios are used, spherical aberration may become appreciable, although it should be noted that the spherical aberration of a single concave spherical mirror is smaller than that of the three- and four-lens anastigmats such as the triplet or Tessar types of the same focal ratio. To correct this residual spherical aberration, Schmidt introduced, in the stop at the center of curvature of the mirror, a thin, non-spherical corrector plate of glass. Even though this plate is non-achromatic it reduces the already very small spherical aberration to 2 or 3 per cent of its original value over the range of wave lengths normally photographed. This permits critical definition over a large field with a focal ratio that is an order of magnitude smaller than is possible with lens systems.

While somewhat similar systems had been suggested independently by others, it was Schmidt's genius as an optician that enabled him to figure successfully the very difficult fourth-degree curves on the corrector plate and make the system a practical instrument.

For critical photographic work with an optical system, it is necessary that the size of the image as set by the aberrations be no larger than the resolving power of the emulsion used. In the detailed design of such a system the dependence of the size of the aberration image on such factors as aperture, focal length, and distance off axis is therefore an essential factor. The theory of the aberrations of a Schmidt camera has been treated by Strömgren (1935), Carathéodory (1940), Bouwers (1946), and Linfoot (1949, 1951, 1955). The following is a simplified development of this theory.

1. ABERRATIONS OF A SCHMIDT CAMERA

1.1. PROPERTIES OF A SPHERICAL MIRROR

In Figure 1, *EF* is a ray through the center of curvature, *E*, of the spherical mirror *BD*, whose radius of curvature is *r*. For the purpose of this discussion this ray will be taken as the axis. *AB* is any other ray parallel to *EF* and at a distance *h* from it. After reflection at the mirror, this ray intersects *EF* at the point *C*. If we set $\sin \theta = h/r$, it is evident from the laws of reflection that

$$EC = \frac{r}{2 \cos \theta} = \frac{r}{2 \left(1 - h^2/r^2\right)^{1/2}}. \tag{1}$$

For rays near the axis, i.e., for h/r very small, *EC* approaches $EG = r/2$. The aberration in focal length is, therefore,

$$GC = \frac{r}{2 \left(1 - h^2/r^2\right)^{1/2}} - \frac{r}{2} \approx \frac{r}{4} \frac{h^2}{r} = \frac{h^2}{8 f}, \tag{2}$$

in which f, the focal length, is $r/2$.

The slope of the ray *BC* with respect to *EF* is approximately $2h/r$. If a photographic plate is placed normal to the axis at the focus for central rays, it is evident that this ray *BC* will intersect the plate at a distance from the axis of

$$GH = \frac{h^2}{4 r} \frac{2 h}{r}. \tag{3}$$

Or, if the plate is moved along the axis for a distance Δ from *G*, the focus for central rays, this distance, δ, becomes

$$\delta = \left(\frac{h^2}{4 r} - \Delta\right) \frac{2 h}{r} = \left(\frac{h^2}{8 f} - \Delta\right) \frac{h}{f}. \tag{4}$$

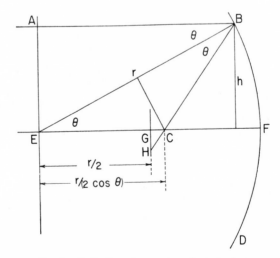

FIG. 1.—Reflection of rays at a spherical mirror

The angle that must be imparted to the ray as it passes the corrector plate to bring it to the same focal point as the central rays is approximately

$$a = \frac{\delta}{f} = \left(\frac{h^2}{8f} - \Delta \right) \frac{h}{f^2}. \tag{5}$$

1.2. Design of the Corrector Plate

Let t be the thickness of the corrector plate at a distance h from the axis and let n be the refractive index of the plate. The deviation, a, produced by the plate, then, is

$$a = (n-1) \frac{dt}{dh}. \tag{6}$$

Equating equations (5) and (6) and solving for dt/dh gives

$$\frac{dt}{dh} = \frac{h^3/8f^3 - \Delta h/f^2}{n-1}. \tag{7}$$

Integrating, one obtains

$$t = \frac{h^4/32f^3 - \Delta h^2/2f^2}{n-1} + K. \tag{8}$$

Let R and D be the radius and diameter, respectively of the aperture of the corrector plate and let $u = h/R$ and let f/D, the focal ratio of the camera, be F. For Δ substitute $aD/64F$. Equation (8) may then be written

$$t = \frac{(u^4 - au^2) D}{512 (n-1) F^3} + K. \tag{9}$$

We may now substitute this value of t in equation (6) to give the amount of the linear displacement of the ray at the focus produced by the corrector plate as

$$\delta = af = \frac{f(n-1) dt}{Rdu} = \frac{(4u^3 - 2au) f}{256F^3}. \tag{10}$$

1.3. Chromatic Aberration

Since the index of glass, n, in equation (8) varies with the wave length, the spherical aberration of the sphere can be accurately corrected for only one value of the index and therefore for only one wave length. If the corrector plate is calculated for use at a wave length for which the glass has an index n but is then used for a wave length for which the index is n', it is evident that the displacement of the beam is

$$\delta' = \frac{(4u^3 - 2au) f (n'-1)}{256F^3 (n-1)} \tag{11}$$

instead of the value given by equation (10). The difference between δ' and δ gives the residual aberration caused by the lack of achromatism of the corrector plate,

$$\delta' - \delta = \frac{(4u^3 - 2au) f (n'-n)}{256F^3 (n-1)}. \tag{12}$$

The radius of the image caused by lack of achromatism of the corrector plate is given by equation (12) when the parenthesis $(4u^3 - 2au)$ has its maximum absolute value in the range, $0 < u < 1$, that is, $0 < h < R$. Table 1 lists the value of the parenthesis over this range of u for several values of a. From this table it is evident that the maximum absolute value of the parenthesis has its lowest value for the case $a = 1.5$. Most corrector plates are figured to give approximately this value of a. For this case the minimum thickness of the corrector plate is at $u = (\frac{3}{4})^{1/2}$ or $h = 0.866R$.

For $a = 1.5$, the maximum absolute value of the parenthesis is 1, and the radius of the chromatic image is therefore

$$(\delta' - \delta)_{\max} = \frac{f(n' - n)}{256F^3(n - 1)}. \tag{13}$$

The wave-length ranges that are covered by various corrector-plate materials without allowing $(n' - n)/(n - 1)$ to exceed certain limits are given in Table 2. In this table it is assumed that n corresponds to $\lambda = 4300$ A.

This chromatic aberration is the factor that normally sets the minimum focal ratio that it is permissible to use in the design of a Schmidt camera for a given purpose. In order to obtain optimum performance, it is necessary that the

TABLE 1

VALUE OF $(4u^3 - 2 au)$

u	a			
	0	1.0	1.5	2.0
0.........	0.000	0.000	0.000	0.000
0.1.......	0.004	−0.196	−0.296	−0.396
0.2.......	0.032	−0.368	−0.568	−0.768
0.3.......	0.108	−0.492	−0.792	−1.092
0.4.......	0.256	−0.544	−0.944	−1.344
0.5.......	0.500	−0.500	−1.000	−1.500
0.6.......	0.864	−0.336	−0.936	−1.536
0.7.......	1.372	−0.028	−0.728	−1.428
0.8.......	2.048	+0.448	−0.352	−1.152
0.9.......	2.916	+1.116	+0.216	−0.684
1.0.......	4.000	+2.000	+1.000	0.000

TABLE 2

WAVE-LENGTH RANGE CORRESPONDING TO VARIOUS
VALUES OF $(n' - n)/(n - 1)$

$(n'-n)/(n-1)$	Fused Quartz	Crown Glass	$(n'-n)/(n-1)$	Fused Quartz	Crown Glass
±0.01......	3850–4960 A	3920–4860 A	±0.03.....	3260–8000 A	3390–7320 A
±0.02......	3520–6040 A	3610–5740 A	±0.04.....	3030–11600 A	....

diameter of the chromatic image $2(\delta' - \delta)$ shall not exceed the limit of resolution, p, of the photographic plate. Thus the minimum focal ratio is, from equation (13),

$$F = \left[\frac{f(n' - n)}{128p(n - 1)} \right]^{1/3}. \tag{14}$$

Or, expressed in terms of the aperture D,

$$F = \left[\frac{D(n' - n)}{128p(n - 1)} \right]^{1/2}. \tag{15}$$

For example, if D is 128 mm, p is set at 0.02 mm, which is about its value for most fast photographic plates, and a wave-length range corresponding to $(n' - n)/(n - 1) = 0.02$ is required, then the focal ratio should not be less than $F = 1$.

1.4. OFF-AXIS ABERRATIONS

As mentioned above, a mirror with an aperture at the center of curvature has no axis, and consequently images are equally good at all points in the field. The corrector plate, however, does have an axis, and consideration must therefore be given to off-axis aberrations.

If the thickness of the corrector plate is expressed as a function of the rectilinear co-ordinates (x, y) of the position on the plate by substituting $u^2 = x^2 + y^2$ in equation (9), one obtains

$$t = \frac{(x^4 + 2x^2y^2 + y^4 - ax^2 - ay^2)\, D}{512F^3(n - 1)} + K. \tag{16}$$

Let β and γ be the displacements of the ray at the focal plane, parallel to the x- and y-axis, respectively, caused by passing through the corrector plate at the point x, y,

$$\beta = \frac{(n - 1)f\partial t}{R\partial x} = \frac{(2x^3 + 2xy^2 - ax)f}{128F^3}, \tag{17}$$

$$\gamma = \frac{(n - 1)f\partial t}{R\partial y} = \frac{(2x^2y + 2y^3 - ay)f}{128F^3}. \tag{18}$$

The off-axis aberrations can then be treated by calculating the change in β and γ as the corrector plate is rotated through an angle ϕ about the y-axis.

This change is caused by two factors. First, since the rays no longer pass the corrector plate at minimum deviation, the deviations are increased by

$$\Delta_1\beta = \frac{\beta(n + 1)(\sin \phi)^2}{2n}, \tag{19}$$

$$\Delta_1\gamma = \frac{\gamma(\sin \phi)^2}{2n}. \tag{20}$$

Second, as the corrector plate is tilted, a point on the mirror, whose co-ordinates with respect to the axis through the center of the corrector plate are x, y, receives light which passed the corrector plate at a point whose co-ordinates are $x/\cos \phi$, y. The changes in the displacement resulting from this are

$$\Delta_2\beta = \left(\frac{1}{\cos \phi} - 1\right)\frac{\partial \beta}{\partial x}, \tag{21}$$

$$\Delta_2\gamma = \left(\frac{1}{\cos \phi} - 1\right)\frac{\partial \gamma}{\partial x}. \tag{22}$$

The resultant total linear displacements of the ray at the image plane are, approximately,

$$\Delta\beta = \Delta_1\beta + \Delta_2\beta = \left[\frac{(n+1)\,\beta}{2n} + \frac{x\,\partial \beta}{2\,\partial x}\right]\sin^2 \phi,$$

$$\Delta\beta = \left(4nx^3 + x^3 + 2nxy^2 + xy^2 - anx - \frac{ax}{2}\right)\frac{f\,(\sin \phi)^2}{128nF^3}, \tag{23}$$

$$\Delta\gamma = \Delta_1\gamma + \Delta_2\gamma = \left(\frac{\gamma}{2n} + \frac{x\,\partial \gamma}{2\,\partial x}\right)\sin^2 \phi,$$

$$\Delta\gamma = \left(2nx^2y + x^2y + y^3 - \frac{ay}{2}\right)\frac{f\,(\sin \phi)^2}{128nF^3}. \tag{24}$$

Table 3 gives the values in the parentheses in equations (23) and (24) for the case $a = 1.5$ and $n = 1.5$. The values are given for one quadrant of the corrector plate. However, it is evident from the formulae that the displacements are symmetrical with respect to both the x- and the y-axis. The unit of measurement in each case is $f(\sin \phi)^2/192\,F^3$. Since the maximum value of the parentheses in Table 3 is 4, the maximum radius, b, of the image caused by this aberration is

$$b = \frac{f\,(\sin \phi)^2}{48F^3}, \tag{25}$$

or, again, setting $2b = p$ the limit of resolution of the plate, we obtain

$$\sin^2 \phi = \frac{24F^3p}{f}, \tag{26}$$

in which ϕ is the limiting semifield for optimum definition. It may be noted that, for a camera designed for the limiting focal ratio F given in equation (14), this reduces to

$$\sin^2 \phi = \frac{3\,(n'-n)}{16\,(n-1)}. \tag{27}$$

Or, assuming again that $(n'-n)/(n-1) = 0.02$, one obtains a field of critical definition of $2\phi = 7°$. For many purposes a considerably larger angle may be used. Thus from Table 3 it appears that about 80 per cent of the light falls within an area whose radius is one-fourth that given by equation (26). Furthermore, if the mirror of the Schmidt camera is large enough to avoid vignetting, the image is completely symmetrical, so that no displacement-with-intensity effect should occur. If this central core of the image is set equal to the resolving power of the plate, a field twice as large in diameter becomes permissible.

The theory of the aberrations in sections 1.1–1.4 is based on the first term of an expansion and is therefore approximate. At low focal ratios the rigorous theory may depart appreciably from the formulae given. Thus at $F1$ the spherical aberration of the mirror is 16 per cent greater than that given in equation (3), and the chromatic aberration is about 12 per cent greater than in equation (13).

1.5. Aberrations Caused by Lack of Collimation

The foregoing theory assumes that the center of symmetry of the corrector plate and the center of curvature of the mirror are coincident. Since these

TABLE 3

VALUES OF PARENTHESES IN EQUATIONS (23) AND (24)

$(a = \frac{3}{2}, n = \frac{3}{2}$; Upper Figure $\Delta\beta$; Lower $\Delta\gamma)$

y	x										
	0	0.1	0.2	0.3	0.4	0.5	0.6	0.7	0.8	0.9	1.0
1.0	0.00										
	+ .25										
0.9	.00	+0.03	+0.10	+0.26	+0.54						
	+ .05	+ .09	+ .20	+ .38	+ .63						
0.8	.00	− .04	− .03	+ .06	+ .27	+0.66	+1.25				
	− .09	− .06	+ .04	+ .20	+ .42	+ .71	+1.06				
0.7	.00	− .10	− .15	− .12	+ .03	+ .36	+0.89	+1.67			
	− .18	− .15	− .07	+ .07	+ .27	+ .52	+0.83	+1.19			
0.6	.00	− .15	− .26	− .28	− .18	+ .10	+0.58	+1.31	+2.34		
	− .23	− .21	− .14	− .02	+ .15	+ .37	+0.63	+0.94	+1.30		
0.5	.00	− .19	− .34	− .41	− .35	− .12	+0.31	+1.00	+1.98		
	− .25	− .23	− .17	− .07	+ .07	+ .25	+0.47	+0.73	+1.03		
0.4	.00	− .23	− .42	− .52	− .50	− .30	+0.10	+0.75	+1.70	+2.98	
	− .24	− .22	− .17	− .09	+ .02	+ .16	+0.34	+0.55	+0.79	+1.06	
0.3	.00	− .26	− .47	− .60	− .61	− .44	−0.07	+0.55	+1.47	+2.73	
	− .20	− .19	− .15	− .09	− .01	+ .10	+0.23	+0.39	+0.57	+0.77	
0.2	.00	− .28	− .51	− .66	− .69	− .54	−0.19	+0.41	+1.31	+2.55	
	− .14	− .13	− .11	− .07	− .01	+ .06	+0.15	+0.25	+0.37	+0.51	
0.1	.00	− .29	− .54	− .70	− .74	− .60	−0.26	+0.33	+1.22	+2.44	
	− .07	− .07	− .06	− .04	− .01	+ .03	+0.07	+0.12	+0.18	+0.25	
0.0	.00	− .29	− .54	− .71	− .75	− .62	−0.29	+0.30	+1.18	+2.40	+4.00
	0.00	0.00	0.00	0.00	0.00	0.00	0.00	0.00	0.00	0.00	0.00

optical parts are separated by the relatively large distance of twice the focal length, the original adjustment and the maintenance of this coincidence often pose difficult problems. It is therefore of importance to consider the accuracy that must be maintained to insure critical definition.

Assume that the corrector plate is shifted a distance L from its proper position in a direction parallel to the x-axis, i.e., perpendicular to the axis of the camera. The change in the deviation produced by the plate at the point x, y is then given by

$$\delta\beta = \frac{L\partial\beta}{R\partial x} = \frac{(6x^2 + 2y^2 - a)L}{64F^2}, \tag{28}$$

$$\delta\gamma = \frac{L\partial\gamma}{R\partial x} = \frac{4xyL}{64F^2}. \tag{29}$$

This results in a typical coma pattern in which the maximum diameter of the pattern is given by the difference $C = \delta\beta(\pm 1, 0) - \delta\beta(0, 0)$, i.e.,

$$C = \frac{3L}{32F^2}. \tag{30}$$

C should not exceed the limit of resolution of the plate, p, and therefore L should not become greater than

$$L = \frac{32F^2 p}{3}. \tag{31}$$

1.6. Correction of Chromatic Aberration for Limited Regions of the Spectrum

For many applications of Schmidt cameras, such as spectroscopy or color-magnitude studies from direct photographs, it is not necessary to focus simultaneously a very large range of wave lengths at one time, although it may be desirable to shift the range studied all the way from the ultraviolet to the infrared. This could, of course, be accomplished by providing each camera with a series of corrector plates, each of which is corrected for the appropriate range of wave lengths.

A much more inexpensive procedure is to make use of the fact that a plane-parallel plate of glass placed in the converging beam introduces a small amount of spherical aberration of a sign opposite that of a concave mirror. Thus, if a ray strikes a plane-parallel piece of glass of thickness d, the emergent ray is parallel to the initial ray but is displaced in the direction of the normal to the plate by an amount

$$T = d\left(1 - \frac{\tan\psi}{\tan\eta}\right), \tag{32}$$

in which η is the angle between the incident ray and the normal to the surface and ψ is the corresponding angle of the ray in the glass.

Assuming an index of refraction N and substituting the law of refraction, this reduces, after neglecting higher powers, to

$$T = d\left[1 - \frac{1}{N} + \left(\frac{1}{2N} - \frac{1}{2N^3}\right)\sin^2\eta\right]. \tag{33}$$

The amount of the spherical aberration, S, that is the displacement between the intersection with the axis of a central ray ($\eta = 0$) and of any other ray is

$$S = \frac{d\ (N^2 - 1)\ (\sin\ \eta)^2}{2\ N^3}. \tag{34}$$

Expressing S in terms of the slope of the ray, i.e., setting $\sin\eta = h/f$, we obtain

$$S = \frac{d\ (N^2 - 1)\ h^2}{2\ N^3 f^2}. \tag{35}$$

After passing through such a plane-parallel plate, the rays for which h/f is large are focused behind those for which h/f is small. This is opposite to the spherical aberration produced by a spherical mirror. Theoretically, therefore, a plane-parallel plate in the converging beam could be used in place of the corrector plate. Equating equations (2) and (35) and solving for d, one obtains the thickness of such a plate required to correct for the spherical aberration of the mirror as

$$d = \frac{N^3 f}{4\ (N^2 - 1)}. \tag{36}$$

For crown glass d is about $2f/3$.

The correction of all the aberration of a spherical mirror by such a plane-parallel plate is impracticable because of the thickness and diameter required. Such a plane-parallel plate is nevertheless very useful to correct for the residual chromatic aberration of the corrector plate. Thus, if the corrector plate is designed for an index n corresponding to a wave length near the short-wave-length end of the range but is used at a longer wave length where the index is n', the correction provided by the plate is then too weak by an amount equal to $(n - n')/(n - 1)$ times the whole correction. This additional correction may then be added by inserting a plate having a thickness d' equal to $(n - n')/(n - 1)$ times the thickness given by equation (36), that is,

$$d' = \frac{N^3 f\ (n - n')}{4\ (N^2 - 1)\ (n - 1)}. \tag{37}$$

For most cases d' is between $0.01f$ and $0.03f$.

In a majority of the cases when one photographs these longer-wave-length ranges, it is necessary to insert a filter to eliminate the shorter wave lengths. By making the filter of the thickness given by equation (37) and placing it immediately in front of the photographic plate, correction for spherical aberration may be attained without the loss of light by additional glass-air surfaces.

Another application for these plane-parallel correctors is the testing with visual light of a plate to be corrected for the ultraviolet, as mentioned in § 2.

1.7. FIELD FLATTENERS

As already mentioned, both the mirror with a stop at its center of curvature and the Schmidt camera yield a focal surface that is a sphere having a radius equal to the focal length and a center of curvature that coincides with the center of curvature of the spherical mirror. In the longer focal lengths it is often possible to bend photographic film or even glass plates to the necessary curvature. Thus glass plates 1 mm thick and up to 35×35 cm are regularly bent to the 3-meter radius of the 48-inch Schmidt camera of the Palomar Observatory. For spectroscopic applications where one is interested in the focus along a narrow strip rather than over a large area, the film or plate can be bent to a cylinder rather than a sphere. Glass plates 1 mm thick bend with practically no breakage to radii as short as 90 cm, and plates 0.75 mm thick bend to a radius of 45 cm with only occasional breakage.

For cameras with shorter radii, one must either use film with its large instability under changes in humidity and temperature or flatten the field with a field-flattener lens placed immediately in front of the plate. Such a field-flattener lens should be plano-convex, the convex surface having a radius of approximately $(N-1)f/N$, in which N is the index of the glass and f is the radius of curvature of the field to be flattened. To reduce aberrations to a minimum, the plane surface of the lens should be placed as close as possible to the photographic emulsion.

If the diameter of the field to be flattened is $2m$, the center of the lens is $Nm^2/2(N-1)f$ thicker than the edge. The chief aberration introduced by the field flattener is spherical aberration, although a slight amount of coma may also be introduced near the edge of the field. In the center of the field such a lens, when placed close to the focus, behaves about the same as a plane-parallel plate of the same thickness and therefore introduces the spherical aberration given by equation (35).

The diameter of the spurious image K, at a plane through the focus for central rays, caused by passage through such a plane-parallel plate is, from equation (35),

$$K = \frac{2\,hS}{f} = \frac{d\,(N^2-1)\,h^3}{N^3 f^3} = \frac{d\,(N^2-1)}{8\,N^3 F^3} , \qquad (38)$$

in which F is again the focal ratio.

By placing the photographic plate at the position of minimum size of the spurious image, this diameter can be reduced to $\frac{1}{4}K$. Furthermore, the corrector plate can be so figured that optimum definition is obtained when a plate of half the central thickness of the field flattener is in place, thereby cutting the spherical aberration in half. However, in order to take advantage of these possibilities, it is necessary to use a radius of curvature for the field-flattener lens slightly different from that given above. When these optimum conditions are used and the central thickness of the lens is substituted for d, the diameter of the residual image, j, caused by spherical aberrations is

$$j = \frac{d \, (N^2 - 1)}{64 \, N^3 F^3} = \frac{m^2 \, (N + 1)}{128 \, N^2 F^3 f} . \tag{39}$$

Setting j equal to p, the limit of resolution of the plate, and solving for m gives the maximum value of the half-field that can be flattened with good definition:

$$m = N \left(\frac{128 \, p F^3 f}{N + 1} \right)^{1/2} . \tag{40}$$

Assuming the usual values of p, it is evident that the permissible field is small for focal ratios of $F/1$ or less.

Linfoot and Wayman (1949) have made an extensive study of the Schmidt camera with field flattener and of possible modification of the curves of corrector plate and flattener to yield optimum definition.

1.8. VIGNETTING

Since the corrector plate and mirror are separated by the large distance of $2f$, substantial vignetting occurs if the mirror is not made appreciably larger than the corrector plate. To have a completely unvignetted field of diameter V, it is evident that the mirror should have a diameter of $D + 2V$, in which D is, as before, the aperture of the corrector plate.

2. METHODS OF FIGURING AND ADJUSTMENT

As indicated by equation (8), the corrector plate must be figured to a fourth-degree curve. This requires the development of techniques different from those used for the conventional spherical surfaces. The procedure most commonly used in the production of a corrector plate is to prepare a plane-parallel plate of approximately the thickness desired. One side is then ground to give the thickness called for by equation (8), using small tools. Several methods have been used for testing the thickness as the grinding progresses. In the case of smaller corrector plates the thickness of various zones may be measured directly with a precision micrometer. Another method which is adaptable to corrector plates of all sizes is to focus a microscope with a precision-focusing mechanism first on the plane-polished face and then on the ground face through the plate. After multiplication by the index of the glass, the difference in the foci gives the thickness. A third method depends on mounting the corrector plate at a small known tilt with respect to another plane plate. Precision ball bearings of accurately equal diameters are then dropped between the plates, and the curve defined by the centers of the balls is noted. This curve, when multiplied by the slope of one plate with respect to the other, yields the curve that has been ground on the corrector plate.

When the plate has been ground to the proper thickness as a function of radius, as shown by one of the above tests, it is then polished. The plate is next mounted in the proper position with respect to the mirror of the camera, and the image is tested with either a knife-edge or a Hartmann test. Further figuring is then carried out as indicated by these tests. For these tests, parallel light should be incident on the system. If this is not available, the tests may be made with a reflecting flat mounted in front of the corrector plate, thereby giving a double traversal of the system by the rays.

For many purposes it is often desirable to have the corrector plate give optimum correction in the violet or ultraviolet, where visual knife-edge tests are difficult or impossible. In this case it is often possible to correct from one region to the other through the introduction of a plane-parallel plate with a thickness given by equation (37) in the converging beam, as explained in section 1.6.

Other procedures for figuring the corrector plates have been suggested and tried. These depend on deforming the plate by mounting it on a ring and evacuating one side in such a way that the plate is deformed into the inverse of the surface desired. If the plate is figured while thus deformed, with one of the usual methods for producing a sphere, and is then allowed to return to its undeformed shape, the desired curve should result. In practice this method has not proved very successful, probably because any errors in the deformation caused by lack of optical accuracy in the supporting ring are ground into the final surface.

In the course of grinding the corrector plate it is customary to grind into the glass a small ring whose center is at the center of symmetry of the surface of the plate. The mirror and corrector plate can then be easily and accurately collimated by bringing this ring into a coincidence with its image as formed by the spherical mirror.

The author is indebted to Mr. Don Hendrix for most of the procedures described in this section.

3. MODIFICATIONS OF THE SCHMIDT CAMERA

As already indicated, the manufacture of the Schmidt corrector plate with its non-spherical surface presents many difficult problems that cannot be handled by conventional techniques. For the same reason, it is not easily adaptable to quantity-production methods. Several procedures have been suggested for replacing the corrector plate with a lens having spherical surfaces whose radii are so chosen as to yield a spherical aberration equal and opposite to that of the mirror.

Maksutov (1944) and Bouwers (1946) have pointed out that a long-focus lens can be given any arbitrary amount of spherical aberration by "bending" it a proper amount, i.e., by using a meniscus form in which the focal length is maintained constant while the depth of the meniscus is varied to give the desired value for the spherical aberration. Maksutov also pointed out that this single lens may be rendered achromatic if the proper relationship is maintained between the front and rear radii, thereby making possible an achromatic system for the whole lens-mirror camera.

With the aid of these systems it is possible to compensate completely for the third-order spherical aberration of the mirror. However, at small focal ratios, fifth or higher orders may still remain because the relative coefficients of these orders are, in general, different for a lens and a mirror. In the conventional Schmidt corrector plate these higher orders are automatically corrected by the methods of figuring and testing described above.

In order to compensate for the spherical aberration of the mirror even with a moderately thick lens, it is usually necessary to use a deep meniscus, i.e., one in which the radii of curvature of the surfaces are comparable with the diameter of the lens. With the high angle of incidence of the light on these surfaces, the correction varies rapidly with angle, and off-axis aberrations tend to be larger than with the conventional corrector plate. These moderately thick lenses with very deep curves are, furthermore, very wasteful of glass and are time-consuming to manufacture. For these reasons, relatively few cameras of this type have been constructed with the apertures required for astronomical purposes.

One modification of this meniscus corrector plate can be made to yield a very large field, namely, the case in which both surfaces of the meniscus are made concentric with the surface of the mirror. A separate aperture stop is placed at the center of curvature. In this case the inner radius and the thickness of the meniscus are the variables used to balance the spherical aberration of the lens against that of the mirror. This system, having no preferred axis, yields equally good definition at all points in the field.

Bouwers (1946) has investigated the case in which the meniscus is placed between the common center of curvature and the focal surface. Henyey and Greenstein (1948) have designed a camera in which the meniscus and the mirror are placed on opposite sides of the common center of curvature and also one in which the meniscus is placed between the focal surface and the mirror. In this case the light traverses the meniscus twice, once in the parallel and once in the converging beam.

These lenses using concentric surfaces no longer have negligible power and therefore give a system that is non-achromatic. Bouwers and Henyey and Greenstein succeeded in making these lenses achromatic by designing the meniscus from two kinds of glass having substantially different dispersions. Since the boundary between the two kinds of glass cannot be concentric with the other surfaces, it is necessary that the two glasses have very nearly the same index, in order that the refraction at the interface between the two glasses shall not cause serious off-axis aberrations. Hawkins and Linfoot (1945) achromatized a similar system by using a two-element corrector plate in addition to the meniscus.

Baker (Whipple 1949) has designed a wide-angle camera for studies of meteor trails which makes use of an extension of these principles. To obtain additional parameters for balancing high-order aberrations, two meniscus lenses are used, one before the common center of curvature and therefore convex to the incoming light, the other between the focal surface and the mirror. To correct still further for the high orders of spherical aberration and the chromatic aberration, a thin corrector plate with a non-spherical surface is introduced at the central stop. This camera, with an aperture of 30 cm and a focal length of 20 cm, yields a well-corrected field about 50° in diameter.

All cameras of this concentric type have the disadvantage that the field is curved, with a radius approximately equal to the focal length. For fields larger than 20° or 30°, great difficulty is encountered in bending an emulsion, even on a film base, to a spherical surface. In the Baker meteor camera with its 50° field it was necessary to use special film molded to a sphere of the proper radius.

Another disadvantage of these designs, particularly for longer focal lengths, arises from the thickness of the meniscus lenses. Thus, in order to obtain compensation for the spherical aberration of the mirror with lenses having concentric surfaces, it is necessary to use lens thicknesses which require light-paths in glass from 0.5 to 1 times the focal length. Consequently, unless unusually transparent glass is obtainable, severe light-losses may occur, particularly at shorter wave lengths.

Two other disadvantages of the conventional Schmidt camera are the curved field and the relatively great length of the telescope tube, which equals twice the focal length. In the case of large instruments this length may add substantially to the cost because of the large dome required.

By combining a corrector plate and a non-spherical mirror, Wright (1935) designed a wide-field instrument with a flat field and a tube length equal to the focal length. Väisälä (1935) generalized Wright's theory to cover a whole family of cameras using non-spherical surfaces on both mirror and corrector plate and yielding a wide range of ratios of tube length to focal length, as well as a variety of field curvatures. In general, the size of the well-corrected field in these designs is smaller than in the Schmidt camera.

Baker (Seyfert 1954) designed a telescope for the Dyer Observatory with a corrector plate, a parabolic mirror, and a compound field flattener placed some distance in front of the focal plane. The field is flat, and the tube length is about 25 per cent greater than the focal length.

Another group of modified Schmidt cameras utilizes a corrector plate and two mirrors in a Cassegrain arrangement. Baker (1940b) has investigated the cases in which one spherical and one non-spherical mirror are used. The Armagh-Dunsink-Harvard telescope designed by him is a representative of the case in which the primary is spherical. Burch (1942), Slevogt (1942), and Linfoot (1944) have also investigated Cassegrain systems of this type. Wayman (1950) studied the special case in which both mirrors are spherical and concentric and the corrector plate is placed at their common center of curvature. Linfoot (1945) achromatized a Cassegrain system through the use of two separated corrector plates.

4. MODIFICATIONS OF THE SCHMIDT CAMERAS FOR SPECTROGRAPHS

For many spectrographic applications it is not necessary to use fully achromatic systems. This permits the use of several modifications that would not yield satisfactory results for general photography. Furthermore, fitting a Schmidt camera into a spectrograph places certain restrictions on the design that are not present in general photography and therefore make other modifications desirable.

4.1. Solid-Block and Thick-Mirror Schmidt Cameras

For Schmidt cameras of short focal length, substantial gains in the limiting focal ratios may be obtained through the use of the solid-block or thick-mirror Schmidt cameras designed by Hendrix (1939) and Hendrix and Christie (1939) and later investigated by Baker (1940a).

In the solid-block design the space between the corrector plate and the mirror is made of one block of glass, the corrector plate being figured on one end and the mirror on the other. Comparing a solid-block Schmidt with a conventional air Schmidt of the same aperture and mirror radius r, it is evident that the spherical aberrations of the mirrors are equal. On the other hand, the focal length and focal ratio of the solid block are $1/n$ times as great as for the air Schmidt, and the speed is therefore n^2 times as great. The chromatic aberration of the solid block is $1/n$ times as great as for the air Schmidt, and the off-axis aberrations between $1/n$ and $1/n^2$ are as great. It is therefore possible to use a solid-block Schmidt with a focal ratio as low as $1/n$ times that given by equation (14) and $1/n^{3/2}$ times that given by equation (15).

The construction of a solid-block Schmidt involves serious practical difficulties because the focus and therefore the location of the plate are at the center of the block. An access hole must therefore be cut from the center of the corrector plate and the bottom of it polished to an optical surface. Because of the difficulty of doing this, the thick-mirror type is usually substituted. In this design the solid block extends from a plane surface passing through the focus to the mirror. The thickness of this block is therefore half of r, the radius of the mirror. Because of the refraction of all off-axis rays entering the solid block, the corrector plate—which is in the form of the conventional thin plate—is placed at a distance $r/2n$ from the focus in order to be at the effective center of curvature of the mirror. The aberrations and therefore the limiting focal ratio are essentially the same as in the solid-block type. Since for both of these types the focal length is $r/2n$, in which n is strongly dependent on the wave length, any off-axis images in white light show large chromatic effects. Consequently, this type of camera can be used only with monochromatic images such as those produced by a spectrograph.

4.2. Schmidt Aplanatic Sphere Camera

Another device for shortening the focus and therefore decreasing the limiting focal ratio of a Schmidt camera is the introduction of an aplanatic sphere at the proper point with respect to the focus of the Schmidt camera (Bowen 1952). As given by the usual theory of an aplanatic sphere made of material of index n, this reduces the focal length to $r/2n^2$ and, at the same time, reduces the linear dimensions of the aberration image produced by the Schmidt camera itself. Unfortunately, the Schmidt camera produces an image surface which is convex toward the incoming light, with a radius equal to the focal length. To satisfy rigorously the aplanatic condition for the sphere at all points of the field, this image surface should be concave, with a radius equal to n times the radius of the aplanatic sphere. Because of this, a small amount of additional aberration is introduced by the aplanatic sphere, except for rays that pass through image points on the circle where these two image surfaces intersect. By making the rear surface of the aplanatic sphere concave with the appropriate curvature, it has been possible to correct for most of this added spherical aberration and at the same time to flatten completely the final focal surface.

To satisfy the aplanatic condition, it is also necessary that the final image be located at a distance from the center of the sphere equal to the radius of the sphere divided by n. A given sphere can be constructed to satisfy this condition rigorously only for one value of n and therefore for one wave length. However, if the sphere is designed to satisfy this condition for a wave length near the short-wave-length end of the spectral range, it has been found possible to correct partially for the errors introduced at longer wave lengths by moving the plate back a short distance, usually a few tenths of a millimeter, from the sphere. Such a Schmidt aplanatic sphere camera yields, if anything, better definition, over a field diameter equal to $0.08f$, than that given by the Schmidt camera alone. This makes possible the use of focal ratios equal to somewhat less than $1/n^2$ of that given by equation (15).

4.3. Twice-through Corrector Plates

In spectrographs using a reflection grating, one of the difficulties encountered is the interference of the camera optics with the incoming collimator beam. To avoid this, it is usually necessary to move all parts of the camera optics to a distance of several times the aperture from the grating. It is then necessary to provide camera optics with an aperture substantially larger than that of the collimator if severe losses due to vignetting are to be avoided at the edges of the field. The introduction of larger optics is always expensive and greatly increases the aberrations, in many cases pushing them beyond the permissible limits.

One method for avoiding this difficulty in the case of the Schmidt camera is to place the corrector plate parallel to and practically in contact with the grating (Bowen 1952). The light then passes the corrector plate twice, once before and once after diffraction at the grating. It can easily be shown that in this case the depths of the curve of the corrector plate should be reduced by the factor $\cos \theta / (1 + \cos \theta)$ from that of the regular once-through plate, in which θ is the angle between the normal to the plate and the collimator beam. For satisfactory performance the axis of the camera should be nearly normal to the grating. The chromatic aberrations are essentially the same as for the conventional corrector plate, and the off-axis aberrations are about 10 per cent less.

5. DESIGNS OF SCHMIDT CAMERAS

Schmidt cameras find two main uses in astronomical research. The first is for direct photography of large areas of the sky. Because of their very superior definition over a wide field, Schmidt cameras are rapidly replacing the older astrographic cameras with lenses of the Petzval or triplet type. Like the older cameras, they are often used with objective prisms for spectrographic surveys. The second use of the Schmidt camera is in spectrographs. The extremely low focal ratios attainable with Schmidt cameras and their modifications make possible very large gains in speed, especially for the spectrographs on the large reflectors. Details of several spectrographs making use of Schmidt cameras are given in chapter 10 of Volume 2.

5.1. Optical Design of Schmidt Cameras for Direct Photography

The focal length and aperture selected for a Schmidt camera depend, like those for any telescope used for direct photography, on the angular resolution and scale and the limiting magnitude required. The limiting focal ratio is set by equations (14) and (15) of section 1.3. Any one of several factors may fix the limit to the plate size that may be used. The first of these is the off-axis aberration of the Schmidt camera as given in section 1.4. The second is the fraction of the light of the incoming beam intercepted by the plateholder. This is likely to be the important factor in cameras of large focal ratio. Finally, the limit is occasionally set by the dimensions of the photographic plate that can be bent to the focal surface without undue breakage or by the size of the field flattener that can be used without introducing objectionable aberrations (see sec. 1.7). In general, it has been found that a square plate will bend to about the same spherical radius as the inscribed circular plate. The square plates are more efficient than the round plates for building up mosaics covering large areas of the sky and are cheaper and easier to obtain.

5.2. Mechanical Design

In general, the mechanical design of the Schmidt camera does not differ greatly from that of the older lens astrographs, the usual design having a closed tube in a fork or English-type mounting. Likewise, drive and control mechanisms are similar to other telescopes of similar size. A few special precautions are necessary, however. Thus all the standard Schmidt cameras locate the plate-holder at the prime focus: because of the large field and small focal ratio, a Newtonian flat would be so large as to intercept an objectionable amount of light from the incoming beam. Knife-edge focusing is therefore impracticable, and the plateholder must be focused by taking focus plates. It is therefore not feasible to refocus at regular intervals during the night to correct for changes caused by thermal expansion or contraction of the tube. In the larger instruments it is customary to eliminate the focal shift by spacing the mirror and the plateholder with invar rods having approximately the same coefficient of expansion as the mirror.

The very large field of critical definition of the Schmidt cameras renders them much more susceptible to differential refraction effects than the older instruments. It is desirable that all long exposures be scheduled for near the meridian. Special attention must also be given to the exact alignment of the polar axis. In some cases it may even be desirable to use slightly different orientations of the axis for fields at various declinations. In order to make these shifts convenient and exactly repeatable, the polar-axis adjustment may be provided with precision micrometers or other indicators.

To reduce these differential effects to a minimum, it is necessary to guide on a star near the center of the field. Since it is impossible to do this by using light from the Schmidt camera, one or more guide telescopes are normally provided. In order that differential motion between the Schmidt camera and the guide telescope shall not cause distortion of the images, special attention must be given to the reduction or compensation of flexure in the two telescopes.

The Appendix (p. 239) lists the characteristics of various existing Schmidt cameras.

REFERENCES

BAKER, J. G.	1940a	*Proc. Am. Phil. Soc.*, **82**, 323.
	1940b	*Ibid.*, p. 339.
BOUWERS, A.	1946	*Achievements in Optics* (New York and Amsterdam: Elsevier Publishing Co.), pp. 1–24.
BOWEN, I. S.	1952	*Ap. J.*, **116**, 1.
BURCH, C. R.	1942	*M.N.*, **102**, 159.
CARATHÉODORY, C.	1940	*Hamburger Math. Einzelschriften*, No. 28.
HAWKINS, D. G., and LINFOOT, E. H.	1945	*M.N.*, **105**, 334.
HENDRIX, D.	1939	*Pub. A.S.P.*, **51**, 158.
HENDRIX, D., and CHRISTIE, W. H.	1939	*Scient. American*, **161**, 118.
HENYEY, L. G., and GREENSTEIN, J. L.	1948	*Am. J. Roentgenol. and Radium Therap.*, **59**, 565.
LINFOOT, E. H.	1943	*M.N.*, **103**, 210.
	1944	*M.N.*, **104**, 48.
	1945	*Proc. Phys. Soc. London*, **57**, 209.
	1949	*M.N.* **109**, 279.

	1951	*Ibid.*, **111**, 75.
	1952	*Trans. I.A.U.*, **8**, 736.
	1955	*Recent Advances in Optics* (Oxford: Clarendon Press).
LINFOOT, E. H., and HAWKINS, D. G.	1946	*M.N.*, **105**, 334.
LINFOOT, E. H., and WAYMAN, P. A.	1949	*M.N.*, **109**, 535.
LINFOOT, E. H., and WOLF, E.	1949	*J. Opt. Soc. America*, **39**, 752.
MAKSUTOV, D. D.	1944	*J. Opt. Soc. America*, **34**, 270.
SCHMIDT, BERNHARD	1932	*Mitt. d. Hamburger Sternw.*, **7**, 15.
SEYFERT, C. K.	1954	*Sky and Telescope*, **13**, 72.
SLEVOGT, H.	1942	*Zs. f. Instrumentenk.*, **62**, 312.
STRÖMGREN, B.	1935	*Vierteljahrsschr. Astr. Gesellsch.*, **70**, 65.
VÄISÄLÄ, Y.	1935	*A.N.*, **254**, 361.
WAYMAN, P. A.	1950	*Proc. Phys. Soc. London, B*, **63**, 553.
WHIPPLE, F.	1949	*Sky and Telescope*, **8**, 90.
WRIGHT, F. B.	1935	*Pub. A.S.P.*, **47**, 300.

CHAPTER 5

Telescope Driving Mechanisms

R. R. McMATH AND O. C. MOHLER

McMath-Hulbert Observatory, Lake Angelus, Michigan

1. INTRODUCTION

A PERFECT driving mechanism for an astronomical telescope should completely stabilize the image produced by the instrument. This means either that the image should remain absolutely motionless with respect to some reference point or that it should move in controlled and predictable fashion when such motion is required by the observational program. One attempts to achieve these aims by variable rotations of the telescope tube about suitably chosen axes and by moving small auxiliary devices—photographic plate carriages, photoelectric cells, optical components—attached to the telescope near the plane in which the image is formed. The choice of axes and the precision of their motion almost entirely determine the convenience and quality of the operation of the telescope.

Two important considerations have led to the nearly universal adoption of a particular type of telescope mounting with a carefully chosen set of axes. The first of these is the recognition that the telescope should, in principle, be directable to all azimuths and altitudes above the horizon. The second arises in the attempt to compensate as directly as possible for the major apparent motion of celestial bodies, which is a result of the earth's rotation. Thus the equatorial, or parallactic, mounting has evolved and is now the usual way of supporting the telescope and providing for the necessary motions. The methods of supplying motions to the equatorial type of mounting will be discussed here. Modifications required for different types of mountings should be apparent, and these have been described in some detail by other authors (Sisson 1954; Fellgett 1956).

An equatorial mounting carries the telescope on two perpendicular axes of rotation: (1) the polar, or hour-angle, axis is fixed relative to the earth and is parallel to the earth's axis of rotation; (2) the other, the declination axis, intersects, or crosses, the hour-angle axis perpendicularly. The simplest form of telescope driving mechanism provides a rotation of the hour-angle axis at the correct invariable rate to compensate precisely for the rotation of the earth.

Although some such form of telescope driving machinery is now generally considered to be an integral part of the instrument, the use of these devices was uncommon before the installation of the great Dorpat refractor in 1826, approximately two centuries after the first telescopic observations. The important role played by Fraunhofer's driving apparatus in the success of the Dorpat instrument was thoroughly appreciated by W. Struve (1826). His recognition and publication of its merits provided a reference standard frequently quoted in establishing specifications for the construction of astronomical telescopes during the nineteenth century.

Most of the early drives controlled the rate of fall of a heavy weight, which, through requisite gearing, moved the hour-angle axis of the telescope. Since the weight was raised to its starting point by hand, the telescopes were actually moved by human power. Indeed, for some telescopes, assistants were hired to turn the gears of the telescope drive (Lassell 1867). The provision of an electric motor for raising the driving weight was one of the first steps in the improvement of the gravity-powered drive. Later developments have substituted electric motors for falling weights as prime movers of telescopes, and the most recent modifications of telescope drives have been concerned primarily with controlling the rate of rotation of the driving motors within close limits or introducing corrections for erroneous rates. Most of these evolutionary changes have been brought about by increasingly insistent demands for greater accuracy in all aspects of telescope performance. The change during a century in the acceptable standard of precision is clearly shown in the contrast between the statement of Lord Oxmantown (1866), the fourth Earl of Rosse, "a joiner and a plumber can execute the work with sufficient accuracy," and the more recent opinion, *"Precision.* This is a consideration of great prominence and importance in astronomical instrument design, where more difficult conditions are imposed than in most general engineering projects" (Sisson 1954).

In striving for the goals of precision just mentioned, modern telescope driving systems should provide accurate, continuously variable motions of both the hour-angle and the declination axis. The original $10\frac{1}{2}$-inch telescope of the McMath-Hulbert Observatory was, as far as is known, the first instrument in which controlled, continuously variable motions about both these axes could be obtained (McMath, Hulbert, and McMath 1932). A precise adjustment of the rates of rotation of the axes of this telescope would maintain the mean position of the image of an astronomical object—star, planet, or small lunar crater —quite motionless in a guiding eyepiece or on a photographic film for half an hour or more. (It should be noted that, because of the effects of refraction, in wide-field telescopes another motion—rotation of the image plane about an axis perpendicular to it—must be provided.)

In addition to nullifying the effect of the uniform rotation of the earth, driving in two co-ordinates can correct for motions of the image that have the following causes: (1) changes in flexure of the telescope and its mounting; (2) incorrect adjustment of the axes or the mounting of the telescope on the axes; (3) variation of refraction with the zenith distance of the observed object; (4) peculiar motions of nearby objects such as the sun, moon, and planets.

Furthermore, controlled motions of the images in arbitrary directions may be used advantageously in many types of observations. For example, (1) widening objective-prism spectra; (2) trailing images along the slit of a spectroscope; (3) panoramic photography of the sun, moon, and planets; (4) elimination of relative motion of a nearby object (moon) and the background star field; (5) production of drift-curves along any diameter for the measurement of solar limb darkening; (6) scanning extended objects (sun, moon, planets, comets, star clusters, nebulae) for the production of maps of intensity, magnetic fields, velocities, etc.

2. GRAVITY DRIVES

The gravity drive, which is powered by a slowly falling weight, is among the oldest of the devices used to turn the hour-angle axis of the telescope. It is still used on many of the largest instruments, but even on observing expeditions to remote regions it has been replaced to a great extent by driving systems using electric motors.

In a gravity drive the difference between the moment exerted by the falling weight and the resisting moment (which may be variable) of the telescope is absorbed by some form of regulator, commonly called a "driving clock." The driving clock adds a controlled frictional resistance to the variable power required to turn the telescope so that the total requirement is constant and the driving weight falls uniformly. The most troublesome imperfections in early telescope drives arose in the driving clock rather than in the means (gear trains, belts or bands, tangent arms) for transmitting the motion of the falling weight to the hour-angle axis, and there have been many dozens of slightly different types of gravity-powered driving clocks invented, most of them incorporating some form of centrifugal governor.

The familiar conical pendulum, used by James Watt for the regulation of the speed of his steam engine, was one of the earliest types of governor employed as a driving clock. As adapted for use with the telescope, it was arranged to increase the pressure on a brake shoe whenever its speed of rotation increased (Sheepshanks 1836). In this way, a measure of control is attained, but the degree of regulation is insufficient to compensate for the many variations in load that are encountered in the course of the normal operation of an astronomical telescope.

Two modifications of Watt's simple governor are in wide use at present. Both these modifications attempt to increase the sensitivity of the device to small changes in the rate of rotation and to increase the range of the controlled power level.

A widely adopted governor was devised by C. A. Young late in the nineteenth century (Fig. 1). The important modification introduced by Young is a linkage which constrains the pendulums of the governor so that they move along the surface of a paraboloid through a small range. Such an arrangement possesses a critical velocity of rotation, and the linkage of the pendulums of the rotating shaft is so constructed that, at the moment when the angular velocity of the governor increases through the critical speed, the brake comes into play with large effect. A carefully constructed governor of this kind will run at a constant speed almost independent of the amount of the driving weight. In a well-made instrument, if the driving weight is doubled, the speed at which the governor will regulate increases by much less than 1 per cent, and a twofold increase in the force required to turn the telescope has an even smaller effect on the speed of the governor.

The second widely used centrifugal governor (Fig. 2) was designed by F. Meyer (1930) for C. Zeiss of Jena. It is the usual type of driving clock found on the newer instruments in Europe, while driving clocks of the Young type are most commonly found on telescopes constructed in the United States. The governors designed by Meyer support their pendulums in a vertical position. The centrifugal force that moves the pendulums outward as the central shaft

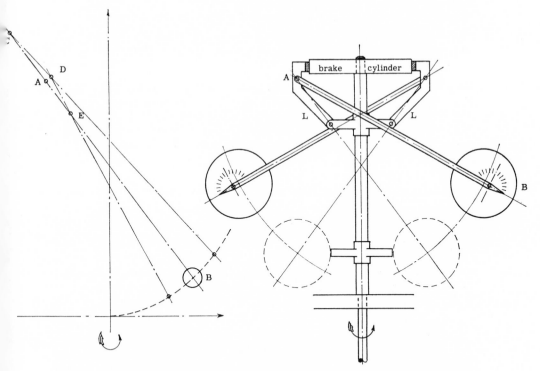

FIG. 1.—Young's centrifugal governor. The drawing on the left indicates that pivoting the pendulum bob B at A constrains it to move on a paraboloid. If through inaccurate adjustment the pivot point is at D, the regulation will be poor. The design of link, L, is important.

of the governor rotates is opposed by the flexure of small, flat springs. The speed of rotation is regulated through a carefully designed brake shoe. A correct rate of rotation of the governor is obtained by adjusting the weight of the pendulums or by adjusting the effective length of the restoring springs. The latter adjustment can be changed while the device is in motion, thus providing a variable-rate drive for the telescope.

Although the gravity-powered "clock" with a centrifugal governor is still

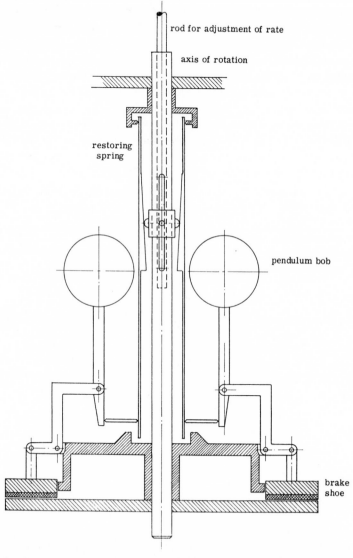

rod for adjustment of rate

axis of rotation

restoring spring

pendulum bob

brake shoe

Fig. 2.—Centrifugal governor of F. Meyer. The rate may be changed while the governor is running by shifting the defining points along the ramps of the restoring springs.

the most common method of driving astronomical telescopes, it is in many ways difficult to explain the generally highly satisfactory performance of these devices. Repeated experiments have shown that even well-made centrifugal governors are not always isochronous and often show capricious behavior. A mere mention of the extremely feeble power output of these devices will make clear the very critical conditions under which they may operate reasonably well. The driving clock of even a very large telescope, such as the 100-inch reflector on Mount Wilson, has a maximum available power output of about $\frac{1}{100}$ horsepower. It is doubtful whether more than half this power can be delivered to the hour-angle axis of the telescope because of losses in the gear train and in the governor, where losses are deliberately introduced to regulate the speed. With only this very small power available, any increase in the driven load, such as may be caused by imperfect balance, change in temperature, or installation of heavy instruments to be carried on moving parts of the telescope, can easily cause lack of regulation or may stall the driving clock completely. In spite of

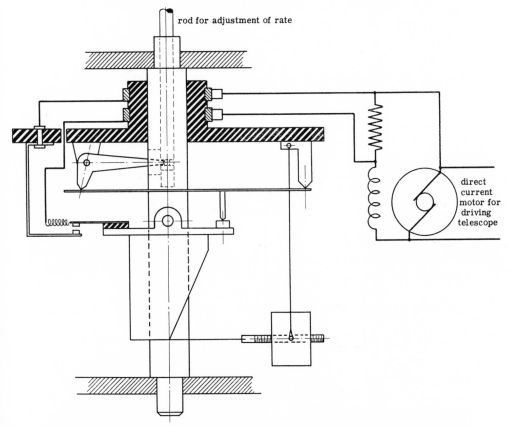

Fig. 3.—Centrifugal governor for control of direct-current driving motor. The rate can be changed by changing the length of the restoring spring. Controls of this type can be made to run with extreme precision.

these very serious defects, it must still be admitted that the gravity clocks often do perform extremely well. However, the numerous variations in clock design are strong evidence that astronomers have frequently sought a better mechanism.

3. ELECTRIC-MOTOR DRIVES

The search for improved driving clocks has led rather directly to some form of speed-controlled electric motor. One of these is a modification of the Meyer governor which uses it to control the speed of a direct-current electric motor driving both the telescope and the governor (Meyer 1930) (Fig. 3). In the elec-

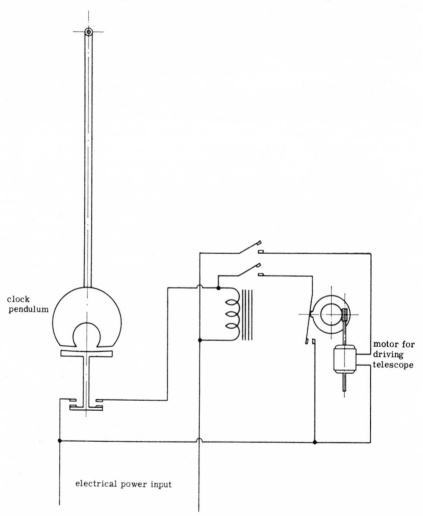

clock pendulum

motor for driving telescope

electrical power input

Fɪɢ. 4.—Clock-controlled electric-motor drive. Rate may be varied by changing the effective length of the pendulum. This is one of the many variations of the Gerrish drive.

tric motor the governor controls a much more responsive reservoir of power than can be supplied by a falling weight. Hence it is much less affected by variations in the power requirements, but the defects of the centrifugal governor still remain.

Many schemes have been proposed that take advantage of the excellent timekeeping properties of observatory clocks, thus circumventing the centrifugal governor. Drives of this kind are on-and-off, phase-sensitive devices that enforce more or less close synchronism between the rotation of the telescope drive and the beating of the pendulum of a good astronomical clock. The Gerrish drive is a direct application of control of an electric motor by a clock.

The principle of the operation of the Gerrish drive is illustrated in the schematic diagram (Fig. 4) of one of its simplest forms. The power for moving the telescope is supplied by a motor adjusted so that it would normally drive the telescope slightly too fast. An arrangement of contacts that are opened and closed in sequence by the clock pendulum and the driving motor interrupts the supplied electric current at such a cadence that the motor runs at the rate required to drive the telescope. The speed at which the motor runs can be varied by changing the effective length of the clock pendulum (King 1901; Cramer 1935).

4. VARIABLE-RATE DRIVES

The driving clocks that have been described so far, if well built, will, under favorable conditions, drive a telescope at a uniform rate practically without error; but, as elaborate forms of observation have become more and more necessary in astronomical research, such driving clocks are no longer adequate. Obviously, few of the schemes mentioned so far or the many similar mechanisms listed in the references could easily provide motion in the declination co-ordinate, since this axis of the telescope is not fixed with respect to the earth, nor can they supply a conveniently variable rate.

It is true that provision for change of rate was included in the driving clock of the great Dorpat refractor and that a variation in the rate of drive can be obtained in both the Meyer governor and the Gerrish drive, but the change cannot be made by the observer from his observing position. A direct solution of this problem has been incorporated in the hour-angle drive system of the 100- and 60-inch telescopes of the Mount Wilson Observatory.

The driving clocks of these instruments are of the type invented by Young, but the constant rate obtained from them has been made easily adjustable by the introduction of a remotely controllable "rater" between the clock and the final worm and gear reduction to the hour-angle axis. The rater (Fig. 5) is a pair of hardened-steel cones and an idler wheel, also of hardened steel. The position of the idler wheel along the cones is adjusted by a small motor controlled by pushbuttons located near the observer's position at the telescope. In this simple way a controllable rate is obtained from an essentially constant-speed driving clock.

Accurate speed-changing devices of this sort can be purchased at small cost, and, if used with a synchronous electric motor operated from commercial power lines, this combination is probably the least expensive adequate telescope drive. An adaptation of the cone-and-disk rater has been used with a variable-speed motor in the production of a highly versatile scanning drive (Babcock 1953b).

An approach to the problem of providing variable rates of large range in two co-ordinates can be made through the use of electric motors whose speed is regulated by devices that need not be carried on the telescope but may, in fact, be located in a thermostatically controlled room and completely protected from the temperature variations that are the chief sources of trouble. The motion of the controlled-speed motors is, in modern designs, transmitted electrically to the portion of the telescope where it is required. Such techniques were employed in the instruments of the McMath-Hulbert Observatory some years ago, and they have proved to be completely satisfactory and especially adaptable to the varying demands of complicated observing procedures (McMath, Hulbert, and McMath 1932; McMath 1937).

There are two common, commercially available electric motors whose rate of rotation can be regulated with great precision: the shunt-wound direct-current motor and the synchronous alternating-current motor. The shunt-wound direct-current motor is well suited to situations requiring wide ranges in speed and reversal of the direction of drive, such as the motions of the declination axis, or the use of the telescope for two-dimensional scanning. Figure 6, A, is a schematic wiring diagram for a direct-current driving motor. This circuit—the Ward-Leonard control circuit—has been used with complete success for driving telescopes, particularly the declination drive, because the motion in this co-ordinate requires a greater range in speed than the hour-angle motion and occasionally reverses direction. In the simplified circuit shown in Figure 6, a, reversal of the motion can be obtained by a mechanical gear shift or by an electrical

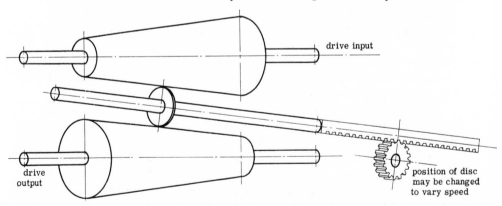

drive input

drive output

position of disc may be changed to vary speed

Fig. 5.—Cone-and-disk speed changer—the Mount Wilson "rater." The cones and the disk are made of highly polished hardened steel. The cones and disk are immersed in oil. Rate-changing devices of this kind are accurate and commercially available.

switch, but the reversal can also be accomplished electrically without inter-
rupting the motion of the control resistor, as indicated in the slightly more complicated scheme of Figure 6, *A*. Within the range of the motors, the speed-torque
relationship tends to maintain a uniform motor speed for a given setting of the
generator voltage. A value of the uniform speed is determined, therefore, by the
potentiometer setting. The setting of the potentiometer is easily controlled remotely from the observer's station, and the speed of the motor can be continuously checked directly, to more than adequate precision, with a modern frequency meter.

Another method of controlling the speed of a motor is illustrated in Figure 7
(McMath and Greig 1934). The direct-current motor drives a generator of alternating current. The rate of rotation of the motor and, consequently, the frequency of the generated alternating current are determined by the frequency

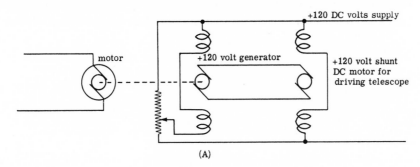

(A)

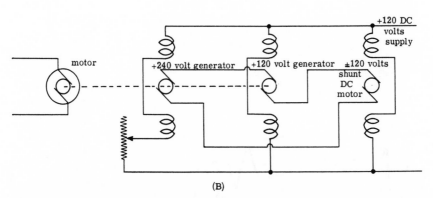

(B)

FIG. 6.—The Ward-Leonard drive. The combination of the direct-current generator and
motor is an excellent constant-speed arrangement for use where the torque requirements are
variable.

of the oscillating circuit. An alternating current generated by a vacuum-tube oscillator and amplifier controls a phase-sensing circuit. A pulsating direct current of constant amplitude is established in the bridged field of the motor when it is running in synchronism with the oscillator, but with a constant phase difference. A rheostat is provided in the armature circuit of the motor so that its speed can be adjusted to a value at which the current flowing in the phase-sensitive circuit assumes control. Either the controlled direct-current motor can be used to drive the telescope directly, or the output of the generator can be used to operate a synchronous telescope-driving motor at the controlled frequency. This type of control provides a variable-rate drive, since the speed of the direct-current motor will vary in step with the frequency of the oscillator as it is turned over a range of approximately 5 per cent of its basic frequency.

With the adoption of the synchronous motor (McMath 1930) as the source of power for driving a telescope, the problem of providing accurate motion becomes that of designing a source of alternating current with stable, but variable,

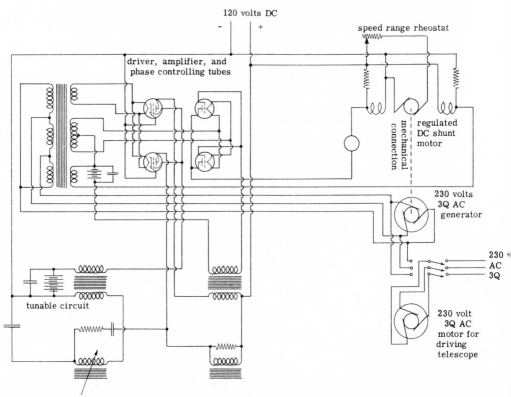

Fig. 7.—Vacuum-tube oscillator control of direct-current shunt motor. The three-phase generator acts as a tachometer, and the difference between the frequency generated by it and the frequency generated by the vacuum-tube oscillator controls the field of the direct-current driving motor so that it runs in synchronism with the oscillator. (3Q read 3φ in each case.)

frequency. There are, of course, many telescopes that do not require drives of the highest precision, and the 60-cycle current supplied by commercial power companies will in most parts of the United States be controlled within close enough limits to provide rather good driving at a constant rate. Maximum variations in the frequency of a well-controlled commercial power line are generally much less than ± 0.06 H, or one part in a thousand. A deviation of this amount will build up an error of 1 second of arc in 70 seconds. The frequency averaged over a period of 1 hour is generally much more nearly constant. Frequency that is essentially without error for a constant-rate drive can be obtained from commercial electrically driven tuning forks that vibrate at 60 H. The output from the fork can be amplified with a good hi-fi amplifier to a power level sufficient to drive a sizable telescope, but, as has been mentioned before, a result of refraction is that even a perfect telescope must be driven at a variable rate if it is to follow celestial objects with the least possible error.

The development of electronic tubes designed for large, undistorted power output and long life at low cost and the similar development of magnetic amplifiers, coupled with the success of the vacuum-tube oscillator as a variable-rate control for the direct-current motor, has led to the construction of synchronous motor drives operated from suitable power amplifiers (Fig. 8). Several such drives have proved in practice to be stable, reliable, convenient, and flexible in operation. The operating frequency, which should be chosen so that specially built synchronous motors are not required, is generated by a vacuum-tube oscillator whose frequency is unaffected by variations in line voltage or temperature. A continuous frequency variation over 10 per cent of the base frequency, controllable from the observer's station, will be sufficient for ordinary programs, but this range must be extended considerably by well-known methods (Beams and Sheppard 1939) if programs involving scanning motions with the telescopes are undertaken. Modern frequency meters make it possible to measure the speed of rotation of the telescope with great accuracy, and such measurement gives the observer a nearly continuous indication of the driving rate.

Another precision source (commercially available) of accurately variable frequency can be obtained in the vibrations of an electrically driven stretched string or wire. The Warren vibratory-wire time standard (Warren 1940) is a device of this type that is used to generate the fundamental frequency for the drive of the 200-inch telescope and other telescopes on Mount Palomar. Its frequency is unaffected by temperature, barometric pressure, or voltage variation in the power supply, within normal limits; yet it has self-contained means for extremely precise and easily controlled adjustment of rate.

An observer unfamiliar with variable-rate driving of telescopes can have little idea of the ease and precision with which the rate of drive can be controlled by tuning a vacuum-tube oscillator or a vibrating wire. The improvement in performance of a telescope previously operated with another kind of mechanism is generally unexpectedly great. Nevertheless, because of deviations in atmospheric refraction from its mean value and somewhat similar excursions of instrumental parameters (flexure, distribution of load, etc.) from their normal courses of variation, no telescope yet built can be driven so perfectly that small corrections of the position of the image are never necessary. An excellent telescope, equipped with variable-rate driving and running at the correct rate initially, requires about half-a-dozen guiding corrections (three in hour angle and three in declination) per hour to keep it pointed to a given star. About the same number of rate changes will be needed, in addition to the predicted changes of rate. (See King 1901, 1931; McMath, Hulbert, and McMath 1932 for methods of computing driving rates for various objects.) If the driving rates are not predicted in advance, many more corrections may be required until an approximate rate has been established.

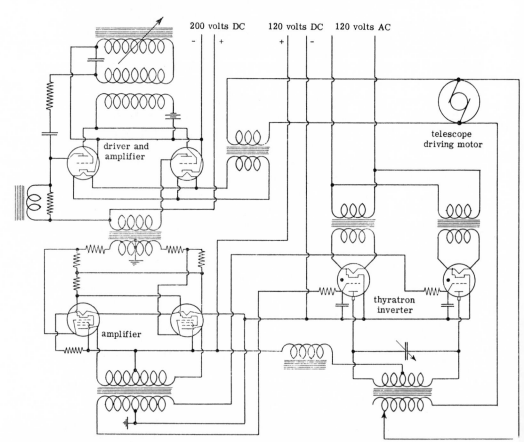

Fig. 8.—Vacuum-tube power supply for telescope driving motor. The output of a vacuum-tube oscillator may be amplified to control a thyratron inverter. Large amounts of power can be supplied in this way from rather simple circuits. The circuitry is highly schematic but indicates essential details required for telescope driving.

The preceding discussion of driving devices applies, as we have already mentioned, only to telescopes with extremely limited angular fields of view, in which single stars are most often the objects being observed. If an object such as the moon or an asteroid, moving in relation to a group of stars, must be held fixed or if one wishes to correct for the apparent rotation by refraction of a field some degrees in width, then a second rate, suitable for the particular circumstances of observation, must be supplied through appropriate optical and mechanical arrangements. A dual-rate telescope for photographing the moon, fixed in position among the stars, is in use at the United States Naval Observatory (Markowitz 1954; chap. 7).

5. PHOTOELECTRIC GUIDING

The residual guiding corrections may be made completely automatic by using photoelectric cells to sense the position of the image and to signal for corrections whenever deviations occur. Motions of the image can be restricted to within 1 or 2 seconds of arc of some mean position, and many of the functions of a refined telescope drive can be performed.

The simplest photoelectric guiders are photoelectric relays that actuate the appropriate slow guiding motions of the telescope. In a typical installation (Alter 1929), the image of the star is formed on the apex of a four-sided pyramid with reflecting faces which divide the starlight into four beams of equal intensity. Each of the partial beams is directed into one of four photoelectric cells arranged in pairs. One pair controls the hour-angle motion, the other pair controls the declination motion. If the image moves from the apex, an out-of-balance current is generated by one or both of the pairs of cells. The out-of-balance current, after amplification, operates the slow motions of the telescope as required to restore the balanced condition. For guiding on extended objects (sun, moon, planets), the four-sided pyramid is replaced with four slits that transmit light from four edges of the object. This general type of photoelectric guiding control is the most common one at present, but there are a number of variations, and the number will doubtless continue to increase.

One of the earliest applications of photoelectric control to astronomical guiding employed a photoelectric cell to correct the position of a double-slide photographic plate carriage (Whitford and Kron 1937) with respect to small deviations of a stellar image. The plate carriage was moved in the hour-angle direction by a small motor whose rotation was controlled by the photoelectric cell so that unwanted motions of the image were followed.

Subsequent to the demonstration of successful photoelectric following of slow drifting of the image, a considerable development has taken place to improve the response to more rapid motion. If an auxiliary optical and mechanical system of low inertia can be attached to a telescope with a reasonably good driving clock, it is possible to control the subsystem photoelectrically and to reduce the short-period erratic motions of the image ("seeing") by a factor of 10.

Among the schemes that have been tried for nullifying the more rapid motions of a stellar image are the following. A plane-parallel plate, mounted in gimbals, can be photoelectrically tilted for the correction of frequencies of ten per second or less (Babcock 1953a). An additional lens may be interposed in the optical path and moved perpendicularly to its optical axis to correct image oscillations at frequencies from 0 to 2 H (Leighton 1956). The image may even be transformed into a stream of electrons in an image-orthicon, and deflections of the electrons corrected from error signals obtained from the original image (DeWitt, Hardie, and Seyfert 1957). After correction, the electron streams can be reconverted into a stationary visual or photographic image.

An interesting suggestion has been made concerning the possibility of correction of telescopic images, not only for relatively low-frequency wanderings, but also for rapid motions and bad definition (Babcock 1953a). These desirable ends can be achieved, in principle, with the help of the eidophor (Fischer and Thiemann 1941). The eidophor contains a possible means of measuring continuously the deviation of the rays from all parts of a telescope objective. This information can then be amplified and used to correct local "distortions" of the figure of the objective. In this way one can obtain simultaneous compensation for small, rapid seeing shifts and imperfections of optical definition. When it is realized that with the 200-inch telescope, for example, stellar images only rarely have diameters as small as $\frac{1}{2}$ second of arc and that the average diameter is much more nearly 2 seconds of arc, the possible importance of the eidophor in achieving a much closer approach to the theoretical performance of a large telescope will be understood and will perhaps lead to more intensive research concerned with the problems encountered in attempting to stabilize a telescopic image.

REFERENCES

ALTER, G.   1929   *Zs. f. Instrumentenk.*, **49**, 553.

BABCOCK, H. W.   1953a   *Pub. A.S.P.*, **65**, 229.

    1953b   *Ap. J.*, **118**, 387.

BEAMS, J. W., and
    SHEPPARD, A. B.   1939   *Rev. Sci. Instr.*, **10**, 59.

CRAMER, O. P.   1935   *Astr. J. U.S.S.R.*, **12**, 226.

DeWITT, J. H.,
    HARDIE, R. H., and
    SEYFERT, C. K.   1957   *Sky and Telescope*, **17**, 8.

FELLGETT, P. B.   1956   *Occasional Notes R.A.S.*, **3**, 143.

FISCHER, F., and
    THIEMANN, H.   1941   *Schweiz. Arch. angew. Wiss. Tech.*, Vol. **7**, Nos. 1, 2, 11, 12.

KING, E. S.   1901   *Harvard Ann.*, **41**, 153.

    1931   *Manual of Celestial Photography* (Boston: Eastern Science Supply Co.).

LASSELL, W.   1867   *Mem. R.A.S.*, **36**, 2.

Leighton, R. B.	1956	*Scient. American*, **194**, 157.
McMath, R. R.	1930	*Pop. Astr.*, **38**, 460.
	1937	*Pub. Obs. U. Michigan*, **7**, 1.
McMath, R. R., and Greig, W. A.	1934	*Pub. Obs. U. Michigan*, **5**, 123.
McMath, F. C., Hulbert, H. S., and McMath, R. R.	1932	*Pub. Obs. U. Michigan*, **4**, 53.
Markowitz, W.	1954	*Astr. J.*, **59**, 69.
Meyer, F.	1930	*Zs. f. Instrumentenk.*, **50**, 58.
Oxmantown, Lord (Earl of Rosse IV)	1866	*M.N.*, **26**, 265.
Sheepshanks, Rev. R.	1836	*M.N.*, **3**, 40.
Sisson, G. M.	1954	*Occasional Notes R.A.S.*, **3**, 96.
Struve, W.	1826	*Mem. R.A.S.*, **2**, 96.
Warren, H. E.	1940	*Trans. Am. Inst. Elec. Engineering*, **59**, 137.
Whitford, A. E., and Kron, G. E.	1937	*Rev. Sci. Instr.*, **8**, 78.

In addition to the references, the following bibliography is intended to serve as a guide to some of the sources of information about telescope driving systems.

Brief descriptions of the principles of operation of many different kinds of drives are given in:

Bischoff, W.	1938	*Zs. Verein. Deutsch. Ingenieure*, **82**, 1393.
Lower, H. A.	1937	*Amateur Telescope Making—Advanced* (Kingsport, Tenn.: Kingsport Press, Inc.), p. 303.
Meyer, F.	1930	. *Zs. f. Instrumentenk.*, **50**, 58.

Gravity-driven clocks assume a large number of different forms. Many of these are historically and mechanically of the greatest interest. Some of them make use of the principle of the clepsydra.

Brydon, H. B.	1939	*J.R.A.S. Canada*, **33**, 379.
Buchanan, W. E.	1903	*English Mechanic*, **78**, 357.
Delmotte, G.	1932	*Bull. Soc. Astr. France*, **46**, 74.
East, A.	1903	*J. British Astr. Assoc.*, **14**, 29.
Friend, I. H., and Sawyer, P. B.	1948	*Sky and Telescope*, **8**, 48.
Hargreaves, F. J.	1930	*M.N.*, **90**, 816.
Haughton, J. L.	1940	*J. British Astr. Assoc.*, **50**, 147.
Heath, T. E.	1907	*M.N.*, **67**, 527.
Hnatek, A.	1916	*Zs. f. Instrumentenk.*, **36**, 295.
Sanders, L.	1949	*J. British Astr. Assoc.*, **59**, 182.
Sellers, F. J.	1930	*J. British Astr. Assoc.*, **40**, 222.
Struve, H.	1917	*Berlin Ber.*, p. 655.
Sweger, P. B.	1954	*Sky and Telescope*, **13**, 202.
Todd, D. P.	1902	*Science*, N.S., **16**, 131.
Venkateswaran, C. S.	1938	*J. Sci. Instr.*, **15**, 265.

The control of the telescope driving motor by the observatory clock was a great advance over the centrifugal governor. Some of the methods of control along these lines are given in the following:

AZAMBUJA, L. D'	1921	*C.R.*, **173**, 494; see also *Observatory*, **44**, 331, 1921.
FELLGETT, P. B.	1950	*Observatory*, **70**, 189.
FESSENKOV, B.	1935	*Astr. J. U.S.S.R.*, **12**, 167.
GRUBB, H.	1905	*Proc. R. Dublin Soc.*, **11**, 34.
HANSON, H. E.	1939*a*	*Rev. Sci. Instr.*, **10**, 184.
	1939*b*	*J.R.A.S. Canada*, **33**, 329.
HARGREAVES, F. J.	1931	*J. British Astr. Assoc.*, **41**, 112.
KAULLA, H.	1932	*A.N.*, **245**, 269.
KELLAWAY, G. F.	1940	*J. British Astr. Assoc.*, **50**, 215.
TINDAL, C. H.	1937	*Rev. Sci. Instr.*, **8**, 251.
YOUNG, C.	1930	*J. Sci. Instr.*, **7**, 264.

A number of speed controls for electric motors have been developed and used in the drives of astronomical telescopes. The following give some samples of this method of control:

BENNETT, A. L.	1941	*Astr. J.*, **49**, 98.
BIÈVRE, C. DE	1942	*Ann. franç. de chron.*, **12**, 23; see also *Ciel et Terre*, **58**, 165, 1942.
CHENEY, W. C.	1951	*Sky and Telescope*, **10**, 70.
DOBRANRAVIN, P. P.	1949	*Priroda*, **38**, 47.
DUFOUR, E.	1929	*Bull. Soc. Astr. France*, **43**, 188.
PETERS, G. H.	1921	*Pop. Astr.*, **29**, 638.

The use of the synchronous motor for telescope driving is discussed in the following:

BROCCHI, D. F.	1940	*Pop. Astr.*, **48**, 271.
MOFFITT, G. W.	1932	*Rev. Sci. Instr.*, **3**, 499.
	1937	*Sterne*, **17**, 113.

Applications of precision sources of variable frequency are described in the following:

COX, H. W.	1938	*J. British Astr. Assoc.*, **48**, 248; **49**, 45 and 81.
DeWITT, J. H., and SEYFERT, C. K.	1955	*Astr. J.*, **60**, 154.
JEFFERS, H. M.	1938	*Pub. A.S.P.*, **50**, 112.
SILVERTOOTH, W., SAWYER, E., and LESTER, E.	1937	*Scient. American*, **156**, 44.
TABOR, L. P.	1939	*Pub. Cook Obs.*, No. 4.
UNTERBERGER, R.	1939	*Zs. f. Instrumentenk.*, **59**, 367.

Photoelectric guiding devices have begun to play a considerable role in the control of astronomical telescopes. The principles of these auxiliaries are frequently described. Some individual applications are given in the following:

BABCOCK, H. W.   1948   *Ap. J.*, **107**, 73.
BAYLE, A.   1931   *Rev. opt.*, **10**, 495.
DUBOV, E. E.   1955   *Izv. Krim. Astrof. Obs.*, **13**, 155.
EDWARDS, H. D., GOD-
  DARD, A., JR., JUZA,
  M., MAHER, T., and
  SPECK, F.   1956   *Rev. Sci. Instr.*, **27**, 381.
FOWLER, F. E., and
  JOHNSON, D. S.   1951   *Electronics*, **24**, 118.
MARIUS, H.   1944   *Mitt. d. Fraunhofer Inst.*, No. 8.
RABBEN, H. H.   1956   *Elektron. Rdsch. Deutsch.*, **10**, 189.
ROBERTS, W. O.   1946   *Electronics*, **19**, 100.
THORNE, T. G.   1950   *Engineering*, **169**, 197.
UTTLEY, A., JONES, S.,
  and MANNS, L.   1948   *Nature* (London), **162**, 144.
WEITBRECHT, R. H.   1957   *Rev. Sci. Instr.*, **28**, 122.

CHAPTER 6

The Transit Circle

C. B. WATTS

U.S. Naval Observatory, Washington, D.C.

1. INTRODUCTION

TRANSIT circles are measuring devices designed for use in determining the spherical co-ordinates—right ascension and declination—of celestial bodies. The co-ordinates of stars thus derived may be differential, the measures being referred to neighboring stars whose positions are accepted as known, or fundamental, in which case the positions of the equator and equinox are redetermined and the final results are independent of earlier work. Observations of the sun, the inner planets, and certain asteroids are utilized in the second case. All our knowledge of the positions and motions of the stars and planets, with the exception of radial velocities, depends directly or indirectly on the work of instruments of this type.

Many of the peculiarities of transit-circle design arise from the circumstance that it is essentially a pointing instrument and is intended (at least in some cases) to measure very long arcs in the sky with as great accuracy as refinements in construction can make possible. In the following pages the principal features of typical examples are described, with some notes on recent developments.

2. DESIGN

Most transit circles resemble in a general way the one shown in Plate I. The reader will recognize characteristic features consisting of a small telescope mounted on a horizontal axis, with two rather large divided circles. The two piers, usually made of stone or concrete, are sheathed with insulating material to smooth variations due to temperature changes. They are free from contact with the floor and rest on a massive foundation of stone or concrete. Attached to the upper surfaces of the piers are the supports for the axis of the instrument and the microscopes for reading the circles. The supports, usually made of steel, can be adjusted through a small range in altitude and azimuth to place the motion of the telescope very nearly in the plane of the meridian.

PLATE I.—The 6-inch transit circle of the U.S. Naval Observatory, Washington, D.C. (Official U.S. Navy photograph.)

PLATE II.—Micrometer of the 6-inch transit circle, U.S. Naval Observatory, Washington, D.C. (Official U.S. Navy photograph.)

The axis of rotation is defined by the pivots, which are hardened-steel cylinders, usually 5–8 cm in diameter, pressed tightly into suitable recesses in the ends of the axis casting. After being put in place, they are carefully ground and lapped, to make them as nearly as possible coaxial and of the same diameter. Each pivot rests on two flat pieces of brass or bronze called the "wyes." They are spaced about 90° apart and are mounted on the same supports that carry the circle microscopes. Most of the weight of the moving parts is carried on wheels thrust upward by counterpoise levers or similar means against portions of the axis machined to receive their pressure. The pivots are usually pierced by cylindrical holes, 3 or 4 cm in diameter, which are useful for admitting light for field illumination and other purposes.

It is customary and convenient to have two divided circles on the instrument, although only one need be investigated for division errors. The other is usually kept in reserve or used in setting the telescope in zenith distance. The circles may be locked against shoulders near the extremities of the axis, and in most cases they can be rotated into any desired relationship with the telescope. Temperature changes make it impracticable to keep both circles sharply in focus in their respective microscopes at the same time. The pivot adjacent to the circle utilized in the observing should therefore be held against an adjustable stop by the thrust of a spring on the opposite pivot. With a conveniently located setting microscope, the telescope is pointed so as to cause the image of the object under observation to trail through the field near the optical axis of the objective.

Division lines are engraved on a metallic strip pressed into a groove near the periphery of the circle. Silver has sometimes been used for this purpose, as well as platinum and gold alloys. An alloy with the composition 78 per cent gold, 16 per cent silver, and 6 per cent copper has been used in several circles at the United States Naval Observatory with satisfactory results. Lines 20–25 μ in width are of convenient size for both visual and photographic use. They are commonly spaced at intervals of 2, 3, or 5 minutes of arc and are usually filled with a black pigment. The division lines should obviously be as nearly radial as possible, and their edges should be smooth and sharply defined. Uniformity in width is also desirable, but great accuracy in the spacing of the lines is not important, since their exact location must be determined by measurement in any case.

The operation of determining the division errors is quite laborious, as it re quires many thousand measures of arcs of various lengths (Lévy 1955). These errors, which seldom exceed 1 or 2 seconds of arc, can usually be determined with an accuracy of $0\rlap{.}''05$–$0\rlap{.}''10$ for the mean of two diameters.

Large graduated circles, even though carefully machined to symmetrical proportions, have occasionally been found to exhibit flexure effects that are not entirely eliminated by the use of multiple microscopes. Since this condition probably arises from local variations in tensile strength, it is wise to keep the circles fairly small and of relatively light weight. A diameter of 65–75 cm appears to be sufficiently large. The circle castings require careful machining to secure the symmetry necessary to avoid circle flexure. Glass circles, about 70 cm in diameter, were provided for the reversible transit circle of the Royal Greenwich Observatory. The division lines, which are of excellent quality, are etched in the glass and are not filled. The weight of a glass circle makes counterpoise levers desirable to avoid distortion (Jones 1944).

The circle microscopes are mounted in pairs at the extremities of diameters to eliminate the effect of eccentricity. Four or six microscopes are usually provided. If they are to be used visually, each is equipped with a small micrometer with which pointings can be made on the division lines. If the scale of the projected image is three or four times that of the circle itself, 1 second of arc in the micrometer is represented by a distance of 4 or 5 μ. Great stability is required of the microscope mountings to avoid too large a change in alignment during the interval between successive determinations of the instrumental constants. Such an interval is ordinarily 2 or 3 hours during an observing tour.

3. OBSERVATIONS

As the task of setting the microscope micrometers and recording their readings is time-consuming, the use of photographic microscopes has become common. These microscopes photograph a short arc of the circle, together with a reference mark, on 35-mm film. The mark may consist of the shadow image of a fine wire, selected to match in width that of the projected images of the division lines. A film base has been found to be sufficiently stable for this purpose, inasmuch as the reference mark is displaced from the division line involved by only a fraction of a millimeter. The measurement of the films can be performed later with a small visual measuring device or, more conveniently, with a photoelectric measuring engine (Watts 1950). An alternative is to retain visual microscopes and to photograph the scales of the micrometers after they have been set manually.

Observations are usually made within 10 minutes of arc of the optical axis, and the objective therefore need not have a large field. It is desirable for the back focus and the length of the telescope tube to change with temperature by nearly the same amount, to avoid frequent adjustments of the relation between the objective and the micrometer. The lenses are constrained in their cell to prevent a possible displacement when the instrument is moved in zenith distance. This may be accomplished by means of springs bearing on the edge of each lens and thrusting it against suitable stops. An elastic ring holds the lenses against a three-point support when the telescope is pointed downward, as is necessary to establish the direction of the vertical over a mercury basin. A shift of the lenses in any position of the telescope amounting to 1 μ would be a serious fault. With the usual dimensions of a transit circle, it would produce a deflection of about 0".10.

The telescope tube is made in two similar sections, which are bolted to the central cube. The cube forms an integral part of the axis. All three of these castings are preferably machined on both the interior and the exterior surfaces to secure symmetry and uniformity in wall thickness. This precaution tends to decrease discontinuities in flexure and may make lateral flexure negligible. By "flexure" in this connection is meant, not the total bending of the tube with gravity, but the difference between the displacement of the objective and that of the micrometer. Flexure in the vertical plane is usually assumed to vary with the sine of the zenith distance. Much study has been given to means for obtaining an accurate measure of it (Atkinson 1955; van Herk 1958).

As bright stars are more difficult to observe accurately than relatively faint ones, it has been found desirable to equip the telescope with a system of screens to avoid an appreciable magnitude equation. These usually take the form of pieces of wire cloth in circular frames that can be interposed singly or in combination in the line of sight. A tilting screen made of slats has some advantages, and one has been used at the United States Naval Observatory (Morgan 1933). The added weight is, however, somewhat objectionable. The screens can be mounted in front of the objective or within the central cube. In either case they are operated by controls near the micrometer.

The carefully balanced and freely moving instrument requires a zenith-distance clamp and a fine-motion control to bring the telescope to a desired pointing. Since the pointing may be disturbed inadvertently by the observer, it is fairly common to leave the clamp on during the course of an observation. This makes it necessary to design the clamp so that it will not deform or displace the axis when it is applied and thereby deflect the telescope in either or both coordinates (Watts 1935).

The micrometer is necessarily somewhat complex. In Plate II the location of the two measuring screws that control the motion of horizontal and vertical slides is apparent. In this micrometer the slides are rectangular frames of steel accurately fitted to ways machined in a block of the same material (Watts 1950). In a different design (Gill 1913) each frame is guided at two points by a polished steel rod of circular cross-section and at a third point by a flat plate. In both designs the thrust of the screw is opposed by springs to eliminate backlash or lost motion. The vertical slide should be of as little weight as practicable, to reduce the effects of a variation in the thrust of gravity that takes place with a change in zenith distance. Both slides carry lines of spider web, moving in planes about 75 μ apart. The lines are usually in pairs, the separation amounting to a few seconds of arc in the field. The micrometer screws have a working range of about 1.5 cm, the pitch being between 0.25 and 0.50 mm.

There are two eyepiece slides controlled by screws, the horizontal screw being geared to the horizontal measuring screw so that the right-ascension line (the "traveling wire") will remain centered in the eyepiece. These screws are also connected by gears to a driving mechanism, which may be either hand- or power-operated. The observer can thus keep an object in the center of the eye-piece field and maintain coincidence of the traveling wire with it during the short interval when it is near the meridian. During some portions of this interval the vertical screw is used to measure small increments of zenith distance from the direction established by the telescope and circle to the object trailing across the meridian. A group of fixed spider lines is useful as approximate reference marks in the field.

A minute shift of the micrometer under the changing influence of gravity would, of course, be objectionable in a pointing instrument, and, to secure great-er stability, it is desirable to omit the draw tube and sleeve usually introduced for focusing. Instead, a small ring casting is interposed between the objective cell and the tube section to which it is attached, and this is machined to the proper thickness to place the spider lines in the focal plane of the objective. Compensation for seasonal changes in temperatures, if necessary, can be made by inserting or removing shims at the flange of the objective cell. A reversing prism, mounted on the eyepiece, enables the observer to rotate the field through 180° when an observation is half-completed, thereby causing a systematic error in bisecting a star image to change sign.

Both micrometer screws have the usual circular graduated scales. The right-ascension screw requires an additional mechanism to record its phase angle at short intervals while it is in motion. In Repsold's (1896) design of the imper-sonal, or traveling-wire, micrometer, a break-circuit wheel is mounted on the shank of the screw. This wheel interrupts a chronograph circuit periodically as it is rotated, recording the instants at which the traveling wire passes through certain points in the field. The introduction of this method, replacing the older one of recording the instants at which the object is observed to cross fixed wires, greatly decreased the observer's personal equation.

A different method of recording the motion of the traveling wire has been used at Washington since 1938 (Watts 1950). The readings of both micrometer screws are photographed on a tape of recording paper, the exposures that repre-sent a transit being initiated by the clock and all others by the observer. This method has the advantage of indicating the position of the traveling wire at uniform intervals of time rather than of distance traveled, regardless of the dec-lination of the object under observation. It is clear that the relation at any instant between the position of the traveling wire and the indication of the circular scale on the screw should be appreciably the same, whether the screw is at rest or rotating in either direction. A test of this condition is facilitated by the latter method of recording transits (Watts 1944).

The spider lines are usually made visible in a bright field by an illuminated diffusing screen located inside one of the pivots. A mirror in the axis reflects the light from the screen obliquely to the center of the objective, where a small adjustable mirror in a cell cemented to the exterior surface of the objective re-flects it back to the micrometer. An eyepiece is usually selected to give a magnification of about 200 diameters.

4. AUXILIARY APPARATUS

Among the several pieces of auxiliary apparatus are the horizontal collimators, which are mounted on piers north and south of the instrument at the level of the axis of rotation. They are used in determining the collimation constant for the right-ascension measures and the horizontal flexure for the measures in zenith distance. Openings in the axial tube make possible the setting of one collimator on the other. While it would be desirable for the collimator objectives to have the same aperture and focal length as the telescope itself, they are usually made somewhat smaller.

Reference to the direction of the vertical in both co-ordinates is established by the use of reflections in a basin of mercury beneath the instrument. Pointings are made with each pair of movable wires on its reflection, and, with the zenith-distance pair, the circle microscopes are also read. A vertical collimator is sometimes used in connection with the mercury basin for instrumental investigations. In this application the auxiliary telescope is horizontal and is supported on a spindle, centered over one of the piers, so that it can be rotated away from the meridian when not in use. It carries in front of the objective a flat mirror properly inclined to enable the observer to set the spider lines on their reflection in the mercury. The vertical collimator can be used to measure a possible term in the flexure varying with the cosine of the zenith distance and also to refer to the direction of the vertical with the transit-circle telescope pointing to the zenith. This is seldom done, however, on account of its inconvenience.

The azimuth of the axis of rotation is determined from observations of close circumpolar stars, preferably at both upper and lower culminations. Since the axis can be shifted slightly by temperature changes, it is necessary to have at least one meridian mark as a temporary reference point. The mark (an illuminated pinhole in a metal plate) is mounted on a stable pier 100 meters or more to the north or south of the instrument. It should be depressed a few degrees, so that it can be viewed below the collimator. For this purpose a lens of suitably long focus is mounted on the collimator pier.

The inclination of the axis of rotation to a horizontal plane can be determined by means of a sensitive spirit level resting temporarily on the pivots. It is now more commonly determined from the nadir measures.

Modern transit circles can be reversed, that is, lifted from the supporting wyes, rotated about a vertical line, and restored to the wyes. The purpose of reversal is to reduce the effect of some of the instrumental errors. Among these are a possible lateral flexure of the tube and uncertainties in the collimation constant, as well as in the corrections adopted for the circle divisions used with the nadir measures.

To investigate the inequalities of the pivots, an axial microscope is often used. This device involves the insertion in one of the pivots of a glass plate on which minute globules of mercury are deposited. The plate is illuminated by light admitted through the opposite pivot. A nearly central mercury spot is observed with a microscope micrometer, and its deviations are recorded as the telescope is moved in zenith distance. The difference in mean radius of the two pivots can also be measured by this method (Hammond and Watts 1927). The application of a different technique is described by Jones (1944). This involves the use of a sensitive gauge, which evaluates inequalities in the surface of the pivots by direct measurement. Another method, originated by A. H. Boerdijk, has been described by De Munck (1954).

In appraising the accuracy of the results obtained with a transit circle, it is necessary to consider whether the work is differential or fundamental in nature. In differential observing the measures extend over relatively short arcs. Much differential work formerly done with transit circles is now carried out more efficiently with photographic equatorials and plate-measuring engines. In this case the positions of a sufficient number of reference stars are determined with transit circles, usually differentially with respect to the stars of a standard catalogue. A fundamental observing program requires the measurement of very long arcs, and, in declination, such measures are affected by uncertainties in atmospheric refraction and instrumental flexure. The effect of refraction is illustrated by the occasional presence of "night errors," which systematically displace the results obtained on a particular night. The observed right ascensions are largely free from similar effects. Scott (1957) has given a brief account of procedures used at the United States Naval Observatory in making and discussing fundamental observations.

If a study of errors is based only on internal discordances, one may expect the probable error of an observation in right ascension to range from 0^s013 sec δ to 0^s020 sec δ for both differential and fundamental work, varying with instrumental techniques. In declination observations the probable error is likely to be about $0''15$ for differential and about $0''30$ for fundamental work.

Many variations in the design of transit circles and their auxiliary apparatus have been made or are in progress. The most extensive change is to be found in the mirror transit circle proposed by Atkinson (1947) and that of Soukharev (1948). In this design the telescope tube is replaced by a flat mirror, the surface of which contains the axis of rotation. The observations are to be made at either of two horizontal telescopes located to the north and south of the instrument. Among the several advantages to be expected are greater freedom from flexure problems and a fixed relationship with respect to gravity among the parts of the micrometers. Instruments of this type are under construction at Ottawa, Pulkovo, and Porto, Portugal.

Photographic and photoelectric devices, replacing the traveling-wire micrometer, are in various stages of development at Copenhagen, Pulkovo, and elsewhere. Both techniques are applicable to the observation of stars and asteroids, but they would probably be difficult to adapt for use with the sun, moon, and planets. The latter objects, however, are not included in many transit-circle programs, and it appears probable that, with sufficient observations of asteroids, the position of the equator and equinox and the obliquity of the ecliptic can be determined without them.

At the Royal Greenwich Observatory a method has been developed of recording on punched cards the clock times of signals originated by the traveling-wire micrometer, and at Bordeaux the use of a selsyn motor to record the settings of the zenith-distance screw is being tried. Experiments in similar techniques are also in progress at the United States Naval Observatory.

The transit circle has largely replaced the transit instrument and vertical circle. Right-ascension and declination determinations were long made with the latter instruments independently of each other, although occasionally in the same observing room. With early transit circles an observer, working without an assistant, required 4 or 5 minutes to make an observation, but recent instrumental developments have reduced this time to 2 minutes or less. It is possible that an automatic transit circle could now be constructed that would observe selected lists of stars and asteroids without requiring more than occasional attention from an operator. However this may be, the dependence of many branches of astronomy on the work of these highly developed instruments is likely to continue.

REFERENCES

ATKINSON, R., D'E.	1947	*M.N.*, **107**, 291.
	1955	*Ibid.*, **115**, 427.
DE MUNCK, J. C.	1954	*Pub. Netherlands Geod. Com.*
GILL, DAVID	1913	*History and Description of the Cape Observatory* (London: H.M. Stationery Office), p. 48.
HAMMOND, J. C., and WATTS, C. B.	1927	*Pub. U.S. Naval Obs.*, **11**, 17.
HERK, G. VAN	1958	*Bull. Astr. Inst. Netherlands*, **14**, 155.
JONES, H. SPENCER	1944	*M.N.*, **104**, 146.
LÉVY, J.	1955	*Bull. Astr.*, **20**, 35.
MORGAN, H. R.	1933	*Pub. U.S. Naval Obs.*, **13**, 7.
REPSOLD, J.	1896	*A.N.*, **141**, 279.
SCOTT, F. P.	1957	*Trans. I.A.U.*, **9**, 713.
SOUKHAREV, L. A.	1948	*Astr. J. U.S.S.R.*, **25**, 59.
WATTS, C. B.	1935	*A.J.*, **44**, 185.
	1944	*Ibid.*, **50**, 181.
	1950	*Pub. U.S. Naval Obs.*, **16**, 333.

CHAPTER 7

The Photographic Zenith Tube and the Dual-Rate Moon-Position Camera

W. MARKOWITZ

U.S. Naval Observatory, Washington, D.C.

1. INTRODUCTION

Two astronomical instruments are described in this chapter, the photographic zenith tube (PZT) and the dual-rate moon-position camera. The first determines the position of stars with respect to the direction of the vertical. The moon-position camera determines the position of the moon with respect to the stars.

These instruments have certain features in common. They are photographic; the exposure times are short, about 10–20 seconds; and the epochs of observation are determined for precise instants which do not depend directly on the times of beginning and end of the exposures. The instruments are designed in accordance with geometric principles. The number of constraints is equal to the number of degrees of freedom, so that the accuracy is largely independent of the continued proper relation of precisely machined parts.

2. THE PHOTOGRAPHIC ZENITH TUBE

2.1. History

About 1909 Frank E. Ross (1915) undertook to design a new instrument of high accuracy for the determination of the variation of latitude. The reflex zenith tube, designed by Sir George Airy (1854), appeared to serve best as a basis for the design. Chandler (1901) had praised the instrument highly.

A schematic view of the reflex zenith tube is shown in Figure 1. The light-rays from a star near the zenith pass through the lens to a basin of mercury; they are reflected, pass through the lens again, and come to a focus about $\frac{1}{4}$ inch above the upper lens surface, where a micrometer is placed. By means of a diagonal, the field is viewed from the side of the tube. The upper portion of the instrument, called the *rotary*, can be rotated through 180°. Such reversal causes the image to appear in the micrometer on the opposite side of the field of view. The observer sets the micrometer thread on the star before meridian passage. The rotary is reversed, and another setting is made after passage. The difference in micrometer settings, allowing for curvature of the star's path, gives the double zenith distance and thus the latitude.

Airy showed that the position of a star image in the field of view is not affected by tilt of the lens if one of its two nodal points is in the focal plane. Translation of the rotary, neglecting the curvature of the mercury surface, does not change the position of the image in the field. The lens which Airy used was a small one, 5 inches in aperture and 116 inches in focal length. Only bright stars could be observed with the reflex zenith tube, which was used chiefly to observe γ Draconis. This star transits near the zenith at Greenwich and was

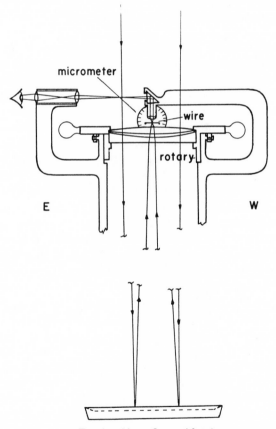

Fɪɢ. 1.—Airy reflex zenith tube

observed for a large part of the year. However, the Greenwich values obtained for the parallax of γ Draconis and for the aberration constant were not satisfactory. Eddington (1911) analyzed the results and concluded that the deficiencies of the reflex zenith tube were its small aperture, the difficulty in determining the focal length, and the second passage of light through the objective. The reflex zenith tube was not used after 1910.

Doolittle (1908), of the Flower Observatory of the University of Pennsylvania, designed in 1904 an improved zenith tube, called the "Wharton reflex zenith tube." In the Airy instrument the nearest nodal point was coincident with the upper surface of the lens, and the micrometer threads had to be placed above. In the Wharton instrument the upper nodal point was designed to be 0.155 inch above the upper surface, and the micrometer threads were placed at that level. The second passage of light through the glass was avoided by a hole 1 inch in diameter, bored through the lens. Under these conditions, however, the position of the image does depend on the tilt of the lens, although only slightly. The Wharton instrument was used from 1905 to 1910. Although it was an improvement over the Greenwich instrument, having an aperture of 8 inches and a focal length of 150 inches, it still had limitations inherent in a visual instrument.

Ross, in his design of the PZT, had to choose between allowing the stars to trail or using a moving-plate carriage. He decided on the second, in order to be able to photograph faint stars. He designed the lens so that the second nodal point was 1 cm below the lower surface of the lens and placed the photographic plate at this point. He thus made the PZT insensitive to tilt and avoided a second passage of light through the lens.

The Ross PZT was placed in operation at the International Latitude Station of the United States Coast and Geodetic Survey at Gaithersburg, Maryland, in 1911 and was used there continuously until December, 1914. Observations were also made there with a visual zenith telescope by the Horrebow-Talcott method. Ross (1915, p. 127) concluded: "The accuracy of the individual latitudes obtained with the photographic instrument appears to be considerably greater than that obtained with the visual instrument." The PZT had been built with funds from the International Geodetic Association; but, in spite of the report by Ross, the PZT was not adopted by the association for use at the international stations, possibly on account of the expense. In 1915 the instrument was purchased by the United States Naval Observatory and brought to Washington, D.C. Observations for the variation of latitude were begun at Washington in October, 1915.

About 1923 John E. Willis suggested that the PZT should be used to determine time as well as the variation of latitude. A timing contact was added to the PZT, and experiments were carried out by Littell and Willis (1929) from 1923 to 1933. After February, 1934, the PZT, now denoted "No. 1," was used for the determination of time. Several improvements in PZT No. 1 were made by Sollenberger (1942, 1945, 1949). A synchronous motor was installed to control the plate drive, and an automatic reversal system was added.

About 1945 it was decided to establish a substation of the United States Naval Observatory, located as near the equator as practicable. Designs for a new instrument, called the "Richmond model," were developed by Sollenberger with the assistance of the writer. This instrument, PZT No. 2, was placed in operation in February, 1949, at Richmond, Florida, located about 25 km south of Miami. PZT No. 3, similar to No. 2, was constructed to replace No. 1 at Washington and was placed in operation in April, 1954. Nos. 1 and 3 were operated simultaneously until May, 1955, when No. 1 was retired from service. Nine other PZT's had been installed at various observatories about the world by 1960.

2.2. THEORY

A lens has two nodal points associated with it. A light-ray which is directed to one nodal point leaves the second nodal point in a parallel direction. The distance from the second nodal point to the focal plane is the equivalent focal

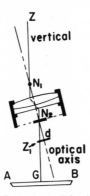

FIG. 2.—Optical principle of PZT

length, EFL. The nodal points normally lie within the elements of the lens; however, a lens may be designed so that a nodal point lies outside. In Figure 2, both nodal points, N_1 and N_2, are shown exterior to the lens.

Positions of nodal points may be located by means of a nodal slide (Jenkins and White 1957), which permits the lens to be rotated about an axis perpendicular to the optical axis. Parallel light is sent through the lens and brought to a focus. A position of the axis of rotation is found such that rotation of the lens does not shift the image; this locates the rear nodal point. The lens is turned around, and the other nodal point is found in a similar manner.

In Figure 2, AB is the horizontal surface of a basin of mercury, and ZN_1 is a ray of light from the zenith The transmitted ray, N_2G, is parallel to ZN_1. The path of the ray is $ZN_1N_2GN_2N_1Z$. The optical axis intersects the path of the ray at N_1 and N_2.

The position of the focal plane may be changed by moving the mercury surface up or down. Let the focal plane be at N_2. Let the plate be fixed with respect to the lens cell. Assume that the lens is held rigidly within the cell. Then neither tilting nor horizontal translation of the lens cell will change the position of the image of the zenith on the plate at N_2. Similarly, the position of the image of a star which is not at the zenith will not be sensibly displaced by such motions. The central rays are, of course, occulted by the plate, but the marginal rays for any star are assumed to come to the same focus.

The position of an image on the plate is affected, however, by rotation of the cell. A rotation of 180° causes displacement of the image symmetrically about the zenith.

In the Airy and Wharton instruments the east-west direction was determined visually from the diurnal motion of the star. In the photographic instrument of Ross, exposures are made with the rotary in alternate positions. A pair of exposures taken with the instrument in the same position determines the east-west direction.

Assume, now, that the focal plane is at a distance d from N_2 and that the plate is in the focal plane. The displacement of Z_1, the image of Z, from the optic axis is $h = d \tan \alpha$, where α is the angle between the optic axis and the vertical. Let f be the focal length, and let $\tan \alpha$ be replaced by α. In angular measure, the displacement is $\beta = g\alpha$, where $g = d/f$. The position of the image of the zenith is thus affected by tilt of the lens when the second nodal point does not lie in the focal plane.

In the modern PZT, the nodal point can be located with a precision of about 1 mm. The focal length is of the order of 4000 mm, so that g can be made less than 0.0003. The inclination of the lens can be kept constant to about 10″, which corresponds to an error in position of 0″.003. This is so small that level readings are not taken except when adjusting the instrument. The value of g for Airy's instrument was 0.002. For a non-reflex instrument, $g = 1$, so that an error in level reading enters with a factor of unity in determining position.

2.3. CONSTRUCTION AND OPERATION

The essential parts of the PZT are shown in Figure 3 and Plate I. The rotary is shown in Figure 4. The plate carriage, C, which moves on three steel balls, is constrained by springs to bear against guides G_1 and G_2. A shutter K_1 is operated by a solenoid, K_2. A box, M, contains a synchronous motor,[1] M_1, a precision drive screw, T, and the program mechanism. The spring S_3 pulls the plate carriage against the end of the drive screw. The guides constrain the carriage so that its motion is rectilinear. A toothed segment, H_1, is attached to the carriage which initiates timing impulses as it moves across the point H_2.

The rotary turns on three ball bearings. In addition, six ball bearings loosely constrain the rotary horizontally. The constraint is a free one, so that upper and lower blocks on the rotary, B_u and B_l, may be brought against the ends of two stops, I_u and J_l. When the instrument is reversed, the blocks are brought against the stops I_l and J_u. The rotation of 180° is checked by means of a pair of microscopes and fiducial marks or with a mirror and a collimating telescope.

---

[1] Blank rectangle above the letter M in Figure 4.

The rotary is reversed in about 5 seconds by means of a motor and gear box. The reversal mechanism is designed so that, as the blocks approach the fixed stops, the speed approaches zero. The blocks are then brought up against the stops with spring tension. Air dashpots prevent bumping of the rotary against the stops.

The synchronous motor, M_1, runs continuously; it is not stopped except for adjustment or repairs. The driving source is a current of 1000 cycles per second generated by the quartz-crystal clock which is being used to time the observations. The motor drives a gear, whose speed is one revolution per second, which has a single tooth placed in each of its two faces. By means of a magnetic clutch, either one of these teeth can be engaged so that the carriage drives forward or backward.

The program mechanism operates as follows to provide a set of four ex-

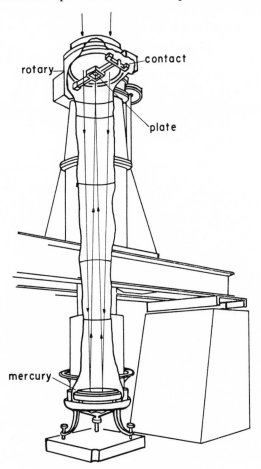

Fig. 3.—Schematic view of PZT

posures. The starting switch is thrown "On," which sends current into a starting solenoid. A cam is lifted and begins turning. After about 2 seconds a cam switch simultaneously opens the shutter and causes one of the two sides of the clutch to engage. The carriage moves from west to east, so as to track the star for 20 seconds. A switch is thrown within M. This closes the shutter and disengages the clutch, stopping the motion of the carriage. At the same time the reversal motor starts, and the instrument is reversed. The cam is now in a position such that the cam switch is open and there is no current in the shutter solenoid or clutch magnets. Thirty seconds after its initial closing, the cam switch again closes and allows current to pass. The shutter opens, and the other

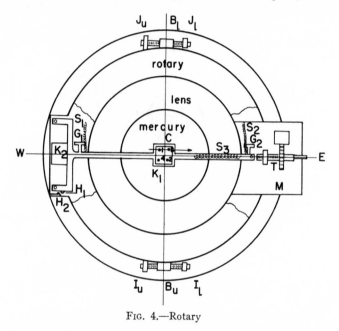

Fig. 4.—Rotary

clutch engages. The second exposure is made with the drive screw turning in the reverse direction. However, the rotary has been reversed, so that the carriage again moves from west to east. After 20 seconds the instrument reverses. The third and fourth exposures are made in a similar manner. Prior to the end of the fourth exposure the starting switch is thrown to "Off." The instrument automatically stops operating after the fourth exposure. The cycle of operations for each exposure is 30 seconds in length.

Consider the exposures made in the same position of the rotary, for example, motor east. The program mechanism is such that the decimal fraction of the second of the time at which the plate carriage occupies some particular position with respect to the lens cell is precisely the same, irrespective of when the starting switch is thrown. Similarly, it remains the same, although at a different value, for motor west. In consequence, the timing signals produced by H_1 and H_2 remain the same from star to star and night to night, so long as the synchronous motor does not stop. Only the decimal fraction of a second is ordinarily retained when determining time. Timing signals, therefore, are not required for each star observed.

The displacement between a pair of images made with the rotary in the same position, such as 1 and 3 or 2 and 4 of the same set, is due to the diurnal motion of the star during 60 seconds. The declination of the star observed is accurately known, and its displacement in arc may be computed. Measurement of the distance between the pair of images on the plate furnishes the scale value of the PZT with high precision. It is determined for each night to about 1 part in 10,000.

The plate is 45 mm square. The plate carriage cuts off a small part (about one-tenth) of the light which enters the lens. The carriage acts as a single-wire grating, which produces a visible diffraction pattern if the star is very bright. The diffraction pattern is symmetrical with respect to the co-ordinate axes through the center of the star.

PZT Nos. 1, 2, and 3 have the optical characteristics given in the accompany-

	No. 1	No. 2	No. 3
Aperture................	200 mm	200 mm	200 mm
Equivalent focal length.....	5167 mm	3786 mm	4577 mm
Field.................	24′	34′	27′

ing table. The objectives of all three were designed for photography with blue-sensitive plates. Nos. 2 and 3 were found to be much faster than No. 1. Slow plates, Eastman 33, are used with Nos. 2 and 3. Stars of magnitude 8.5 are photographed under average observing conditions.

Although the field of the PZT is small, an adequate number of stars is available for observation. For stations in latitudes higher than that of Washington, apertures of 250 mm have generally been used. Since, however, the speed of photographic plates has been increased in recent years, the larger apertures may not be necessary in future construction.

The reflecting mercury basin is 20 cm in diameter and 1.5 cm deep. It is made of steel and has a copper insert amalgamated with mercury in the upper surface. The insert has a depression of 3 mm, which retains the mercury.

The reflecting basin floats in a second mercury basin. To clean the mercury, the reflecting basin is lowered until it rests on supporting blocks. Mercury is added if necessary, and the surface is skimmed with a plastic rod 2 cm in diameter. The basin is then raised until the mercury surface makes contact with a focusing rod.

The PZT is prepared for operation by cleaning the mercury surface, focusing, and inserting a plate. The PZT may be operated by remote control or automatically throughout the night. Automatic programmers have been developed at Richmond, Ottawa, Tokyo, and Neuchâtel.

Since the PZT observations are made photographically and without guiding by an observer, the instrument is impersonal. The plates are measured with a standard type of measuring instrument. Latitude and time are determined from measurement of differences in the positions of four images of each star. Personal equation in bisecting the images cancels out.

The measurement and reduction of plates at Washington are made with the aid of punched cards and the IBM 650 magnetic-drum computer. The apparent declinations and predicted Universal Times of transit of each star are calculated in advance with this computer.

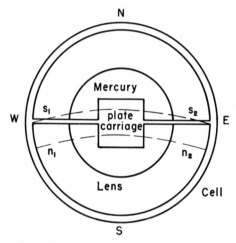

Fig. 5.—Path of stars in focal plane, as seen from above

2.4. Formation of Images

Figure 5 shows the path in the focal plane of stars which transit near the zenith, as seen from above. The track of a star which transits north of zenith is n_1n_2, and that of one south of the zenith is s_1s_2. To obtain sharp images, the plate carriage is driven from west to east. Assume that the exposures are started with the rotary motor east. Four exposures are made as follows, with respect to the mean in time:

Exp.	Time	Motor	Exp.	Time	Motor
1..........	-55^s to -35^s	East	3.........	$+ 5^s$ to $+25^s$	East
2..........	-25 to $- 5$	West	4.........	$+35$ to $+55$	West

If the plate did not move during the exposure but the shutter was opened for each exposure, there would be obtained four trails of a south star, as shown in

Figure 6, *a*. If the plate moved but there was no reversal, four images would appear, as in Figure 6, *b*. In practice, the rotary is reversed between exposures, and the four images form a quadrilateral, as shown in Figure 6, *c*. When the exposures are symmetrical with respect to time of meridian passage, the images form a rectangle.

Two groups of stars are photographed on the same plate each night. If those of the first group are photographed with the motor east-west east-west, those of the second group are taken west-east west-east. As shown in Plate II, four bands of stars are obtained, two for each group.

The formation of images 1 and 2 is shown in detail in Figure 7. Each exposure is started with the center of the plate 10^s west of the meridian. At the end of the exposure it is 10^s east. Reversal of the rotary brings the center of the plate back to 10^s west.

It is assumed that the nodal point lies in the plane of the plate. Then the image of the zenith coincides with the nodal point. The meridian is the north-south line through the zenith. The images of the zenith and meridian are fixed with respect to the lens cell while an exposure is made, but their positions on the plate change. Hence it is not possible to indicate the zenith and meridian on the developed plate.

The double zenith distance is the north-south component of the distance between images 1 and 4, or 2 and 3, corrected for curvature of path.

The image of a diurnal circle on the plate is a curved line. Let ζ be the angular distance of a star north of the prime vertical and let ζ_0 be the value when the star is on the meridian. Then, very nearly,

$$\zeta - \zeta_0 = \frac{15^2 \tau^2 \sin 2\delta \sin 1''}{4},\qquad (1)$$

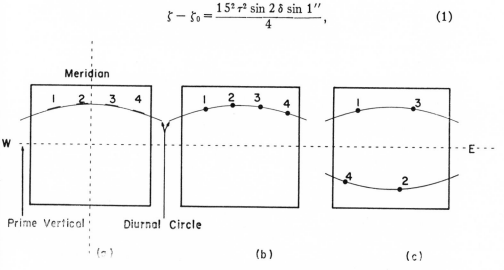

Fig. 6.—*a*) Trails with plate stationary. *b*) Plate moves, but without reversal. *c*) Images formed with plate moving and with reversal.

where τ is the hour angle of the star in seconds of time and δ is its declination. Since the field of the PZT is small, we may replace δ by ϕ, the latitude of the station. Equation (1) becomes, for Washington,

$$\zeta - \zeta_0 = 0\overset{\prime\prime}{.}0002667\,\tau^2 \; . \tag{2}$$

The displacement due to curvature of path is found by integration between the limits of τ as given above for each exposure. The measured zenith distance of a star at Washington is $0\overset{\prime\prime}{.}309$ north of its zenith distance when on the meridian.

2.5. DETERMINATION OF TIME

Figure 8 shows exposures being made for the two positions of the rotary. In each position of the rotary the carriage moves from west to east. In Figure 8, *a*, the contact is shown at the instant of opening and in Figure 8, *b*, at the instant of closing. Both the opening and the closing of the contact generate timing impulses which are recorded with respect to a clock. One part of the contact is attached to the plate carriage and the other to the lens cell, so that

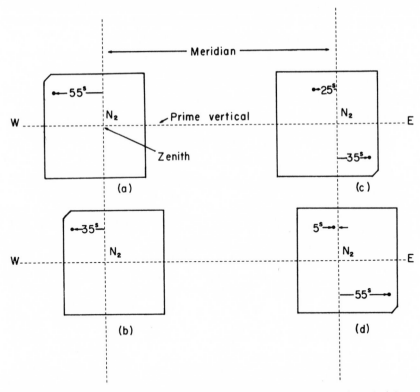

FIG. 7.—Formation of images 1 and 2. *a*) Beginning of 1, $t = -55^s$. *b*) End of 1, $t = -35^s$; rotary begins reversal. *c*) Beginning of 2, $t = -25^s$. *d*) End of 2, $t = -5^s$; rotary begins reversal.

the instants at which impulses are generated are independent of backlash in the plate-drive gearing or of lateral displacements of the rotary.

Let the epochs of the timing pulses as read on the clock be t_1, t_2, t_3, and t_4, respectively, for the four exposures. At each of these times the position of H_1 with respect to H_2 is the same. It follows, therefore, that the positions of the node, zenith, and meridian on the plate are identical, respectively, at these times.

The positions of the star in the sky and its image on the plate at times of impulse are given in the accompanying table. The p's are hour angles, measured

Time	In Sky	On Plate	Time	In Sky	On Plate
t_1........	p_1, east	h_1	t_3........	p_3, west	h_3
t_2........	p_2, east	h_2	t_4........	p_4, west	h_4

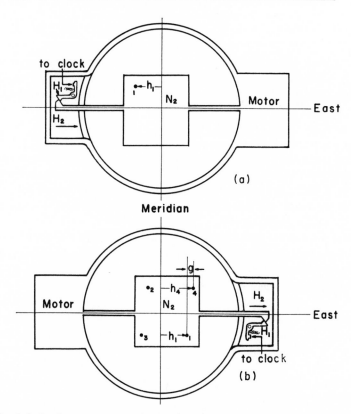

FIG. 8.—Relation between contact, plate, and nodal point at opening or closing of contact. a) Motor east, contact at instant of opening. b) Motor west, contact at instant of closing. The letters H_1 and H_2 should be interchanged.

in time, and the h's are in linear units. The two are related by a known scale factor.

At epoch $(t_1 + t_4)/2$, the position of the star is $(p_1 - p_4)/2$ east of the meridian. Having four images, the plate may be oriented parallel to the prime vertical. The distance $h_1 - h_4$ is measured, and, since the scale value is known, $(p_1 - p_4)/2$ is obtained. Thus it is possible to determine the position of the star with respect to the meridian for a known epoch. Utilizing all four exposures, we find that, at epoch

$$t_0 = \frac{t_1 + t_2 + t_3 + t_4}{4},$$

the position of the star east of the meridian is

$$p_0 = \frac{p_1 - p_4 + p_2 - p_3}{4},$$

which is obtained by measuring

$$h_0 = \frac{h_1 - h_4 + h_2 - h_3}{4}.$$

2.6. SCALE VALUE

The latitude of a station is given by the formula $\phi = \delta - \zeta$, where ϕ is the latitude, δ is the declination of the star, and ζ is the north zenith distance at time of transit. The zenith distance is obtained by multiplying a measured distance by the adopted scale value.

An erroneous scale value will affect the observed latitudes with the opposite sign for north and south stars. A scale value may be determined from the condition that north and south stars shall give the same latitude. The scale value so determined will be affected, however, by errors in the assumed declinations.

We may derive the scale value independently from the diurnal motion of the stars, as previously explained. The value thus obtained is not sensibly affected by errors in the declinations.

The displacements measured on PZT plates vary from 0 to about 0.5 mm in determining time, and from 0 to about 35 mm in determining latitude. The determination of an accurate scale value is therefore more important in determining latitude than in determining time.

Two scale values are determined each night, σ_1 from the condition that the latitudes shall be alike and σ_2 from the dirunal motion. It is possible that a developed plate has a different scale value in the two co-ordinates because of distortion of the emulsion. The value σ_1 is used in the preliminary reductions. A correction based on the average value of σ_2 for each group during the year is applied later. Hence, systematically, the scale value used in the final latitudes depends only upon σ_2.

2.7. THE PZT CATALOGUE

The catalogue of right ascensions and declinations used in the PZT reductions is based internally on observations made only with the PZT itself. The positions as a whole are placed on a fundamental system, such as FK4. Thus the PZT catalogue is not affected by the accidental and periodic errors of star catalogues.

The PZT stars observed are divided into eight groups of ten stars each. Two groups of stars are observed for $6\frac{1}{2}$ weeks. At the end of this time one group is dropped, and a new group is added. This process is continued for the entire year, until the two initial groups are observed again.

For the initial year of observation a preliminary PZT catalogue is formed by using positions given in star catalogues. For each night the condition is imposed that all the stars shall give the same latitude. The differences of the observed latitude for each star from the mean for each night gives a set of corrections to the assumed catalogue positions. Each group is observed on about 30–40 nights. These observations provide corrections within the group. Corrections to each group are also obtained, since the groups are observed in pairs. Individual corrections are thus derived to the initial positions, which are internally self-consistent. It should be noted that the positions obtained with the PZT are completely independent of the initial positions, except that the mean of the declinations of all the stars remains the same as that of the preliminary catalogue.

A catalogue formed in this manner is suitable for determining the variation of latitude; but it is not suitable for determining absolute latitude. For this purpose the mean declination of the stars must be placed on a fundamental system.

A PZT catalogue of right ascensions is formed in a manner similar to that for declinations. The condition is imposed that on any one night all the stars shall give the same clock correction.

As an example, observations with the Richmond PZT began in February, 1949. By March, 1950, a catalogue based on the PZT observations had been formed, and these were used thereafter for the determination of time and latitude. After 6 years of observations, revised positions and proper motions were derived.

For the Washington PZT, both the positions and the proper motions depend internally on the PZT observations alone, as the results from over 20 years of observation were available in forming catalogues for each co-ordinate.

On account of precession, one PZT star is lost about every 2 years and must be replaced with another. The replacement star is observed for 4 years to bring it into the PZT system before the change. An attempt is made to maintain the mean zenith distance of each group near zero.

2.8. PZT Adjustments

2.81. *Azimuth.*—The plate carriage should move in an east-west direction. An error in orientation of the instrument will produce an elongation of the star image in the north-south direction. Exposures are for 20 seconds, and during this time the image moves approximately 250 seconds of arc. An error of $0°.1$ in the orientation of the carriage will produce an elongation of $0''.5$. The images obtained with the PZT vary in diameter from about 3″ to 5″. There is no difficulty in determining the mid-point of an image, so that orientation of the PZT is not critical. In practice, the PZT can be oriented to within 2′. The orientation may be checked as follows.

A bright star is allowed to trail until it reaches a position near the center of the plate. The driving clutch is engaged, and the star is tracked for 20 seconds. The star is then allowed to trail again, but without reversing the rotary. If the azimuth is correct, the two trails will coincide at the point where they meet the star image.

An error in azimuth does not cause an error in latitude or time, provided that the reversal is 180°. Consider images 1 and 4. The position of the plate with respect to the nodal point is the same at the beginning of exposure 1 as at the end of 4. Similarly, it is the same at the end of exposure 1 as at the

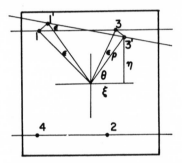

FIG. 9.—Reversal

beginning of 4. Hence the mean position of the plate with respect to the nodal point is the same for exposures 1 and 4. This holds also for the pair 2 and 3.

2.82. *Reversal.*—It is necessary that the PZT rotary shall reverse through 180° to within a few seconds of arc. Two microscopes are used to set on two fiducial marks. Let the readings of the microscopes when the motor is east be A_e and B_e, respectively. Similarly, let A_w and B_w be the readings when the motor is west. Let ϵ be the excess over 180° in reversal when the motor rotates from east to west through north. Then, in seconds of arc,

$$\epsilon = \frac{(A_w + B_w) - (A_e + B_e)}{m K \sin 1''}, \tag{3}$$

where m is the magnification of the microscope objective and K is the distance between the microscopes in millimeters.

The effect of an error in the reversal angle is shown in Figure 9. We may assume that images 2 and 4, taken with motor east, are correctly placed. If the reversal angle were 180°, images 1 and 3 would appear as shown. However, if there is an error in reversal, the images will appear at 1′ and 3′.

Let the rectangular co-ordinates of an image with respect to the center of rotation of the rotary be ξ and η, and let the polar co-ordinates be ρ and θ. The η-axis is parallel to the meridian. We readily obtain the differential formulae

$$d\,\xi = -\,\eta d\,\theta\,, \qquad d\,\eta = +\,\xi d\,\theta\,.$$

The error in the observed double zenith distance due to the error ϵ is the mean value of $\xi\epsilon$ for images 1 and 3. During the exposure, ξ changes. Mean values are $-525''$ and $+175''$, respectively. If $\epsilon = 5''$, the resulting error in the single zenith distance and in the derived latitude is $0''.002$.

The error in the double meridian distance is $-\eta\epsilon$. The maximum value of η is about $800''$. If $\epsilon = 5''$, the maximum error in the observed mean meridian distance and therefore in the time is found to be $0^s.0008$. The average value is $0^s.0004$.

The value of ϵ may readily be kept to about $2''$, so that corrections for error in reversal need not be applied.

The Washington and Richmond PZT's utilize two pairs of screws as stops for each position of the rotary. In making adjustments for the reversal angle, the rotary is brought against one pair of stops. Each one of these stops is moved forward and backward slightly, in turn. The microscopes must indicate that the rotary is being moved when either of the two stops is moved. This shows that both blocks on the rotary are bearing against the screws. The instrument is reversed, and the same procedure is used with the other pair of stops. In the final adjustment, only one of the four screws is used for obtaining the correct orientation. The orientation is stable; it is checked once a month.

2.83. *Level.*—The PZT rests on two steel beams, which are supported by four leveling screws. The rotary carries two levels, placed at right angles. The rotary is leveled by adjusting the leveling screws so that the same reading of each level is obtained for the two positions of the rotary. The level readings remain constant to within $10''$ for successive reversals.

After the rotary is leveled, the lens is leveled within the rotary. For this purpose a special level is used which can be placed against the lower surface of the lens. The optical axis of the lens can thus be kept vertical to about $10''$.

2.84. *Focus.*—To focus the PZT, a stainless-steel rod is pulled down from the tube, and the mercury basin is raised so as to touch the end of the rod. Changes in focal setting may be made by adjusting the length of the rod. The position of best focus is found by trial. The length of the rod is not changed thereafter.

The best setting of the length of the rod can be determined to about 0.5 mm. This means that the focal distance of the lens is critical to about 1 mm.

2.85. *Nodal point.*—The back focal length of the lens (BFL) may be obtained by measuring the distance from the lower surface of the lens to the mercury surface and then to the photographic plate. The equivalent focal length (EFL) may be obtained either from a laboratory measurement or from the diurnal motion of stars. The second nodal point is located below the lower surface of the lens a distance equal to BFL−EFL. The plane of the photographic plate must be located close to the second nodal point.

Specifications for the lens of PZT No. 3, manufactured by the Perkin-Elmer Corporation, required that the EFL should be 4570 ± 150 mm and that the nodal point should be 11 ± 1 mm below the lens. It is interesting to see how well these specifications were met.

Tests made at the National Bureau of Standards showed that EFL = 4579 ± 1 mm, BFL = 4589 ± 4 mm at a "dominant wavelength of approximately 480 millimicrons."

The effective scale value derived from diurnal motion is 45″.080 per mm. The geometric scale value is smaller by the factor (1−0.00028) because of atmospheric refraction near the zenith. The true scale value is thus 45″.067 per mm, which gives the value 4577 mm for the EFL. The probable error is ±0.5 mm.

Measurements made at the PZT show that the lower surface of the lens is 2299 ± 0.5 mm above the mercury surface and 10 ± 0.1 mm above the emulsion of the plate. The BFL is 2 × 2299 − 10 = 4588 ± 1 mm. Hence, as determined by astronomical observation, the second nodal point is 11 ± 1 mm below the lens. The agreement between the laboratory and astronomical determinations of the properties of the lens, allowing for possible differences in effective wave lengths employed, is very good.

2.9. Sources of Error

During the year May 5, 1954, to May 5, 1955, three PZT's were in operation. Nos. 1 and 3, which were located 11 meters apart at Washington, photographed the same stars simultaneously. PZT No. 2 was operated at Richmond, Florida, about 1500 km to the south. The operation of these three PZT's during this year afforded an unusual opportunity to study the sources of error. The number of nights of observation were 194 for PZT 1, 187 for PZT 3, and 277 for PZT 2. Simultaneous observations were made with PZT 1 and PZT 3 on 171 nights. The average number of stars observed per night were thirteen for PZT 1, fourteen for PZT 3, and fifteen for PZT 2.

The principal sources for error are listed below. The letter (c) means that the error affects PZT's 1 and 3 in common, when the same star is observed. Other errors are not in common. The errors are due to the following causes:

Short-period refraction anomalies, of the order of 1 minute; origin external to PZT house (c)
Long-period refraction anomalies, of the order of 1 day; origin external to PZT house (c)
Error in adopted star position (c)
Refraction anomalies within PZT house
·Measurement of plate
Film distortion
Tilt of mercury surface

Consider a star observed simultaneously by PZT's 1 and 3. Let v be the observed difference in time. Let v_1 and v_3 be the respective errors in time, a_1 and a_3 the respective non-common errors, and c the common error. Then

$$v_1 = a_1 + c , \qquad v_3 = a_3 + c , \qquad v = a_1 - a_3 .$$

For a large number of observations, mean values are related as follows:

$$v_1^2 = a_1^2 + c^2 , \qquad v_3^2 = a_3^2 + c^2 , \qquad v^2 = a_1^2 + a_3^2 . \qquad (4)$$

Mean values of v_1^2 and v_3^2 are obtained from the residuals for each night with respect to the mean for each PZT. The mean value of v^2 is obtained from the differences in time. Equations (4) may be solved for mean values of a_1^2, a_3^2, and c^2. Probable errors of $v_1, v_3, v, c, a_1,$ and a_3 were calculated from these data. Table 1

TABLE 1

PROBABLE ERRORS OF OBSERVATION

Error*	Observation of*	PZT 1	PZT 2	PZT 3	PZT 1 − PZT 3	PZT 2 − PZT 3
e_1.........	One star	10.6	9.6	8.5	....	....
e_2.........	One star	....	....	....	10.5	....
e_3.........	One star	6.1	....	6.1	....	....
e_4.........	One star	8.7	....	5.9	....	....
e_5.........	One night	3.0	2.5	2.3	....	....
e_6.........	One night	4.7	4.6	4.4	....	....
e_7.........	One night	3.6	3.9	3.8	....	....
e_8.........	One night	....	....	....	5.4	6.2
e_9.........	One night	2.5	....	2.5	....	....
e_{10}........	One night	4.0	....	3.6	....	....
e_{11}........	One night	2.6	....	2.8	....	....

* For further explanation see text.

gives these probable errors and others derived for PZT 2. Thus e_1 is the probable error of $v_1, v_3,$ or v_2, e_2 being the probable error in v.

The common error, c, whose probable error is e_3, is due to refraction anomalies and errors in the adopted star positions. The positions have been well determined, so that refraction anomalies are the principal source of the common error. Since the value of e_3 is almost as large as e_1 for PZT 3, it follows that refraction anomalies are the principal limitation on the accuracy of determining time for a single star with the PZT. The probable error of the non-common error is e_4.

The internal probable error of a time determination for one night is e_5. The external probable error, e_6, is obtained from the observed *minus* adopted clock corrections for each night. In obtaining the adopted clock correction, strong smoothing, extending over several months, was employed. The same clock correction was adopted for Nos. 1, 2, and 3. Because of this, e_6 is considered to be the external probable error. The systematic error for a night is e_7. It is obtained from the formula

$$e_7^2 = e_6^2 - e_5^2 .$$

If the quantities e_6 were independent, the probable error e_8 of a difference for the night of (PZT 1 − PZT 3) or (PZT 2 − PZT 3) would be $0.^s0064$. The second quantity agrees closely with this value. This is to be expected because PZT 2 at Richmond and PZT 3 at Washington are well separated, so that the results should be independent.

The value of e_8 is significantly smaller for (PZT 1 − PZT 3), so that there is a common night error, e_9, which affects PZT 1 and PZT 3 at Washington.

The non-common error which affects each PZT for the night is obtained from the formula

$$e_{10}^2 = e_6^2 - e_9^2 .$$

The error, e_{10}, is composed of an accidental part equal to e_5 and a systematic part, e_{11}, obtained from the formula

$$e_{11}^2 = e_{10}^2 - e_5^2 .$$

Causes which might contribute to e_{11} are tilt of the mercury surface, error in referring PZT to the clock, and refraction anomalies in or near the PZT house.

Table 2 gives the components of e_6, in time and arc, for PZT 3. It is seen that

TABLE 2

COMPONENTS OF ERROR FOR PZT 3

e_5, from accidental errors of stars...............	$\pm 0.^s0023 = \pm 0.''027$
e_9, systematic part, external to PZT building.......	$\pm$ .0025 $\pm$ .029
e_{11}, systematic part, affecting PZT...............	± 0.0028 ± 0.033

these are nearly the same in magnitude.

On account of systematic effects, no great increase in precision can be gained by observing a large number of stars in one night. The probable error e_6 for nights with four to eight and nine or more stars is given in the accompanying table. The weight of an observation with 16 stars is about 1.5 times as great as

No. Stars	Mean	No. 1	No. 3	No. 2
4–8........	6	$0.^s0048$	$0.^s0056$	$0.^s0053$
9 or more...	16	0.0046	0.0041	0.0045

that of one with 6 stars, although the number of stars is 2.7 times as great.

Probable errors in latitude were also studied. The probable error of one star with respect to the mean for the night is e_{12}. To obtain the external probable error for one night, e_{13}, a smoothed latitude-curve was drawn, based on the results of both PZT's 1 and 3 for May, 1954—May, 1955. From these data are calculated the internal probable error for one night, e_{14}, and the systematic error for the night, e_{15}, using the relation

$$e_{15}^2 = e_{13}^2 - e_{14}^2 \, .$$

Values are given in Table 3.

Table 4 gives a comparison of the probable errors in time and latitude for the two PZT's for a single star and for one night. The agreement for the two coordinates is close.

TABLE 3

PROBABLE ERRORS IN LATITUDE

	PZT 1	PZT 3
e_{12}, one star.............................	0″125	0″106
e_{13}, one night, from adopted latitude-curve...	.054	.055
e_{14}, one night, accidental part..............	.035	.028
e_{15}, one night, systematic part.............	0.041	0.047

TABLE 4

COMPARISON OF PROBABLE ERRORS

	PZT 1		PZT 3	
	Time	Lat.	Time	Lat.
One star.......................	0″124	0″125	0″099	0″106
One night, accidental part........	.035	.035	.027	.028
One night, systematic part........	.041	.041	.043	.047
One night, total.................	0.055	0.054	0.051	0.055

To summarize, the probable error of one night of observation with PZT 2 or 3 is 0.̊0045 in time and 0″055 in latitude.

3. THE DUAL-RATE MOON CAMERA

3.1. HISTORY

Proposals to determine the position of the moon with respect to the stars by photography were made as early as 1895 (Wade 1905). The first systematic program was carried out jointly by the Harvard and Princeton Observatories from 1911 to 1917 under the direction of H. N. Russell (Russell and Pickering 1913; Russell and Fowler 1916). By means of an occulting disk, mounted several feet in front of the telescope, it was possible to photograph the stars for 10 minutes and the moon for about 0.2 second. Later techniques have utilized a small shutter which is placed in front of the image of the moon, near the photographic plate.

The techniques described involve making a short exposure of the moon to eliminate trailing and a long exposure of the stars to photograph faint ones. Since the moon and stars are not photographed simultaneously, two sources of error arise: (a) the position of the telescope when the moon is photographed may not be the same as its average position for the stars, and (b) displacements due to refraction anomalies may not be the same for the moon as for the stars.

In 1951 the writer designed the dual-rate moon-position camera, which allows the moon and stars to be photographed simultaneously (Markowitz 1954). The first dual-rate camera was placed in operation at the United States Naval Observatory in 1952. Twenty cameras, of a second model, were constructed for use during the International Geophysical Year. This model is shown in Figure 10.

3.2. PRINCIPLES OF OPERATION

The rays of light from the moon pass through a dark, plane-parallel glass filter, which is placed in front of the photographic plate. The filter is tilted during the exposure, thus shifting the image of the moon by optical refraction. The filter also reduces the light of the moon so as to produce an image on the plate of suitable density. By proper selection of the rate of tilt and orientation of the axis of tilt, the moon can be held fixed relative to the stars for simultaneous exposures of 20 seconds. The epoch of observation is the instant when the filter is parallel to the plate, irrespective of when the exposure begins or ends, since at this instant there is no displacement of the moon relative to the stars.

During the exposure, a synchronous motor and micrometer drive the plate carriage by means of a drive arm and a movable steel ball. The distance of the ball from the center of rotation of the arm is adjusted so as to give the correct speed, which depends on the declination of the moon, to track the stars.

A second synchronous motor and micrometer, mounted on a movable platform, drive a tilt arm which tilts the filter. The distance of the micrometer axis from the center of rotation of the tilt arm can be varied, so that the rate of tilt can be made to correspond to the speed of the moon relative to the stars. The platform which carries the tilt assembly can be moved so that the axis of tilt is perpendicular to the apparent path of the moon with respect to the stars.

A contact is mounted on the tilt arm to provide a chronograph record. The reading of the tilt micrometer when the filter is parallel to the focal plane is found by autocollimation with the aid of a clear glass plate. The reading of the micrometer when the contact opens or closes is obtained with an electric meter. Since the micrometer turns at a known speed, one may calculate the correction to the chronograph reading to obtain the instant of parallelism.

In practice, no attempt is made to obtain this correction with high precision. The camera is rotated 180° between successive exposures, and plates are always measured in pairs, one for each of the two positions. Systematic effects due to an error in the chronograph correction or to optical imperfection of the filter are thereby eliminated. The filter is 1.8 mm thick. It transmits about one five-hundredth of the entering light.

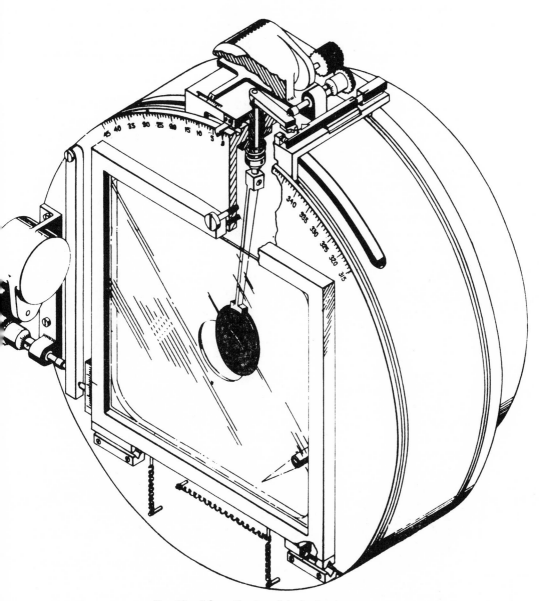

FIG. 10.—Schematic view of dual-rate camera

A special telescope was designed in 1957 for use with the moon camera at the Naval Observatory. The lens, constructed by the Perkin-Elmer Corporation, has an aperture of 200 mm and a focal length of 4115 mm. The two-element lens, which provides good images, was designed for use with blue-sensitive plates. This choice was made to allow examination of the plates during development. An electric-motor sidereal drive is provided, but it is not used when an exposure is being made.

Exposures are made automatically with a cycle timer. The moon is centered in the finder, and a starting switch is closed. The telescope drive motor stops, and the synchronous motors on the camera start. After 10 seconds a rotating, shutter within the camera opens. Ten seconds later it closes, the synchronous motors stop, and the telescope motor drives again. The timer may be set to make 20-second exposures.

Exposures are normally made for 10 seconds at Washington, using slow plates, Eastman II-O. Measurable images of stars of photographic magnitude 9.0 are obtained under favorable conditions. The plates are 16 × 16 cm in size.

3.3. Design of Camera

The requirements for tracking the moon are more severe than those for tracking a star. If the plate moves uniformly, but not quite at the correct sidereal rate, the star trails uniformly. Its position at the middle of the exposure can be accurately found. For the moon, the bright limb is utilized in measurement. If the moon trails, the edge obtained in the photograph will not correspond to its position at the middle of the exposure. It was considered that if the trailing of the moon could be held to $0''.1$, the error in the derived position, due to this cause, would be less than $0''.05$.

The tracking of the moon is accomplished in two parts: (a) driving the center of the plate to track the stars and (b) removing the differential motion with the tilting filter. Two methods may be used to track the stars: the telescope remains stationary and the plate moves, or the plate is fixed and the telescope moves.

The requirement that the tracking shall be accurate to $0''.1$ is severe. A good telescope drive may have the required precision, but it appeared difficult to obtain such precision with the telescope available in 1951. Experience with the PZT had demonstrated that stars could be tracked accurately for 20 seconds by moving the plate. This method was therefore adopted when designing the dual-rate camera.

If the plate is driven parallel to the equator at the speed required to track a star at its center, the plate is rotated, effectively, about this center. Short tangential trails are produced for stars not at the center.

The rotation is $\gamma = 15'' \, t \sin \delta_0$, where t is the length of exposure in seconds and δ_0 is the declination of the plate center. The length of the trail in seconds of arc is $l = 0.017\gamma R$, where R is the distance of the star from the center of the plate in degrees. Maximum values of the quantities are $t = 20$ seconds, $\delta_0 = 29°$, and $R = 1°$. The maximum value of l is $2''.5$. This quantity is too small to produce a noticeable effect, since star images are enlarged by atmospheric refraction effects. Since the trailing is uniform, no error is involved in determining the position of the center of a star image. For the Washington plates, $t = 10$ seconds, and R seldom exceeds $0^{\prime\prime}.7$. The maximum value of l for Washington is about $1^{\prime\prime}$, and the average is about $0^{\prime\prime}.5$.

The moon is essentially circular, so that a small rotation of the plate has virtually no effect on determining the position of the center of the moon.

We consider the tolerances necessary in order that a trailing of the image of the moon less than $0^{\prime\prime}.1$ shall be produced in 20 seconds by any one cause.

3.31. *Frequency.*—The moon moves about $300^{\prime\prime}$ in the sky in 20 seconds. The frequency of the current which supplies the plate-drive synchronous motor should be accurate to 1 part in 3000.

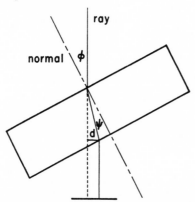

Fig. 11.—Displacement of ray by plane-parallel plate

3.32. *Drive arm.*—The length of the plate drive arm is about 170 mm. The setting of the movable steel ball should be correct to 0.06 mm.

3.33. *Orientation.*—The plate carriage should move parallel to the equator. An error of $1^{\prime}$ in orientation will produce a north-south trail of $0^{\prime\prime}.09$.

3.34. *Tilt drive.*—The moon moves about $10^{\prime\prime}$ in 20 seconds of time, with respect to the stars. The tilt-arm setting distance is about 25 mm. A precision of 1 part in 100 is required; so the setting must be accurate to 0.25 mm.

3.35. *Tilt axis.*—A precision of 1 part in 100 is required in orienting the axis of tilt, that is, about $0°.5$.

The dual-rate cameras are made so that, if desired, the plate drive is not used.

3.4. OPTICAL DISPLACEMENT

Figure 11 shows the optical displacement of a ray of light by a plane-parallel plate. The displacement is

$$d = k \sin \phi \, (1 - u \cos \phi \sec \psi) , \qquad (5)$$

where k is the thickness of the plate, ϕ is the angle of incidence, ψ is the angle of refraction, and $1/u$ is the index of refraction.

The tilt mechanism of the dual-rate camera operates so that $\tan \phi$ changes uniformly with time during an exposure. Hence it is necessary that the displacement of the image shall be nearly proportional to tan ϕ. To see how well this condition is satisfied, consider the following example.

Let $k = 2$ mm and $u = 0.655$. Let the scale value of the telescope be $50''/$ mm. Then the displacement in arc is $D = 50''d$, which is closely approximated, it is found, by $D_1 = 34''.53$ tan ϕ. The accompanying table gives D and D_1 and

ϕ	D	D_1	$D - D_1$
2°.....	1″2048	1″2058	−0″0010
4......	2.4131	2.4146	− .0015
6......	3.6278	3.6292	− .0014
8......	4.8523	4.8529	− .0006
10.....	6.0906	6.0886	+0.0020

their difference for values of ϕ up to 10°.

The moon moves 6″ with respect to the stars in about 11 seconds. It is seen that, for exposures as long as 22 seconds, the relative motion of the moon can be compensated for with high accuracy by the method employed.

3.5. MEASUREMENT AND REDUCTION

The plates are measured by projection with a Mann measuring engine, which was developed for the moon program. This is a two-screw machine with two stages—a coarse stage for rapid rotation and a fine stage. A lever and ratchet allow the plate to be accurately rotated 6° at a stroke. The two screws are fitted with transparent dials which read directly to millimeters and microns. Coleman digitizers were attached by the Naval Observatory so as to allow a direct shaft read-out on IBM punched cards. This read-out system is similar to one developed by A. N. Adams of the Six-Inch Transit Circle Division.

The measurement of a plate consists of the following steps:

1. The plates are prepared for measurement by drawing an inked line on the glass side, joining the stars selected for measurement. A mark is made near the center of the moon with the aid of a plastic transparent disk which has circles inscribed on it. The x- and y-screws are set so that the center of rotation of the fine stage is near the center of the reticle of the measuring microscope. The plate is inserted with the artificial mark near the center of rotation.

2. The positions of the stars are measured in x and y.

3. The x-screw is used to bring the plate to the center of rotation in x. The y-screw is then used to measure the radius of the moon, r, at successive 6° intervals.

4. The plate is rotated 180° from the initial position, and the stars are again measured in x and y.

Steps 2 and 4 determine the position of each star in x and in y from the center of rotation of the precision stage. Step 3 determines the position of the center of the moon with respect to the same point. Hence the position of the moon with respect to the stars is obtained.

PLATE I.—Photograph of PZT 3. (Official U.S. Navy photograph.)

PLATE II.—PZT plate enlarged three times. The bright star, Vega, shows diffraction images caused by the plate carriage. Vega is not used to determine latitude and time; it is photographed along with a star on the program.

The equation of condition used to determine the position of the center of the moon is

$$a \cos \theta + b \sin \theta + c = r ,$$

where a and b are the rectangular co-ordinates of the center with respect to the center of rotation, θ is the orientation of the radius vector, and c is the radius of the moon. A solution for a and b is made by least squares, using measures made on about thirty points on the bright limb of the moon. The solution also furnishes c, but, since the edge of the moon on a photographic plate is not sharp, the radius obtained is not considered significant.

The determination of the position of the center of the moon is independent of personal equation in setting on the limb of the moon, provided that the settings are made in a consistent manner. The stage of the measuring engine rotates, so that the field when measuring the moon appears the same for each point measured. This minimizes personal equation.

The star positions used are those of the Yale Zone Catalogues, which have been placed on punched cards.

The observed position of the moon is corrected for parallax, using adopted geocentric co-ordinates for the observing station. There are thus obtained observed values of the apparent geocentric right ascension and declination of the moon for an epoch of Universal Time (U.T.). The co-ordinates are referred to the true equator and equinox of this date.

Beginning with 1960, computed co-ordinates, based on the lunar theory of E. W. Brown, are tabulated in the national ephemerides as a function of Ephemeris Time (E.T.). The observed co-ordinates are entered in these tables, and the Ephemeris Time at which the observation was made is obtained by interpolation. An example is given in the *Improved Lunar Ephemeris, 1952–1959* (U.S. Nautical Almanac Office, 1954), which describes the basis on which the lunar ephemeris is calculated.

The epoch of a photographic observation of the moon is recorded with respect to U.T. Measurement and reduction of the plate furnish the corresponding E.T. These give the quantity

$$\Delta T = \text{E.T.} - \text{U.T.}$$

The reduction of the moon plates is carried out with the aid of a magnetic-drum calculator, the IBM 650. The development of the formulae of reduction and the programing for the IBM 650 are due to R. Glenn Hall.

3.6. PROBABLE ERRORS

A comparison of the results from plates taken on different nights in the same lunation indicates a probable error of $0\overset{''}{.}15$ in either co-ordinate for one night. The value obtained from a series of lunations, however, is about $0\overset{''}{.}25$. Systematic effects, which vary with the libration of the moon, have been noted (Markowitz 1959a). Such effects would be expected if the moon were not spherical.

C. B. Watts is deriving corrections to the profile of the moon, so as to reduce all observable profiles to a common origin. The application of these corrections may remove some of the systematic effects observed.

3.7. DUAL-RATE SATELLITE CAMERA

The dual-rate principle may be applied to the photography of artificial satellites. An experimental dual-rate satellite camera was constructed at the United States Naval Observatory in 1958. The aperture is 178 mm, the focal length is 1000 mm, and the glass image shifter, which rotates continuously, is 12 mm thick. Photographs were taken of several rapidly moving artificial satellites (Markowitz 1959b). The dual-rate principle will probably be used to advantage in tracking very faint, distant, artificial satellites, as the light from the satellites can be integrated over an interval of time.

Dr. R. Glenn Hall has contributed greatly in the programs with the instruments described and has provided valuable help in the preparation of this description.

REFERENCES

AIRY, G. B.   1854   *Astr., Mag., and Meteor Obs. of the Greenwich Obs.*,
                                       Appendix I.
CHANDLER, S. C.   1901   *A.J.*, **22**, 57.
DOOLITTLE, C. L.   1908   *Flower Obs. Pub.*, Vol. **3**, Part 1.
JENKINS, F. A., and
  WHITE, H. E.   1957   *Fundamentals of Optics* (New York: McGraw-Hill
                                       Book Co., Inc.), p. 77.
LITTELL, F. B., and
  WILLIS, J. E.   1929   *A.J.*, **40**, 7.
MARKOWITZ, W.   1954   *A.J.*, **59**, 69.
                               1959a   *Ibid.*, **64**, 106.
                               1959b   *J. Geophys. Res.*, **64**, 1115.
ROSS, F. E.   1915   *Latitude Observations with the Photographic Zenith
                                       Tube at Gaithersburg, Md.* (Spec. Pub. No. 27,
                                       U.S. Coast and Geod. Survey.)
RUSSELL, H. N., and
  FOWLER, M.   1916   *Ann. Harvard Obs.*, **76**, 127.
RUSSELL, H. N., and
  PICKERING, E. C.   1913   *Ann. Harvard Obs.*, **72**, 1.
SOLLENBERGER, P.   1942   *Pop. Astr.*, **50**, 74.
                               1945   *A.J.*, **51**, 145.
                               1949   *Actes du Cong. de Chronométrie* (Geneva), pp. 110
                                       and 116.
U.S. NAUTICAL ALMANAC
  OFFICE   1954   *Improved Lunar Ephemeris 1952–1959: Joint Sup-
                                       plement to the American Ephemeris and the*
                                       (British) *Nautical Almanac.* Washington.
WADE, E. B. H.   1905   *M.N.*, **66**, 46.

astonishing stability, but, owing to the defective arrangement of the instrument, no full advantage of this remarkable property could be taken.

Various astronomers have been successful either in correcting this optical defect or in rendering the astrolabe an impersonal instrument. The excellent results obtained by Dr. Paul Muller, the well-known double-star observer, with a micrometer containing a doubly refracting prism led the author to the concept of a more complete solution, which will now be described and which is the essential feature of the impersonal astrolabe (Danjon 1948, 1955, 1958a).

At the focus of the telescope a double Wollaston prism made of quartz is

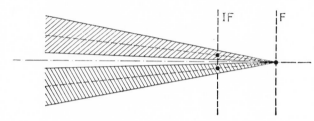

FIG. 2.—False image distance produced by focusing error in the astrolabe of Claude and Driencourt.

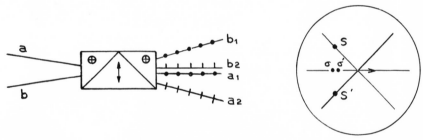

FIG. 3.—Image formation in a double symmetrical Wollaston prism. The images S and S' are suppressed.

placed. In such a prism (Fig. 3), the point of intersection of the two polarized rays arising from a ray perpendicular to the incident face is found to be in a plane accurately parallel to this face, irrespective of the incident height of this ray. If a simple Wollaston prism, composed of only two quartz prisms, is used (Fig. 4), the point of intersection would be located in a plane inclined with respect to the incident face. In the latter case, the distance between the two images of the same star will vary directly with the incident height. The separation angle of the double prism (Fig. 3) is precisely equal to the angle between the axes a and b of the two pencils of light transmitted by the objective. The splitting of the pencil a gives two pencils, a_1 and a_2, as is shown in Figure 3, while the splitting of pencil b gives pencils b_1 and b_2. It is seen that a_1 and b_2 are parallel and that therefore the distance of the two corresponding images σ and σ' no longer de-

---

CHAPTER 8

The Impersonal Astrolabe*

ANDRÉ DANJON

Director, Paris Observatory

1. INTRODUCTION

THE discoveries of the motion of the terrestrial poles and the variability of the period of rotation have aroused renewed interest in the problems of positional astronomy. The aim of this chapter is to describe our program at the Paris Observatory in pursuit of these problems and, in particular, the instruments developed.

2. DESIGN AND CONSTRUCTION

A few years before World War II, the author published the description of a new type of transit instrument for the determination of right ascensions. The results obtained at Strasbourg with a prototype of small dimensions (aperture 6 cm) having been very encouraging, a new series of tests was commenced at the Paris Observatory in 1946. Meanwhile, an instrument of similar design but of 12 cm in aperture was constructed. The early observations made with this larger instrument revealed unforeseen difficulties, which required a new design for the mounting.[1] For the time being, the study of this instrument was discontinued, and the facilities of the Paris Observatory were concentrated on the construction of an instrument of a different type: the impersonal astrolabe, which is the main topic of this chapter.

There was another reason for giving priority to the astrolabe, of which an experimental model had already been constructed at the Observatory in 1950 and progressively improved. In 1952 the International Council of Scientific Unions decided to organize the International Geophysical Year and to incorporate in its program a determination of world longitudes and latitudes. The observatories participating in the operation were recommended to observe stars

---

* Adapted by the author and the editors from the George Darwin Lecture, May 9, 1958, by permission of the Royal Astronomical Society, London.

[1] The larger transit instrument is now under construction and will be installed during 1961.

selected in the Fundamental Catalogue FK3 (or in the improved catalogue FK3R). It was agreed that preference should be given to modern instruments giving simultaneously and with the highest possible accuracy the two co-ordinates, time and latitude. The zenith telescope gives both co-ordinates but requires a special catalogue limited to zenith stars, in which, therefore, non-fundamental stars have to be introduced. The astrolabe is the only instrument that permits both co-ordinates to be determined by the observation of fundamental stars alone.

A large-size astrolabe was ordered from the Société Optique et Précision de Levallois (OPL). The design was worked out in close co-operation with the technicians of this firm. The new instrument differs from the experimental model mainly in its larger dimensions and improved mechanical design.

The astrolabe was put into service in July, 1956, and has been in use without interruption since. Over forty thousand transits have been observed, which is adequate for evaluating the qualities of the instrument, if not for establishing definitive results. The observations have been carried out mainly by Drs. L. Arbey and B. Guinot, and Mlle Débarbat.

Under the most favorable atmospheric conditions, the OPL astrolabe permits the transit of a star, at a well-determined zenith distance differing very slightly from 30°, to be recorded with an accuracy of $\pm 0''.09$ (standard deviation), assuming that the errors of the catalogue have been corrected. The deviation increases with atmospheric scintillation, and its most frequent value is $\pm 0''.17$. For only 6 per cent of the nights is it larger than $\pm 0''.26$. The observations have proved to be free from systematic errors, a result of outstanding importance for the use of the impersonal astrolabe as a fundamental instrument.

It was soon realized that the use of the instrument was not restricted to the determination of time and latitude but that it could be used as well for the improvement of the FK3 catalogue and for the determination of the fundamental astronomical constants. The accuracy of the results is due partly to the intrinsic qualities of the instrument and partly to the application of the so-called "method of equal altitudes of stars."

The principle of the instrument is as follows. Suppose that we fix an equilateral glass prism in front of a horizontal telescope in such a way that its edges are horizontal and one of its faces vertical (Fig. 1). A beam of light coming from a star entering the face AB at right angles is then reflected from AC and emerges through the lower half of BC. Another portion of the beam falls on AC after having been reflected from the surface of a mercury basin. It is reflected by AB and emerges through the upper half of BC. Thus two images of the star, S and S', are seen in the telescope; these appear to move in opposite directions, one upward and the other downward. They coincide when the star is at a zenith distance of exactly 30°; and the instant of coincidence is noted. As the prism angle is not exactly 60°, there are three unknowns, namely, the correction of the clock, the latitude, and the excess of the zenith distance over 30°. Therefore,

at least three stars, in different azimuths, must be observed. In fact, many than three stars are observed; each of our groups contains, in general, tw eight stars. The plotting of position lines, a method familiar to navigators, an approximate graphical solution, but the final solution should be mad least squares.

The astrolabe in its original form was designed by Claude and Drien (1905). It was initially a very simple instrument, consisting of a telesco prism, a mercury horizon, and adjustment devices. The observer noted the

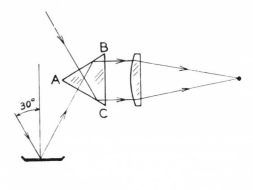

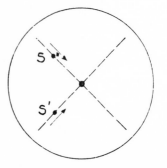

FIG. 1.—Principle of the prism-astrolabe of Claude and Driencourt

of coincidence of the two images of the star by the eye-and-ear method o the hand-tapping method. Thus each star gave only a single determinatic time, which was affected by personal equation. It was then intended to b instrument for use in the field and not one of high precision. There was an source of error resulting from the images being displaced when the positic the eye-piece was slightly changed. The reason is that the images are for by two pencils of rays the axes of which are not strictly parallel but are incl to each other at an angle of 2° or 3° (Fig. 2). If the focusing is altered, the tance between the two pseudo-images changes, which produces the same e as a variation in the prism angle. It will be shown later that this angle ha

pends on the adjustment of the eyepiece. The two other images, S and S', are eliminated by suitably placed screens. Moreover, the coincidence of the two images σ and σ' can be obtained by a displacement of the quartz prism parallel to the axis of the telescope. This coincidence can be maintained by traversing the prism at a rate proportional to the sine of the azimuth and to the cosine of the latitude. The micrometer screw, which drives the prism, carries a disk with contacts connected to a chronograph. The astrolabe, already corrected for its optical defects, then becomes impersonal. The observer needs only to correct

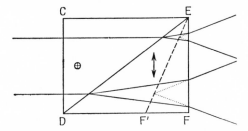

FIG. 4.—Single Wollaston prism, causing the plane of intersection to be oblique

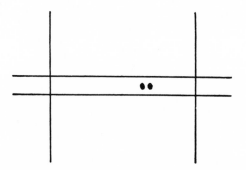

FIG. 5.—Reticule and the two images

the movement produced by a motor, so as to maintain the coincidence of the two images. In fact, this coincidence is obtained not by superposing the two images but by placing them side by side along the same horizontal line between two illuminated wires, as shown in Figure 5.

It would take too long to describe in detail the arrangements adopted for the component parts of the astrolabe (Danjon 1958a). Figure 6 shows a simplified section of the instrument, and Plates I, II, and III show the instrument itself. The objective of the OPL model has an aperture of 10 cm and a focal length of 1 meter. A diaphragm containing two equal lune-shaped holes gives vertically elongated diffraction images with axes in the ratio of 3 to 5. The faces of the prism are rectangles of 8 × 10 cm. The dimensions of the micrometer screw are rather unusual: 25 mm in diameter and 5 mm in pitch (Pl. III). If the star is observed exactly east or west, the screw makes a complete revolution in 2.61 seconds. The speed of the motor is constant and is adjusted to the latitude of the station. When the astrolabe is turned around its vertical axis to observe another star, a speed reducer automatically varies the rate of rotation of the screw proportionally to the sine of the azimuth. The observer is able to regulate the motion of the screw manually by means of a wheel (20 in Fig. 6). One rota-

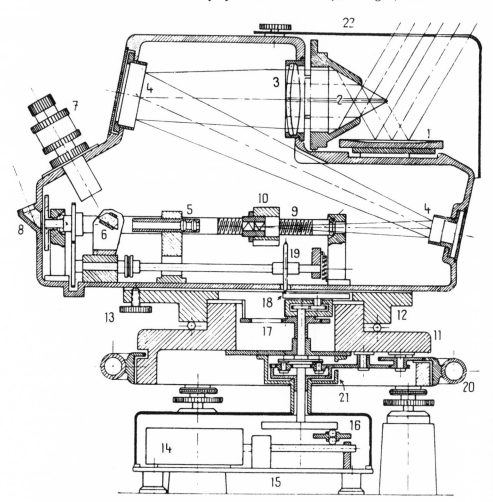

FIG. 6.—Vertical section of OPL astrolabe (schematic). *1*, Mercury basin; *2*, prism; *3*, objective; *4*, plane mirrors; *5*, carriage; *6*, reflecting prism; *7*, eyepiece; *8*, prism for reading drum; *9*, micrometer screw; *10*, birefringent prism and supporting carriage; *11*, bell-shaped support for turntable, *12; 13*, level adjustment; *14*, motor; *15*, speed reducer; *16*, first differential; *17*, gear (La Hire); *18*, second differential plate; *19*, second differential gear wheel; *20*, differential corrector wheel; *21*, differential corrector; *22*, cover.

tion of the wheel corresponds to a change of 40″ in the zenith distance if the astrolabe is oriented east or west. To make the instrument as compact as possible, the beam of light is broken twice by mirrors made of fused quartz and located between the objective and its focus.

3. PERFORMANCE AND ACCURACY

The images formed by the first OPL astrolabe were not completely satisfactory; they were not equidistant from the objective and one of them showed slight astigmatism. One could bring them into the same plane by introducing two Wollaston prisms, one normal, the other inverted (Fig. 7). This type of birefringent prism was adopted for all OPL astrolabes, but an arrangement was

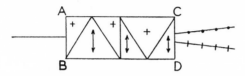

FIG. 7.—Compensated Wollaston prism (1956)

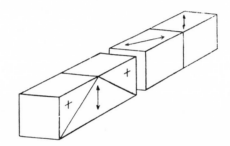

FIG. 8.—Compensated Wollaston prism (1960)

sought which would be simpler to construct and at the same time would correct the above-mentioned aberrations more effectively (Danjon 1958, p. 329). The double symmetrical Wollaston prism of Figure 3 was reintroduced, preceded by a compensator consisting of two plane-parallel quartz plates with their crystallographic axes inclined at 45° to the incident pencil. As mounted in the astrolabe, the axes of the compensator are horizontal (Fig. 8). Its length is approximately equal to that of the double Wollaston prism. This made necessary a slight modification of the mounting, but the image quality was distinctly improved.

The two images each show colored fringes on one side—one above, the other below—caused by the secondary spectrum of the objective and the dispersion of the Wollaston prism. These fringes can be removed by means of a filter which absorbs the blue and far red parts of the spectrum.

The accuracy of astrolabe observations is due in part to the careful manufacture by the Société OPL and in part to the working conditions and the principles of the equal-altitude method. On the latter points we may comment as follows: as the instrument rotates around a vertical axis, its flexures are not liable to vary with the azimuth. Its design provides protection against sudden changes of temperature. The results of time and latitude observations do not even depend on the absolute value of the prism angle; they could be affected only by a variation in this angle during the observation. But results obtained since July, 1956, have demonstrated that there is no systematic variation in this angle in the course of the night, not even in the course of a year, and that the zenith distance remains invariable within a few hundredths of a second of arc. Our observational program includes twelve groups, each of twenty-eight stars chosen from the FK3 or its supplements. These groups are identified by letters a, b, . . . , k, l.

A single observer, during a single night, can observe at least two consecutive groups, often three, or even more (Guinot 1958). The computed zenith distance, corrected for refraction, would have the same value for all these groups if the

FIG. 9.—Differences in zenith distance between interconnected groups of stars

prism angle were constant and if the catalogue were not affected by systematic errors. In fact, two consecutive groups observed in the course of the same night give different values, as is shown by Figure 9. In the course of a year, differences a − b, b − c, . . . , l − a are obtained. The distribution of these differences does not reveal any systematic variation with right ascension, which indicates that the prism angle is independent of the annual variation in temperature and that errors in the catalogue are solely responsible for the differences obtained. Furthermore, we have been able to verify that the zenith distance of transits does not vary systematically during the course of the night, although, as a rule, the temperature of the instrument decreases from the evening to morning. This is illustrated by the smallness of the closing error computed by Guinot. For the completed years they are as follows: 1957, $-0''\!.02$; 1958, $+0''\!.09$; and 1959, $-0''\!.07$, the standard deviation in each case being $\pm0''\!.10$. It must be emphasized that the prism has been very carefully annealed and that its mounting does not exert any prejudicial stresses; these two conditions are probably essential.

Consider the advantages of the method of equal altitudes devised by Gauss about a hundred and fifty years ago for field operations; its application to problems of fundamental astronomy has so far been restricted to special cases such as, for instance, the determination of latitude by the Talcott method, which is still in use in the International Latitude Service, and the observation of transits in the prime vertical by the method of W. Struve. However, it is very valuable, in its general form, for linking together stars whose declinations differ by several tens of degrees and whose right ascensions differ by several hours.

The declinations of the stars that can be observed with the astrolabe are between $\phi - 30°$ and $\phi + 30°$, ϕ being the latitude of the station. In Paris, these limits are $+18°50'$ and $+78°50'$, or $+20°$ and $+78°$ in practice. Their hour angle at the time of the transit has the limits $-H$ and $+H$, H being found from the equation $\sin H = \frac{1}{2} \sec \phi$. For Paris $2H = 6^h36^m$, and for Herstmonceux, 6^h59^m. The observation of one group requires about $1\frac{1}{2}$ hours, so that it is possible to link together stars whose right ascensions differ by as much as 8 hours.

When two transits of the same star are observed, one east and the other west, the mean of the observed times gives the right ascension, a, and the declination, δ, is easily computed from the difference of the transit times. The determination of the right ascension is not very accurate when the declination of the star is near either limit, while the determination of the declination is not possible when the hour angle of the transit is close to H. It would be advantageous to set up astrolabe stations in several latitudes in order to fill these gaps. For instance, in Paris, good values of the right ascensions are obtained for declinations between $+20°$ and $+78°$, and good values for the declinations from $+20°$ to $+50°$ and from $+68°$ and $+78°$. With a high-precision instrument the method of equal altitudes discloses at once the individual errors of the catalogue, as these errors are important compared with the accuracy of the observations. As stated above, the average value of the standard deviation for one transit is about $\pm0".17$, and under favorable conditions the deviation is as small as $\pm0".09$. As each group is observed about twenty times per year, the plotting of the position lines is correct within a few hundredths of a second. In a few years the precision of the determination will be as accurate as $0".01$. Individual errors being expressed by a dispersion of the position lines in the diagram, some of them intersect the circle, whose center and radius are obtained from a least-squares adjustment, and some others remain outside the circle. The systematic errors of the catalogue may be revealed by an asymmetry of the diagram.

The diagram in Figure 10, a, was drawn from the results obtained on January 22, 1958, on group d. The same group was observed in 1957, and the displacements to be given to the position lines to make them tangent to the circle were already known. Figure 10, b, shows the same diagram corrected from the observations obtained in the preceding year. Their quadratic mean error decreases from $0".21$ to $0".09$, and the asymmetry disappears. This example illustrates clearly the effectiveness of the method of equal altitudes in correcting the position of stars, but it must be remarked that this operation is merely an internal adjustment affecting each group independently and that it is by no means sufficient to correct the catalogue.

It should be noted that, whatever the instrument used, observation of a single group of stars cannot disclose systematic errors of a catalogue which are equivalent to a change in the co-ordinate system and which do not affect the relative positions of the stars. Such effects may be produced by an error in the value of the precession or of the nutation. As the relative positions of the stars remain unchanged but the position of the pole and the origin of the co-ordinate system are erroneous, the diagram of the position lines is translated without distortion, and therefore neither its symmetry nor the radius of the circle of the position lines is affected. But the co-ordinates of the center of the circle are altered, and consequently also the time and the latitude. The method of equal altitude of stars, which clearly reveals individual errors and local errors affecting the various regions of the sky, cannot therefore provide any evidence of a systematic error in the reference system by a single observation of a given group. Such errors can be found only by a chain program of observation, with group-to-group connections, covering at least one entire year. These errors will then appear in the group errors in the form of a variation depending on a.

In this respect there is no privileged instrument. Suppose that we observe with a meridian circle the transits of a group of stars of limited range in right ascension. If the pole of the catalogue is at a distance $\Delta \nu$ from the true pole of rotation, in consequence of an error in the precession, and if a_m is the observed

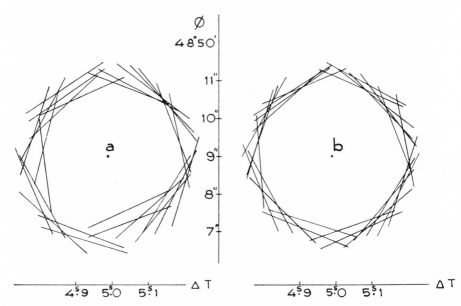

Fig. 10.—Position lines: *a*) uncorrected, *b*) with individual corrections applied

a) $\Delta T = 4^s.987 \pm 0^s.006,$
$\Delta \phi = -1''.01 \pm 0''.06,$
$R = -2''.27 \pm 0''.04,$
$\sigma = \pm 0''.21.$

b) $\Delta T = 4^s.987 \pm 0.002,$
$\Delta \phi = -1''.01 \pm 0''.03,$
$R = -2''.27 \pm 0''.02,$
$\sigma = \pm 0''.09.$

mean right ascension of the group, the azimuth of the meridian circle, computed from the observations, will have an error equal to $\Delta\nu \sin a_m \sec \phi$, but the representation of the observations by means of this faulty azimuth will still be excellent. Therefore, no improvement in the catalogue can be expected. Here again the "chain adjustment" will enable one to determine the errors of the catalogue.

Theoretically, therefore, the method of equal altitude of stars and the method of meridian transits are equivalent in this respect; but, in practice, their applications are very different. In the first place, the stability of the astrolabe can be guaranteed with much greater certainty than that of the meridian circle. In particular, the astrolabe allows the value of the prism angle to be accurately controlled, and this is the only instrumental constant whose variation would be prejudicial to the accuracy of the observations. We know by experience that errors produced by changes in the prism angle are negligible compared with the accidental or systematic errors of the fundamental catalogue. Moreover, the observations with the astrolabe have a single terrestrial reference in the vertical. The discussion of the latitude observations have proved, as shown below, that the daily variations in the zenithal refractions are imperceptible, at least in Paris.

4. COMPARISON WITH THE TRANSIT INSTRUMENT

The conditions are quite different in the transit instrument. The solid body which serves as the direction of reference is not now a simple glass prism but a telescope with its trunnions. The line of sight is determined by the optical center of an objective—consisting of two lenses which can be linked neither rigidly together nor to their mounting—and the spider's web carried by the movable frame of a micrometer. The objective and the micrometer are linked together by a metallic tube exposed to continuously variable conditions of temperature, as this tube radiates from one side or the other according as the star observed is north or south. The axis of rotation is defined by two trunnions carried by a heavy metallic part exposed to the same temperature variations. Consequently, the position of the instrument changes with respect to the vertical from star to star, and, as the flexures are not rigorously symmetrical with respect to the meridian plane, lateral deflections are unavoidable. To measure the collimation of the instrument and the inclination of its axis of rotation, the telescope is pointed toward the nadir in a direction quite different from the positions it occupies for the observation of stars. One may question what happens to this collimation and inclination when the telescope is pointed toward a star. To obtain an accuracy of $0''.1$, it is necessary that the mechanical or thermal deformations of the instrument be less than $1\ \mu$. Experience shows that they are, in general, much larger than this limit. Chandler (1887) had already asserted that the method of equal altitudes is better suited to give accurate results than was meridian astronomy. We have reached this conclusion by comparing the physical properties of the astrolabe and the transit instrument. But there is another reason, of a geometrical nature, which confirms it. With the method of equal altitudes, transits of stars can be observed all around a complete circle (almucantar) on the celestial sphere; and that is why the radius of the circle and its pole, which is the zenith of the station, are so well determined. Meridian observations provide different conditions, as the observations can be made only over 45° of zenith distance, that is, along an arc which covers only one-quarter of the circumference on the meridian; thus the position of the pole of this arc, which defines the direction of the rotation axis of the transit instrument, is, in practice, less accurately determined than that of the zenith of the astrolabe.

Even if it were perfect, the transit instrument by itself could not conveniently provide for the "chain adjustment," because such adjustment cannot be effected without referring, as an intermediate step, to an azimuth mark or a collimator. I know nothing more disappointing than the observation of a mark. I have often observed those of the Strasbourg Observatory, which were set up very carefully by Winnecke. Even when at first sight they appeared to be stable, they suffered from sudden variations, amounting frequently to 1 second of arc. If the mark is located not far from the instrument, then its azimuth is not well defined. If it is far from the instrument, its direction is frequently deviated by lateral refractions. But, in any case, a terrestrial mark is far from being as reliable as the prism of the astrolabe for defining a direction of reference. Its stability cannot even be assured through the course of a night, and far less during daytime.

Better results may be expected from a collimator than from a mark, because the collimator can be installed in the interior of the meridian room and can then be efficiently protected against temperature variations, as is true also of its pillar and the surrounding ground. For this reason I have used two collimators, one east and the other west, with the transit instrument mentioned before, the principle of which will now be briefly described (Fig. 11, *left*). In front of the objective of a telescope whose axis lies in the meridian plane is mounted a reversing prism, which covers its surface with the exception of two segments. Two images of the star appear in the field, one direct, one reflected, which move in opposite directions. The images coincide when the star transits the plane of the reflecting face, which differs, at most, by a small amount from the direction of the meridian plane. The position of the prism is then determined by auto-collimation, by means of the lateral collimator (Fig. 11, *right*) pointed toward its reflecting face. The readings made with this collimator provide the necessary correction for reducing all the transits to the same plane. The second collimator is used when the instrument is reversed. Various operations enable one to control the horizontality of the collimator by means of a mercury horizon, and its azimuth by the observation of fundamental stars. It is stressed that the line of sight is much better defined by the prism than by the optical axis of the conventional meridian telescope. The major difficulties occurring in the meridian telescope are automatically eliminated, but other problems arise which we are endeavoring to overcome. If there is a noticeable difference in temperature between the interior and the exterior of the meridian room, the reflected image of the cross-wires, as seen in the collimator, is unsteady. This, however, is easily corrected. The most troublesome effect is caused by the position of the prism in front of the objective. If the prism differs in temperature from that of the surrounding air by even a few tenths of a degree, it is enveloped by a layer about 1 cm thick, within which there exists a marked temperature gradient. The pencil of rays crossing this layer becomes divergent if the prism is warmer

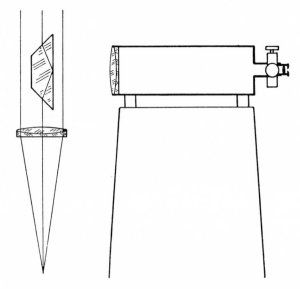

FIG. 11.—Principle of the new-type transit instrument. Transit with prism, *left;* collimater, *right.*

than the air and convergent if it is cooler; in both cases the image given by the free aperture is altered. If the air around the prism is stirred by means of a fan, the layer disappears, and the image resumes its normal aspect.

A similar effect is produced in instruments in which metallic parts cross the light-path. I have observed, for instance, by a very sensitive interferometric method, that the bright extensions which surround the stellar images in a reflecting telescope are caused by the presence of the supports of the secondary mirror, which, cooling off by radiation during the night, are surrounded by a layer of warmer air, producing a refraction effect and not a diffraction effect, as is generally assumed. André Couder eliminates this effect by covering the secondary mirror supports with polished aluminum.

The case of the reversing prism of our transit instrument cannot be treated so easily, and I have had to adopt a more radical solution: the prism of the projected instrument will be placed in an atmosphere of helium, this gas having a refractivity ten times smaller than that of air and a conductivity six times higher. The idea is not new; Lyot had made plans for a reflecting telescope of aperture 150 cm without a dome to be installed at the Observatory of the Pic du Midi, the tube of which, sealed by a glass plate at its upper part, would have been filled with helium. These detailed explanations are given to show how different can be the theoretical and the actual properties of an instrument. We shall now return to the discussion of "chain adjustment." Years will elapse before we know whether the new transit instrument is as well adapted to this requirement as the astrolabe.

5. ANALYSIS OF OBSERVATIONS

The legitimacy of the chain program has been disputed. This criticism is based, in particular, on the closing errors, sometimes quite large, found for certain latitude stations equipped with zenith telescopes. The mean value of the closing errors for the years 1956 and 1957, for the four stations of the International Latitude Service, was $-0''.124$ between the evening group and the middle group and $-0''.101$ between the middle group and the morning group. But the individual values show a large scatter. The extreme annual means were $-0''.345$ for Ukiah and $+0''.162$ for Kitab. If these closing errors had the same value for all the stations, they could be eliminated by correcting the constant of aberration, but they are different from one station to the other. This dispersion can be assigned only to instrumental or meteorological factors. I believe that the first occur more frequently and are, in general, more harmful.

It may also happen that the local terrain or large buildings in the vicinity of the instrument will give rise during the night to atmospheric turbulence, which produces appreciable accidental refractions. Such cases may be exceptional, since the observatory site will be selected with knowledge of these facts. But a temperature drop during the night affects the level and the micrometer screw of the zenith telescope, and these effects contribute to the closing error of the chain program.

The astrolabe does not have such disadvantages. Dr. Guinot, who has determined the corrections of our groups, has found a very small closing error for the first year of observation. He first smoothed the observations (cf. Fig. 10 and accompanying discussion), in order to free them from individual and local errors. He then computed the differences between consecutive groups observed *by the same observer in the course of a single night.* He started with group j and returned to this group after a complete year. Table 1 gives the differences in time and latitude with the related standard deviations. These results have been confirmed by those of the second and third years of observations.

Certain differences, mainly in right ascensions, reach surprisingly high values. In the course of the same night, groups b and c give clock corrections differing by 23 milliseconds. What is more remarkable is the smallness of the closing errors

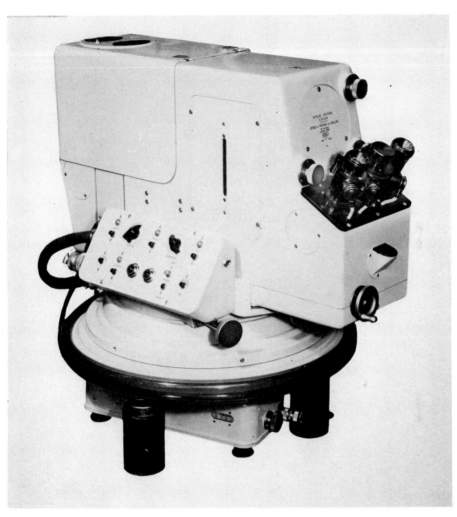

PLATE I.—General view of OPL Astrolabe

PLATE II.—OPL astrolabe with prism and mercury basin

PLATE III.—Micrometer and small roller wheel moving the Wollaston prism

which are much below their uncertainties. We can therefore assume that the chain method of adjustment is permissible, and we can conclude that not only the astrolabe but also the atmosphere of Paris is very stable. If, contrary to my opinion, the closing errors observed elsewhere were not chiefly due to instrumental causes, we would then have to admit that, by bad fortune, these other stations had all been located in exceptionally unfavorable sites and that Paris enjoyed uniquely privileged conditions! I strongly refuse to believe in the poor

TABLE 1

1956–1957

Groups	Time (Unit: $0\overset{s}{.}001$)	Latitude (Unit: $0\overset{''}{.}01$)	n
j–k.............	$+15.0\pm4.1$	-2.9 ± 3.1	5
k–l.............	$+ 3.2$ 2.2	$+0.5$ 4.0	12
l–a.............	$- 8.0$ 1.7	$+3.0$ 3.6	10
a–b.............	-10.0 2.5	-3.1 2.9	11
b–c.............	$+23.0$ 1.7	$+5.7$ 1.8	10
c–d.............	-12.1 1.7	-3.8 2.0	12
d–e.............	$+ 3.0$ 1.7	$+1.9$ 2.0	13
e–f.............	$+ 0.5$ 1.1	-2.6 1.2	13
f–g.............	$- 0.5$ 1.5	-7.3 1.6	14
g–h.............	-12.8 1.5	$+7.4$ 2.5	13
h–i.............	$+ 1.7$ 1.8	-4.9 1.4	15
i–j.............	$- 1.6$ 1.5	$+2.6$ 2.5	16
Closing error	$+ 1.4\pm7.1$	-3.5 ± 8.7	....

TABLE 2

	a	b	c	d	e	f	g	h	i	j	k	l
Time........ ($0\overset{s}{.}001$)	$+0.1$	-10.0	$+12.9$	$+0.7$	$+3.6$	$+3.9$	$+3.3$	-9.6	-8.0	-9.7	$+5.1$	$+8.2$
Latitude...... ($0\overset{''}{.}01$)	$+1.5$	$- 1.3$	$+ 4.7$	$+1.2$	$+3.6$	$+1.2$	-5.8	$+2.0$	-2.1	0.0	-2.6	-1.8
Zen. Dist...... ($0\overset{''}{.}01$)	-7.3	$+ 1.4$	$+ 2.4$	$+0.8$	-7.4	$+2.3$	$+1.8$	$+7.4$	-3.2	$+2.4$	$+2.9$	-3.5

quality of the other latitude stations, and I persist in accusing the zenith telescopes, the control of which seems to me very difficult. By "control" I mean a permanent and absolute control such as that which is provided for the astrolabe, at least twice per night, by the determination of the prism angle and not a mere testing of the instrument at long intervals.

Having conclusively established that the application of group corrections is permissible, Dr. Guinot computes the corrections required to refer the determinations of time, latitude, and zenith distance to a provisional system more consistent than that of the FK3 (Table 2).

Figure 12 represents the group corrections for time and latitude reduced to nearly the same scale, as an arc of 1 millisecond at the zenith in Paris is nearly equal to 0″.01. It appears at first sight that the right ascensions of the FK3 are less homogeneous than the declinations. This difference may be partly explained by the uncertainty of the proper motions, the computation of which depends to some extent upon meridian observations made before the introduction of the traveling-wire micrometer. But that such deficiencies still exist in the FK3 is a proof of the inability of conventional methods to link together stars with very different right ascensions.

We shall know in a few years whether the corrections given in Table 2 are stable or whether they vary in the course of time. In the latter case their varia-

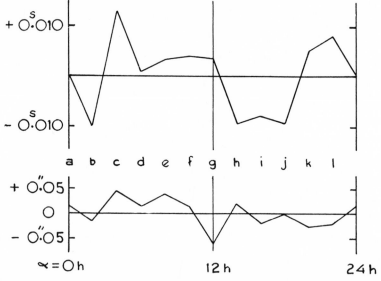

Fig. 12.—Group corrections in α and δ

tions will enable us to derive corrections to the constants of precession and of nutation. But we shall have to wait for 19 years until we can accurately separate these constants.

It is well known that the *constant of aberration*, k, is readily found from the closing error in latitude. The values obtained for the first three years are 20″.48, 20″.47, and 20″.52. Guinot (1958, p. 29) has shown that time determinations can also be used for this purpose. If the accepted value of k is inexact, the difference in the clock corrections obtained from two consecutive groups must vary in the course of a year. This method gives $k = 20″.51$. All these values of k have low weight, but they show once more that it may be desirable to change the accepted value of 20″.47 for a higher value.

It is not surprising that the determination of the constants requires long series of observations, but, apart from this long-term program, the data given

in Table 2 have immediate applications to (1) the determination of the irregularities of Universal Time; (2) the study of the variation of latitude; and (3) the
establishment of a catalogue of stars referred to the provisional system of the
astrolabe.

The first of these applications has been studied by Dr. Arbey and the author,
the two others by Dr. Guinot. My two associates have refrained from making
any selection of the observational data. They have rejected no observations
and have retained incomplete groups as well as those observed by personnel
under training. But they have weighted the results according to their standard
deviations by means of a suitably decreasing scale. They have then computed

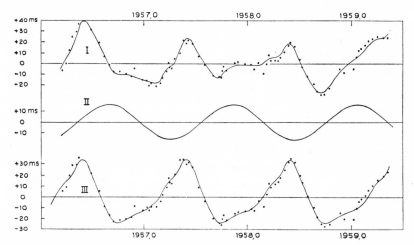

FIG. 13.—Periodic terms in TUO for Paris. The ordinates of curve *I* are the sum of curves
II (Chandler term in variation of longitude) and *III* (seasonal variation of the terrestrial
rotation plus the annual variation in longitude).

the means, including from ten to nineteen groups, but usually thirteen. All these
means have nearly the same weight, and they are shown by the points on the
following figures derived from astrolabe observations grouped as just explained.

Figure 13 represents fluctuations in the time TUO (Observed Universal
Time) deduced from observations made in Paris, measured against the uniform
time scale, TCs, defined by the cesium standard of Essen and Parry (adopted
frequency 9,192,631,770 cps). These comparisons were made by Dr. Arbey. The
differences TCs − TUO are available since 1955.5. In order to eliminate the
progressive variation in this quantity, the quantity $419\theta + 95\theta^2 - 28\theta^3$ (where
$\theta = t - 1957.00$), has been subtracted.

The corrected differences are represented by curve *I* (interval 1956.2 −
1959.4); harmonic analysis shows two periodic components, one that of Chandler (period 1.20 years) represented by the sine curve *II* of Figure 13, and the
other an annual variation (curve *III*). The annual component is the sum of the

seasonal variation of the terrestrial rotation and the variation of longitude at Paris, due to the forced nutation, while the Chandler term is due to the free nutation. The differences O − C, with an arithmetic mean of 2.8 milliseconds, have at times a systematic trend, but they remain small (Danjon 1959, 1960).

With the Chandler term in the longitude of Paris known, the corresponding component of the movement of the pole perpendicular to the Paris meridian can be deduced. Guinot and Débarbat (1960) thus find, for the same 3-year interval,

$$0''23 \cos \frac{2\pi}{1.20} (t - 1956.05),$$

t being expressed in years. This expression may be compared with that of the component parallel to the Paris meridian, given below.

The determination of the latitude offers less complexity than that of the determination of time, as it is derived directly from the observations after the group junctions are completed. Figure 14, derived by Dr. Guinot, represents the latitude of the Paris astrolabe since mid-1956. The groups were selected in such a way that they will be observable without change until the year 2000. Homogeneous data will then be available for the determination of the secular wandering of the pole. This is not the case at the moment.

Analysis has shown that the variation of the latitude ϕ between 1956.5 and 1960.0 is well represented as the sum of a sine-wave with a period of 1.20 years (Chandler term), an annual variation, a, reproduced each year identically, and a progressive variation:

$$\phi = a + 0''22 \sin \frac{2\pi}{1.20} (t - 1956.04) + 0''008 (t - t_0),$$

the time t being measured in years. Thus the Paris astrolabe alone has sufficed to determine the Chandler polhode. It is practically circular and is described at a uniform rate.

We still have to indicate the order of magnitude of the errors involved in both determinations. The average standard deviation of a group observation is ± 5 milliseconds in time and ± 0''06 in latitude, including incomplete groups

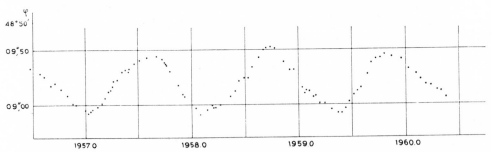

FIG. 14.—Variation of the latitude of Paris from 1956.5 to 1960.4 (all points have the same weight; they represent means of about 14 groups).

(the best determinations gave much smaller values, ± 2.3 milliseconds and $\pm 0''.025$, respectively). These figures refer to the consistency within a group. If we consider the observations of groups by referring to the smoothed curve, then the standard deviations are larger, 8 milliseconds and $0''.07$.

We shall now discuss Guinot's results relating to the establishment of a catalogue of fundamental stars. In 1955 he presented to the General Assembly of the International Astronomical Union a note on the error Δa_δ of the FK3 derived from the results of the protype astrolabe, which was the only one in service at that time. Figure 15 shows the similarity of the results obtained since with the OPL astrolabe, although the observed stars are mostly different in the two cases.

Dr. Guinot has further undertaken to determine with the astrolabe the co-ordinates of as many stars as possible, referred to the provisional system de-

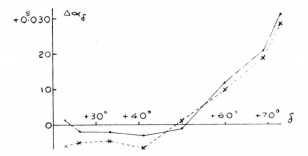

FIG. 15.—Difference Δa_δ (Astrolabe—FK3). *Full line:* experimental astrolabe (1954); *broken line:* OPL astrolabe (1957).

rived from the group corrections. He first computed the translation, T, which should be applied to each of the position lines to take into account (1) the internal smoothing of each group (it has been verified that these corrections are not affected by magnitude or color equations) and (2) the corrections of Table 2. He then derived from T the correction to the tabular co-ordinates of each star. If two transits, east and west, were observed, with T_E and T_W the corresponding values of T, and if A is the azimuth of a transit reckoned from the south, positive toward the west, and η is the parallactic angle, then the corrections to apply to the co-ordinates of the catalogue are

$$\Delta a \text{ (Astrolabe} - \text{FK3)} = \frac{T_E - T_W}{2 \,|\sin A\,|\cos \phi},$$

and

$$\Delta \delta \text{ (Astrolabe} - \text{FK3)} = -\frac{T_E + T_W}{\cos \eta}.$$

In certain special cases, a single transit can be used—for instance, when the star is close to its maximum elongation. In that case it can be assumed that $\cos \eta = 0$; the right ascension is then given by the following relation:

$$\Delta\alpha \,(\text{Astrolabe} - \text{FK}\,3) \;=\; -\frac{T + \Delta\delta\cos\eta}{\sin A\,\cos\phi}.$$

The same formula gives $\Delta\delta$ for stars close to the southern limit in declination, since it may then be assumed that $\Delta\alpha \sin A = 0$.

In this way, Dr. Guinot has established a preliminary catalogue containing 115 stars of the time and latitude program. For 47 stars two co-ordinates are known, for 56 stars only the right ascension is known, and for 12 only the declination is known. Such a catalogue may be independently derived for each year. The first three sets of values so obtained show excellent agreement with one another (Guinot 1959, for the first 2 years).

A second OPL astrolabe has been put into service, and special groups of stars, different from those of the routine program, were observed, in order to extend the catalogue to all fundamental stars visible at Paris. A catalogue of nearly 500 stars from the FK3 and the FK3 Supplement is in course of reduction and will be completed in 1961. Meanwhile, the following remarks may be of interest.

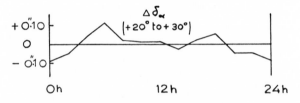

FIG. 16.—Values of $\Delta\delta_a$ (astrolabe—FK3)

For the declinations, the astrolabe catalogue and the FK3 are in good general agreement. The average of the differences is

$$\langle\Delta\delta\rangle\,(\text{Astrolabe} - \text{FK}\,3) \;=\; -\,0\overset{''}{.}002$$

and is not significant. This is only a check of the adjustment. Figure 16 shows the behavior of $\Delta\delta_a$ for stars in the zone $+20°$ to $+30°$. Systematic differences are small, but the statistics relate to only a limited number of stars, and a common error could affect the declinations of both catalogues.

In right ascension the differences are larger, and the distribution is more systematic, as is shown in Figure 17. Each star is represented by a circle, whose diameter is proportional to the difference $\Delta\alpha$ (Astrolabe — FK3), black when the difference is positive and open when it is negative, except when the difference is smaller in absolute value than 5 milliseconds, in which case a cross is used. There is a region of high declination, between 23^h and 11^h, where the differences are large and positive. Because of this anomaly, the difference $\Delta\alpha_\delta$ increases rapidly beyond $+50°$. This illustrates the disadvantage of dividing

Δa into two terms. The FK3 system is homogeneous between 11^h and 23^h. In this interval it would be sufficient to correct the individual positions to obtain a good catalogue with very small systematic errors, for the co-ordinates as well as for the proper motions. On the other hand, applying the correction Δa_δ in this interval would be injurious, for then it would be necessary to compensate for it by applying another correction, Δa_a, of the opposite sign, the total correction being a function of both a and δ.

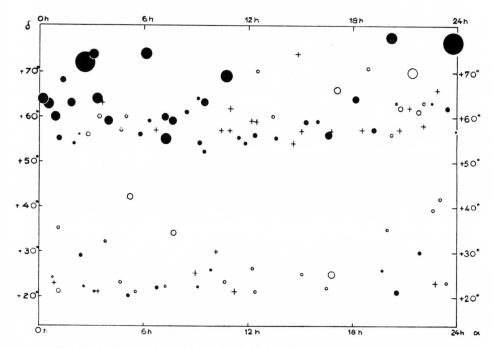

FIG. 17.—Differences (Astrolabe OPL−FK3) in right ascension for 103 stars of FK3. *Open circles:* negative differences; *filled circles:* positive differences; *crosses:* absolute differences less than 0.005 second.

It is surprising that the existence of these regional errors has not hitherto been realized. The reason is that it had become customary to analyze the errors algebraically instead of considering simply Δa and $\Delta \delta$. It would seem advantageous to abandon this method, which can in no way be justified. For the compilation of the FK4, it would be well to consider the individual and local errors as well as the systematic errors, the latter mostly arising from errors in the adopted positions of the pole and the equinox.

The lack of stars in the central zone of Figure 17 is not due to the impossibility of determining their right ascensions; quite the opposite: in this zone the right ascensions are the most precise. However, these stars are not of interest for either time or latitude determinations and were therefore omitted from the first program. The current program will fill this gap.

Figure 18 represents the mean values of $\Delta\alpha \cos \delta$ between $+60°$ and $+75°$. There are two conspicuous discontinuities at about 11^h and 23^h. The representation of such residuals by trigonometric series would be nonsensical. The conclusion is that the conversion of the FK3 to the FK4 cannot be derived from harmonic analysis.

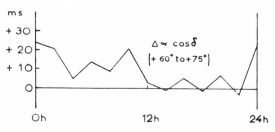

FIG. 18.—Values of $\Delta\alpha \cos \delta$

6. CONCLUSIONS

For meridian observations the accuracy decreases from the equator as $\cos \delta$; thus large discrepancies observed for high declinations can be attributed to random errors. But the accuracy of the measurements of right ascension with the astrolabe depends on the sine of the azimuth. For Paris it is the same for the zone from $+20°$ to $+22°$ as for the zone $+68°.5$ to $+73°$. Hence if the $\Delta\alpha$'s are much larger in the second zone than in the first, the catalogue is responsible. The uncertainty of the group corrections could explain discrepancies of the order of 5 milliseconds but not of 20 milliseconds or more. The anomaly of the FK3 is found again, but to a lesser extent, in the N30 catalogue of H. R. Morgan. However, positive corrections should still be applied to the right ascensions between 23^h and 11^h beyond $+50°$. But the first astrolabe catalogue still has too few stars to allow for detailed discussion.

The previous discussion, while in part admittedly somewhat provisional, will emphasize the advantages of the method of equal altitudes. Applied to the impersonal astrolabe, the method provides its own reference point, which enables one to evaluate the results objectively. The several unknowns—namely, time, latitude, corrections to the catalogue and to the fundamental constants—can be separated to a degree not otherwise attained in meridian astronomy. Instead of amending the catalogue hour by hour, large areas can be dealt with, which are easily linked together. The results are explicit, and their discussion is unambiguous. The methods developed hold out great promise in the field of fundamental astronomy.

REFERENCES

ARBEY, L.   1955 Ve Congrès International de Chronométrie, Paris,
                                    1, 129.

BALL, J., and SHAW, H.
    KNOX   1919   A Handbook of the Astrolabe (Cairo: Government
                                    Press).

CHANDLER, S. C.   1887   Ann. Harvard Coll. Obs., **17**, 179.
CHANDON, E., and
    GOUGENHEIM, A.   1935   Rev. Hydrograph., **12**, 1.
CLAUDE, A., and
    DRIENCOURT, L.   1905   Rev. gén. sci., pp. 972 and 1071.
                            1907   J. de Phys., December, 1907.
                            1910   Description et usage de l'astrolabe à prisme (Paris:
                                    Gautier-Villars).
DANJON, A.   1948   C.R., **227**, 320.
                            1955   Bull. Astr., **18**, 251.
                            1958a   Ibid., **21**, 323.
                            1958b   M.N., **118**, 411 (Darwin Lecture).
                            1959   C.R., **249**, 209.
                            1960   Ibid., **250**, 1399.
GUINOT, B.   1958   Bull. Astr., **22**, 1.
                            1959   Ibid., **23**, 91.

GUINOT, B., and
    DEBARBAT, S.   1960   C.R., **250**, 2124.

CHAPTER 9

Astronomical Seeing

J. STOCK*

McDonald Observatory

AND

G. KELLER

National Science Foundation

1. INTRODUCTION

1.1. DEFINITIONS

THE atmosphere of the earth influences astronomical observations made from the ground in a number of ways. It changes the direction of light as well as its intensity. Both effects may be considered to consist of a constant and a fluctuating term. The sources of the various terms are not necessarily found in the same part of the atmosphere, and neither are they necessarily produced by the same mechanism. The constant term of the deflection of light passing through the atmosphere is called the *refraction*, while the constant term of loss of light on its way through the atmosphere is called *extinction*. These two phenomena are not discussed here. The random fluctuations in the direction of starlight are referred to as *seeing*, while the random fluctuations of the intensity of starlight received on the ground are referred to as *scintillation*. These two terms apply only to fluctuations caused by random variations in the refractive index in the atmosphere; only the phenomena so caused are discussed in this chapter.

1.2. SEEING

When a stellar image is observed through a telescope with high magnification, the observed image structure, even with perfect optics, does not usually correspond with the theoretical diffraction pattern. Instead, the diffraction rings may be resolved only partly or not at all. In addition, an irregular motion of the image is often observed. The distortion of the image as well as its motion may vary considerably with time and with the location of the observer. These

---

* On leave of absence as scientific adviser, Chile Observatory Project.

random displacements of part or all of the light received by the telescope are called *seeing*. The appearance of seeing depends strongly on the aperture of the telescope. With small apertures, the displacements of the entire image are often the main effect; but, with large apertures, a spreading and blurring of the image are observed, with little or no motion of the image as a whole.

1.3. Scintillation

A certain type of scintillation can readily be observed with the unaided eye. The "twinkling" of stars falls into this category. With photoelectric methods, the amplitudes of the random variations of the intensity, or scintillation, can be measured with precision and the frequency spectrum of the amplitude variations studied. The scintillation depends in a characteristic way on the aperture of the telescope in the sense that the amplitudes decrease with increasing aperture. This effect becomes quite apparent in visual observations. The twinkling of stars is usually not apparent to a visual observer using binoculars.

1.4. The Source of Seeing and Scintillation

The seeing is caused by inhomogeneities of the refractive index in the atmosphere. The large amplitude of the scintillation, often exceeding the mean atmospheric extinction, leaves no doubt that it is of a nature similar to that of seeing, rather than due to irregularities in the atmospheric absorption. In an exact treatment of these problems the propagation of electromagnetic waves through an inhomogeneous medium must be considered. A simplified discussion on the basis of geometrical optics, however, is adequate for an understanding of many of the observed phenomena. This approach is followed here.

Inhomogeneities of the refractive index may be expected in the turbulent parts of the atmosphere; the latter may occur anywhere. In the present context it is often found, however, that the most effective turbulence is located in layers within a few hundred feet from the ground and within 3 km (10,000 feet) or so from the level of the tropopause. Turbulent air inside the observatory dome and within the observing instruments themselves frequently causes serious disturbances. The effect of a homogeneous turbulent region of limited thickness upon the statistical behavior of the observed image structure and intensity are described below. The total statistical effect of all the turbulent regions in the light-path may be found, in the first approximation, from an appropriate summation of the effects of the individual regions.

If a plane wave front enters a turbulent layer, it will emerge as a distorted wave front and travel as such to the ground (cf. Fig. 1). Two phenomena are readily deduced from the figure: (*a*) Below the turbulent zone the *direction* of light will show a dispersion. This dispersion is independent of the distance from the turbulent zone. (*b*) The *intensity* in the wave front below the turbulent zone is not uniform. The lack of uniformity increases with increasing distance from the zone, at least until the average lateral displacement of a light-ray is comparable with the average separation of the turbulent elements.

Changes in the turbulence pattern in the light-path cause the temporal changes associated with seeing and scintillation.

The foregoing remarks make it clear that seeing can be caused anywhere in the atmosphere, while turbulence near the ground will be ineffective as a source of scintillation. Taking into account the fact that the refractive power of the atmosphere decreases with increasing altitude, we conclude that the source of the seeing is more likely to be found near the ground, while scintillation may be expected to be produced largely at some elevation above the ground. Therefore, it is not surprising that seeing and scintillation show little, if any, correlation. This fact justifies separate treatment of the two phenomena.

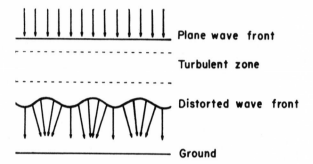

Fig. 1.—Distortion of wave front after passage through an atmospheric zone of turbulence

2. SEEING

2.1. GENERAL REMARKS

Although the interpretation of seeing is not an astronomical subject, the seeing phenomenon imposes such limitations on astronomical research that its discussion here is justified. Since the astronomer is concerned more with the effect on astronomical observations than with the nature of the phenomenon, our discussion is so oriented. As was remarked before, theoretical considerations are presented on the basis of geometrical optics.

Contributions to the theory and observation of seeing phenomena are widely scattered throughout the literature of optics, astronomy, and atmospheric physics. A bibliography of the literature prior to 1952 will be found in Nettleblad (1953) and from 1952 through 1956 in Keller, Protheroe, Barnhart, and Galli (1956, chap. 8). Perhaps the most important single contribution to the general theory of seeing and scintillation is that of van Isacker (1953). Derivations of the expressions used in Sections 2.3 and 2.4 of this presentation will be found in Keller et al. (1956), Keller (1953), and Keller and Hardie (1954).

2.2. The Aperture Effect

It is apparent from Figure 1 that, with a ground-based telescope of *small* aperture, only a narrow, almost parallel, bundle of light is observed, whose direction will vary as the pattern produced by the turbulent zone moves past the instrument. Thus arises a sharp, or nearly sharp but erratically moving, image. On the other hand, with a sufficiently *large* aperture, the entire range of directions will be observed simultaneously, the average direction being identical with that of the undisturbed bundle above the turbulent zone. This means that a blurred image with a steady position will be observed. Telescopes with intermediate apertures show a somewhat blurred and, at the same time, moving image. For star images produced by a series of telescopes of different aperture (all optically perfect), the *time* averages of the angular light-distributions will be the same.

For a turbulent zone near the ground, the foregoing results may be expressed in a more specific way, if it is assumed that the turbulent layer consists of cells of various sizes with a refractive index different from that of their surroundings. Then cells with horizontal dimensions of the order of the aperture of the telescope or smaller will, in a first approximation, act as small lenses and defocus all or part of the light entering the telescope, thus causing blurred images. Large cells, on the other hand, act primarily as prisms, since, at a given moment, only a portion of a cell covers the telescope aperture; thus large cells cause image motion.

2.3. The Physical Constitution of Turbulent Zones

It is clear, then, that if the turbulence is near the ground, the sizes of turbulence elements can be estimated from the seeing observations with different apertures. The temperature and pressure differences between the turbulence elements and their surroundings will be of interest also, as well as the thickness of the turbulent layers needed to account for the observed seeing effects.

The optical characteristics of a turbulent element depend on the difference δf between the refractive index of its air and that of the surroundings. Now

$$\delta f = \frac{\delta \rho}{\rho_0} (n_0 - 1) \, ,$$

where $\delta \rho$ is the difference in density between the turbulent element and the surroundings; ρ_0 is the density of air at normal temperature and pressure; and n_0 is the corresponding index of refraction. Since the velocities of the turbulent air are highly subsonic, it may be assumed that density differences between adjacent air elements are the result of temperature differences and not pressure differences. Under these conditions, for a perfect gas,

$$\frac{\delta \rho}{\rho} = - \frac{\delta T}{T} \, ,$$

where δT is the temperature difference of the turbulent element and ρ is the mean density of the surrounding air. Thus

$$\delta f = -\left(\frac{\rho}{\rho_0}\right)\left(\frac{\delta T}{T}\right)(n_0 - 1) \cdot$$

If the element is close to the telescope and the latter at sea level, one has, with $n_0 - 1 = 2.9 \times 10^{-4}$ ($\lambda = 4700$ A),

$$\delta f \approx -10^{-6}\delta T \ .$$

A rough estimate of the effect of a single turbulence element is obtained by assuming that in front of a telescope is placed a spherical cell having the same diameter. If the refractive index within the cell is uniform with the value

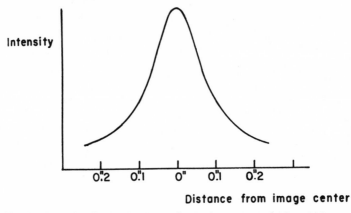

Intensity

0".2   0".1   0"   0".1   0".2

Distance from image center

FIG. 2.—Intensity distribution in star image due to atmospheric turbulence

$n_0 + \delta f$, and if $\delta f = 10^{-7}$, the image profile will be observed as shown in Figure 2. The abscissae are proportional to δf. If the average dimensions of the turbulence elements are estimated, a comparison of the observed image profile with Figure 2 leads to combinations of δf and the thickness of the turbulence zone which can account for the data.

2.4. LIGHT DISTRIBUTION IN THE SEEING IMAGE

A qualitative discussion may be made considering two extreme kinds of seeing, termed "good" and "bad." In good seeing the turbulent layer may be likened to a thin, irregular diffracting screen wherein the optical thickness of the diffracting elements is so small that a good fraction of the incident light passes through the layer in an undiffracted (zero-order) plane wave. Images are then obtained of a quality limited primarily by the optical properties of the telescope, though they are surrounded by halos of diffused light caused by diffraction in the turbulent layers. Conditions may be termed "good" when the quantity

$$K^2 = \frac{2\pi^3}{\lambda^2} NL_m^2 \delta^2 f < 1 \ .$$

Here N is the average number of turbulent elements which the light-rays pass through on their way; L_m is a measure of the average size of the elements; $\delta^2 f$ is the mean-square fluctuation of the refractive index; and λ is the wave length of light. Since the length of the optical path through the turbulent layer increases with the zenith distance of the object observed, N does also. Hence good seeing is promoted by (1) thin turbulent layers, (2) small zenith distances, (3) small element sizes, (4) small temperature fluctuations, and (5) use of a long wave length of light for observation. It can be shown that the fraction of light transmitted into the undisturbed image is approximately $\exp(-4K^2/\pi)$.

When conditions are such that $K^2 > 1$, the seeing is said to be "bad." It can be shown that under such conditions the image of a point source seen with an ideal telescope will always be spread out into a Gaussian distribution such that

$$I(v) = \left(\frac{I}{2\pi b^2}\right)\exp\left(-\frac{v^2}{2b^2}\right),$$

where $I(v)$ is the intensity of radiation per steradian in the direction making an angle v with the center of the image and $2b^2$ is the mean-square angular deviation of the rays from the center. Now

$$2b^2 \approx 2\pi N \delta^2 f ;$$

hence, under conditions of bad seeing, the size of images can be minimized by observing near the zenith, since N varies here also with the secant of the zenith distance. Little is now to be gained, however, by going to longer wave lengths.

2.5. Seeing and Meteorological Phenomena

Although the seeing is caused by meteorological factors, of either a local or a large-scale nature, it is not yet possible at present to predict the seeing with certainty for a given meteorological situation. Certain conditions, however, have a known influence on the seeing. If mixing of air masses of different temperatures occurs, extensive turbulence zones are produced, and large values of δT may exist. This occurs, among others, in two typical situations: (a) in a cold front and (b) in an inversion layer. The latter is particularly typical of dry climates. At night the surface cools rapidly by radiation, and little of this radiant energy is absorbed by the atmosphere because of lack of water vapor. Thus cold air forms close to the ground. The higher layers of the atmosphere show little change in temperature, unless there is wind. The thickness of the layer of cold air steadily increases during the night. The vertical temperature gradient shows an inversion at the top of the cold air. Turbulence with large values of δT may exist near the inversion. In level areas the inversion may reach elevations of several hundred meters during the night. In mountainous areas the cool air formed on the slopes and at the top of the mountains is drained into the valleys, rapidly filling these with cold air. Then the inversion may rise during the night to more than 1000 meters above the valley floor.

Both phenomena and their relation to seeing are readily studied if continuous temperature recordings are also made. A rapid temperature decrease, lasting several hours or more, indicates that a cold air mass is moving into the area. A rapid temperature drop of short duration, if observed on a mountain in a dry climate during a windless night, indicates that the temperature inversion has risen above the observer. A rapid temperature decrease is almost invariably accompanied by poor seeing, although the mechanisms mentioned above may not always be the cause. A steady or even slightly rising temperature during the night seems to be a necessary, though not a sufficient, condition for good seeing.

Strong winds are often, though not always, connected with poor seeing. If the cases are eliminated when the temperature is dropping rapidly at the same time—here the mechanism is obvious—the relation is no longer so pronounced. Turbulence produced by structures in the vicinity of the telescope cannot, in general, have a strong effect on the seeing, because the thickness of the turbulence zones is insufficient. However, with a poorly insulated or ventilated dome, the building and inside air may have temperatures differing by many degrees from the outside air. A gust of wind may cause mixing near the dome slit. With a large telescope the total optical path length to the Cassegrain focus is substantial, which may cause a pronounced cumulative seeing effect.

3. METHODS FOR SYSTEMATIC SEEING OBSERVATIONS

Seeing studies for astronomical purposes may be classified into two categories: (a) studies at existing observatories and (b) field tests. In the first case, the facilities of a fully equipped observatory are available, and the purpose is the study of seeing as such or the search for systematic tendencies, seasonal variations, etc. The knowledge of such tendencies may be useful for selecting observing programs. Field tests are intended to provide material for the selection of a site for a new observatory. Portable, or at least movable, equipment is needed in such cases.

3.1. STATIONARY EQUIPMENT

3.11. *Image diameters for telescopes of large aperture.*—The only seeing feature observed through a large aperture is the profile of the image. It has been shown that the profile is usually nearly Gaussian. The images do not have sharp edges, and consequently diameter estimates may depend on the brightness of the stars used. With some experience, such estimates become consistent over a fairly large magnitude range. Sufficient magnification must be used to resolve the images into disks. The magnification may thus have to be chosen according to seeing conditions. Photoelectric measurements through diaphragms of different sizes show how much of the starlight is included within a visually estimated diameter. The value usually falls between 70 and 90 per cent.

3.12. *Image-motion estimates.*—If no large aperture is available, it is best to

PLATE I.—Interferometer used in site testing for the proposed 60″ AF-AURA telescope in Chile. (Photograph, J. Stock.)

go to very small apertures, so that most of the seeing effects appear as image motion. In this case it is sufficient to estimate the maximum excursion of the image from its average position. Such estimates again yield a radius within which the image will stay for 80–90 per cent of the time, nearly the same value as obtained in the first method. If the image also appears fuzzy, its intrinsic diameter has to be estimated also. To obtain the diameter which would have been observed, had a large-aperture telescope been used, one computes the square root of the quantity $(2 \times \text{maximum excursion of image})^2 + (\text{image diameter})^2 - (\text{diameter of diffraction pattern})^2$. This method requires a steady telescope with a good drive.

3.13. *Photographic trails.*—Image motion can be obtained readily by trailing focal images of bright stars across a photographic plate. This method has the advantage of giving a permanent record. Also, it allows the deduction of the entire image profile expected for large apertures. The method, however, works satisfactorily only if most of the seeing effects appear as image motion, not as image size.

3.14. *Observations through two apertures.*—Very satisfactory results can be obtained if two small apertures are placed in front of a telescope of large aperture. If one observes the images slightly out of focus, two still sharp but separated images can be seen. The relative motion and structure of the two images provide very useful measures of what the image appearance would be in a telescope of aperture equal to the separation between the holes. From photographic trails of the two images, image profiles for the larger telescope can be deduced.

It follows, then, that the same type of observation can be made with an interferometer-type instrument, wherein the two images are observed side by side rather than in superposition. When possible, the separation of the two apertures should be made as large as the aperture of the largest telescope which is to be used on the site. Since only relative displacements are measured, this method requires no accurate drive, internal rigidity being more important than accurate guiding. The difficulty mentioned above of measuring the intrinsic width of the individual images from photographic trails also applies here.

3.2. Methods for Field Tests

3.21. *Resolution of the diffraction pattern.*—One of the most widely used methods was proposed by Danjon (1926). It is based on estimates of the resolution of the diffraction pattern of stellar images observed through apertures of 20–25 cm. The estimates made in a scale described by Danjon are then transformed by an empirical relation to angular measures. Allowance for the actual aperture used can readily be made. Such estimates can be carried out easily and with accuracy. Seeing effects which appear as image motion through a 20–25-cm aperture, however, are not included, although they are at times the main contributors to the image profile observed through a much larger aperture. The usefulness of this method depends on how well image distortion and image motion observed through a 20-cm aperture are correlated. Though a correlation does seem to exist, accurate predictions for image profiles produced by a large aperture cannot be made.

3.22. *Image motions.*—Field instruments are usually without an accurate drive. The method (of Sec. 3.12) for stationary equipment can still be used, if the motions of an image drifting through the field of a telescope are observed. In this case, only the component perpendicular to the diurnal motion can be used, and it is convenient to let the star drift between two cross-hairs of known separation. However, vibrations of the telescope due to wind shake, etc., are detrimental to such observations.

3.23. *Interferometer-type instruments.*—The two-aperture method for stationary equipment is mentioned in Section 3.14. This method does not require a good drive, and it is insensitive to vibrations of the instrument. Here estimates of the diameter and the relative motion of the two images yield information on the seeing condition. Again, it is advantageous to have a pair of cross-hairs or a grid of known separation in the field. The instrument used in the Chile Observatory test program is shown in Plate I.

4. DESIGN OF INSTRUMENTS TO MINIMIZE SEEING EFFECTS

For the present purpose it is convenient to subdivide the air through which the light must travel from a celestial source to the photodetector into three main parts. The first part consists of all the air lying between the top of the atmosphere and a point where the thermal behavior of the air is affected appreciably by local topographic features. Minimization of adverse seeing effects in this part of the path can be achieved only by intercomparison of the seeing conditions in widely different geographical areas and subsequent selection of the most favorable ones. The second part of the light-path lies between the lower boundary of the first part and that point at which the telescope and associated dome has an important effect on the thermal structure of the air. Adverse seeing effects generated in this portion of the light-path can be minimized by careful study of local features in the light of the considerations cited in Section 2.5, followed by comparative tests of individual proposed locations. The third part of the light-path is that in which the thermal pattern of the air is governed by the structure of the telescope, dome, and auxiliary instrumentation. It is this last portion of the light-path toward which the present remarks are directed.

Even a seemingly mild inhomogeneity in the optical properties of the air within an optical instrument can be surprisingly damaging to the image definition. From the discussion of Sections 2.3 and 2.4 it is easy to show that near sea level, if the various portions of a wave front pass, on the average, through N elements of air having temperatures differing from the mean ambient temperature by an r.m.s. amount δT in degrees centigrade, the r.m.s. deviation of the light of a point source from its mean position is approximately $(N)^{1/2}\ \delta T$ seconds of arc. Thus even a single element in the light-path with a temperature deviation of 1° will enlarge stellar images to a diameter of 1 second of arc on a photographic plate exposed for even a few seconds.

A number of methods have been suggested and tried, with varying degrees of success, for suppressing seeing effects in optical instruments. The first is to devise a combination ventilation and temperature-control system that will assure that the temperature of the air within the instrument is as nearly uniform as possible and at the same temperature as the outside air above the dome. Such systems have been described by Couder (1953), Rösch (1955), and Sisson (1957). A practical difficulty with this system is encountered when diurnal temperature changes are rapid, in which case it may be difficult to maintain the temperature of portions of the equipment, particularly large glass or quartz mirrors, in thermal equilibrium with the air. It may be that it will be possible to develop temperature-controlled metallic mirrors, in which case this difficulty might be overcome. When the instrument is to be used for solar observations, the problem is compounded by the rapid heating of the air and optical elements by the solar radiation. For this reason, experiments with a temperature-controlled telescope structure and metallic mirrors are being conducted at the Kitt Peak National Observatory in connection with the construction of a large solar telescope.

Brief periods of exceptionally good instrumental seeing have been obtained by Leighton (1957) by utilizing the first 100 seconds after first opening the 60-foot Mount Wilson solar tower to the sun's light.

Another approach to the problem is based on the fact that, at any given instant, the wave front being focused at adjacent points in the focal plane have traversed pretty much the same elements of inhomogeneous air. To the extent that this is true, the images of adjacent point sources will be displaced and distorted in the same manner, a fact that opens up the possibility of analyzing one or more of the images to determine the nature of the distortion and using this information to introduce optical corrections, as suggested by Babcock (1953) and actually achieved, so far as lateral displacements are concerned, by Leighton (1956) and DeWitt, Hardie, and Seyfert (1957).

If the image is bright enough, it is well known that sharper definition can generally be obtained by using the shortest exposure possible, in order to minimize the effect of changes in the distortion and lateral shifting of the image which occur as the pattern of inhomogeneous elements shifts around. Stopping the aperture of the objective down to 4 or 6 inches is usually helpful also, since (at the cost of some resolving power, which usually cannot be achieved anyway because of seeing distortions) the number of distinct inhomogeneous elements through which all parts of the incoming wave front pass at any instant is reduced, thus reducing the instantaneous distortion (while at the same time increasing the average lateral displacement). The use of an image amplifier has great advantages in this approach to the problem, since it enables one to use shorter exposures and to work with fainter sources. Frederick (1960) has been able to photograph binary stars having separations as small as 0.3 second of arc with the aid of a two-stage cascaded-image intensifying tube and exposures of the order of $\frac{1}{100}$ second of time. There is a fundamental limitation on the faintness of the objects which can be observed by this method, however, since, even with a system having 100 per cent photon-recording efficiency, it is clear that at least one photon must be received from each point on the object to be recorded in the short exposure times of $\frac{1}{100}$ second required in order to "freeze" the turbulence pattern. Use of a larger aperture will not help because one cannot then be sure that the individual photons from different parts of the object will suffer the same lateral displacement.

Perhaps the most elegant approach to the problem is to evacuate the air from all parts of the optical system for which this can be done. McMath (1955) has had striking success with this procedure in connection with the high-dispersion solar spectrograph at the McMath-Hulbert Observatory. A complete solution to all seeing problems (although at the cost of introducing some other formidable instrumental problems!) may be had by placing the entire equipment at an altitude sufficiently high that a negligible amount of air lies in the light-path to the instrument. Using a 12-inch reflector suspended from a balloon at an altitude of 80,000 feet, Schwarzschild (1959) has obtained photographs of the solar granulation of unprecedented definition. Using exposure times of approximately $\frac{1}{1000}$ second, the theoretical optical resolution of $\frac{1}{3}$ second of arc has been achieved in the best photographs over a field of 83 by 107 seconds of arc. Construction of a 36-inch balloon-borne telescope for high-resolution photography of night-sky objects is now being undertaken by Schwarzschild and his co-workers.

5. SCINTILLATION

5.1. GENERAL REMARKS

As in the case of seeing, a detailed study of scintillation is of more interest to students of optics than to astronomers. The following brief discussion is intended to provide only a quasi-quantitative description of the most important effects. It is hoped that it may be of some assistance to the astronomer who may be faced with the problem of avoiding or minimizing scintillation problems.

For the reasons given in Section 1.4, the illumination of the surface of an objective lens or mirror in the light of a single star is never completely uniform. The irregular patchwork of illumination which is actually present at any instant is called the *shadow pattern*. The integrated illumination over the unvignetted and unocculted area of the objective determines the amount of starlight arriving at the focal plane at that instant. The rapid temporal changes in the shadow pattern are accompanied by changes in the integrated illumination, and scintillation results. Numerous observations have shown that the individual light and dark patches are of the order of 10 cm across. Consequently, the r.m.s. amplitude of scintillation tends to be larger for small-aperture instruments. Protheroe (1955) found that a mean value of the scintillation at Columbus, Ohio, is of the order of 40 per cent of the mean intensity for an aperture of 2.5 cm when one observes close to the zenith during the night. For large-aperture instruments the fluctuations are much less, dropping to the order of 5.0 per cent for a 30-cm objective. (This quantity varies over a wide range, however.) This is called the *aperture effect*.

As in the case of seeing, the literature on scintillation is widely scattered. Bibliographies of the literature through 1956 will be found in the two references cited in Section 2.1.

5.2. Shadow Patterns

Direct observation of instantaneous shadow patterns is difficult because even the brightest stars do not furnish enough light to permit the use of exposure times needed to stop the motion (of the order of $\frac{1}{500}$ second) with ordinary photographic techniques. On the other hand, the statistical properties of a pattern can be studied by the use of high-efficiency photomultiplier cells which sense the illumination in the pattern at specific points separated by a preassigned amount. If the correlation between the intensity fluctuations at such points is then plotted as a function of the separation, the autocorrelation function of intensity fluctuations is obtained. The pattern is frequently not isotropic and certainly becomes coarser with increasing zenith distance. As an example, however, Barnhart, Keller, and Mitchell (1959) have obtained fairly typical autocorrelation functions for stars near the zenith which can be approximated by the expression

$$Q = \exp - \frac{(\Delta r)^2}{2 (\Delta r)_0^2},$$

where Δr is the separation of the correlated points in centimeters and $(\Delta r)_0$ is of the order of 2 cm.

5.3. Spectrum of the Fourier Components of the Shadow Pattern

It is sometimes instructive to study the relative amplitudes of fluctuation of various dimensions in the shadow pattern. This information is expressed in a statistical manner by the spectrum function, B. It is essentially the Fourier transform of the autocorrelation function, Q. For the isotropic case, using the sample Q introduced in the preceding section,

$$B(w) = 8\pi \langle h^2 \rangle_{Av} (\Delta r)_0^2 \exp [- 2\pi^2 (\Delta r)_0^2 w^2] .$$

Here w is the wave number in cm^{-1} of a Fourier component; $2\pi w B(w) \Delta w$ is the sum of the squares of all the Fourier coefficients of the intensity fluctuation with wave numbers lying in an interval Δw around w; and $\langle h^2 \rangle_{Av}$ is the mean-square amplitude of intensity fluctuation in the pattern. As might be expected, B decreases rapidly for wave numbers larger than $1/(\Delta r)_0$.

5.4. APERTURE EFFECTS

It would be expected that the use of a large aperture would have the effect of partially averaging out fluctuations in the total light received at the focal plane. One may suppose that the number of patches seen through the aperture is proportional to the square of its radius R_2 and that the fluctuation of the integrated intensity from its mean value varies with the square root of the number seen. Since the time-average illumination is proportional to the square of the aperture, the ratio of the fluctuation to the mean illumination varies as $1/R_2$. More detailed analysis shows that when R_2 is larger than $(\Delta r)_0$ by a factor of 2 or so, the following relation holds approximately, assuming the autocorrelation function given in Section 5.2:

$$\frac{[\langle I^2 \rangle_{Av}]^{1/2}}{I_{DC}} = \frac{\sqrt{2}}{\sqrt{\pi}} \frac{(\Delta r)_0}{R_2} \frac{\langle h^2 \rangle_{Av}^{1/2}}{h_0}.$$

Here $\langle I^2 \rangle_{Av}$ is the mean-square fluctuation in intensity of light received through a circular aperture of radius R_2; I_{DC} is the corresponding time average intensity; and h_0 is the mean illumination of the aperture per unit area. Protheroe (1955) has obtained data for values of R_2 ranging from 1.25 to 16 cm which agree surprisingly well with this formula. It seems clear, therefore, that scintillation effects can be suppressed by using a larger aperture.

5.5. RELATIVE EFFECTS OF SCINTILLATION FLUCTUATIONS AND SHOT-NOISE FLUCTUATIONS

Random arrival of photons from a star gives rise to fluctuations in the observed light-intensity at the focal plane, which are referred to as *shot noise*. As in the case of scintillation itself, the ratio of the r.m.s. variation in number of photons received in a given interval of time to the total number received in that interval varies as $1/R_2$. Consequently, the relative importance of scintillation fluctuations and shot-noise fluctuations does not depend on the aperture. It does depend, however, on the brightness of the star and on the optical efficiency of the telescope and associated equipment, since increasing either of these increases the number of photons received per second and consequently reduces the ratio of the shot-noise amplitude to the total light received, while at the same time leaving the corresponding ratio for the scintillation unchanged. As an example, if we consider a star of the same spectral type as the sun's, observed near the zenith with a telescope of 30-cm aperture under conditions of r.m.s. scintillation of 5 per cent, assume an optical efficiency of the telescope of 0.8, use a photocell with a photon efficiency of 10 per cent with a band pass of 1000 A around a center wave length of 4700 A, and assume that the scintillation noise is present up to frequencies of the order of 200 c/s, it can then be shown that scintillation fluctuations and shot-noise fluctuations will be comparable in r.m.s. amplitude for stars of apparent photographic magnitude of about +6.6.

5.6. The Physical Constitution of the Turbulent Zone
and Its Relation to the Shadow Pattern

As was pointed out in Section 1.4, the light and dark patches in the shadow pattern are related, at least in a statistical fashion, with corresponding patches of hot and cold air in the upper atmosphere. Let us suppose that these patches of air are confined to a horizontal layer of thickness Δz lying at a vertical height z above the observer. Let us suppose that the variations in index of refraction f in this layer are described by a Fourier series. If we further assume that the turbulence is homogeneous and isotropic, we can describe the frequency of elements of different sizes by the spectrum function $b(w)$, for which w is the wave number in cm^{-1} of a Fourier component and $4\pi w^2 b(w)dw$ is the sum of the squares of all the Fourier coefficients with wave numbers lying in the interval Δw about w. If the turbulence and hence the scintillation are not unusually severe, a number of authors have shown that a relation between $b(w)$ and the spectrum function for the shadow pattern $B(w)$ can be obtained (see Keller et al. 1956):

$$\frac{B(w)}{h_0^2} = \frac{16\pi^2 \Delta z\, b(w)\, \sin^2(\pi z\lambda w^2)}{\lambda^2}.$$

Here λ is the wave length of light in centimeters. The formula indicates in a general way the manner in which atmospheric conditions are related to the characteristics of the shadow pattern and hence to the amplitude of scintillation. Large temperature fluctuations cause large differences in the index of refraction, hence large values of b and B. A thick layer produces a larger B than a thin layer. If the star is not at the zenith, then the formula holds if z and Δz are taken to be, respectively, the slant distance along the light-path from the telescope to the layer and through the layer. Thus, at large zenith distances, Δz becomes large, and the sin^2 term increases until it begins to oscillate between 0 and 1. Thus it is not surprising to find, as Mikesell, Hoag, and Hall (1951), Protheroe (1955), and others have observed, that scintillation is usually stronger for stars at large zenith distances.

For stars near the zenith and values of z, λ, and w of practical interest, we usually have $\pi z\lambda w^2 < 1$, and the foregoing formula can be simplified to read

$$\frac{B(w)}{h_0^2} \approx 16\pi^4 z^2 \Delta z w^4 b(w) .$$

In this form two other observational facts are easily understood. First, no dependence on λ appears, and hence the lack of color dependence of the scintillation found by Mikesell et al. and Protheroe follows. Second, the right-hand side of the equation decreases rapidly as w decreases, which accounts for the absence of large element sizes in observed shadow patterns, even though there is reason to believe that large turbulent elements do, in fact, occur in the atmosphere.

5.7. The Frequency Spectrum of Scintillation

Protheroe (1955) and Mikesell *et al.* (1951) have made observations of the frequency spectrum of scintillation. It is found that the fluctuations in intensity of the light have frequencies varying from 0 to perhaps 500 c/s. The r.m.s. amplitude per unit band width is more or less constant up to 75 c/s and decreases fairly smoothly to zero at the high-frequency limit. During winter months, when meteorological conditions are more severe, it is found that the amplitudes at all frequencies are larger, but those at the higher frequencies relatively more so, probably because of the higher wind velocities that prevail at that time of year. The scintillation at all frequencies increases with increasing zenith distance, but the relative increase is more marked at lower frequencies. This effect may be understood in terms of the first formula of Section 5.6. The lower frequencies are generated by the larger turbulent elements, for which the value of w, the wave number, is small. When w is small, the $\sin^2$ term is very small. When one observes at a larger zenith distance, z increases, and hence the $\sin^2$ term increases rapidly. Now this will happen for all values of w, until the $\sin^2$ term approaches unity. This approach will occur first for the larger values of w. As z continues to increase, $B(w)$ then increases faster for small values of w, which means that the amplitude of the larger elements in the shadow pattern is enhanced relative to the smaller ones.

5.8. Scintillation and Meteorological Phenomena

A number of studies have been made of the relation of upper-air phenomena to the behavior of shadow bands and scintillation by Protheroe (1955), Gifford and Mikesell (1953), Mikesell (1955), and Barnhart *et al.* (1959). The auto-correlation method mentioned in Section 5.2 can be used with considerable accuracy to measure the speed and direction of motion of shadow patterns. When these shadow-pattern velocities are compared with wind velocities measured at various altitudes by rawinsonde, it is found that in nearly all cases the velocity of the pattern agrees with the wind velocity at altitudes near the tropopause. Occasionally, agreement is also found with wind velocities at other altitudes, but this is not generally the case. The presumption is that the scintillation is caused primarily by a turbulent layer of mixed hot and cold air located near or at the tropopause.

Although the most striking of the temporal changes in the shadow pattern is its lateral motion, important intrinsic changes occur fairly rapidly. Barnhart *et al.* (1959) find for a sample of 12 nights that the pattern changes completely in periods of time varying from 6.5 to 13 milliseconds. During this period the pattern as a whole moves distances of the order of 15–27 cm.

REFERENCES

Babcock, H. W.	1953	*Pub. A.S.P.*, **65**, 229.
Barnhart, P. E., Keller, G., and Mitchell, W. E., Jr.	1959	*Report TR59-291*, Air Force Cambridge Research Center, Bedford, Mass.
Couder, A.	1953	*Pub. Obs. Haute Provence*, Vol. **2**, No. 53.
Danjon, A.	1926	*C.R. Acad. Sci. Paris*, **183**, 1032.
DeWitt, J. H., Hardie, R. H., and Seyfert, C. K.	1957	*Sky and Telescope*, **17**, 8.
Frederick, L. W.	1960	Paper read at the 105th meeting of the American Astronomical Society.
Gifford, F., Jr., and Mikesell, A. H.	1953	*Weather*, **8**, 195.
Isacker, J. van	1953	*Pub. Inst. R. Météorol. de Belgique*, B, No. 8.
Keller, G.	1953	*Astr. J.*, **58**, 113.
Keller, G., and Hardie, R. H.	1954	*Astr. J.*, **59**, 105.
Keller, G., Protheroe, W. M., Barnhart, P. E., and Galli, J.	1956	*Reprint No.* **39**, Perkins Observatory, Delaware, Ohio.
Leighton, R. B.	1956	*Scient. American*, **194**, 157 (No. 6).
	1957	*Pub. A.S.P.*, **69**, 497.
McMath, R. R.	1955	*Sky and Telescope*, **14**, 372.
Mikesell, A. H.	1955	*Pub. U.S. Naval Obs.*, 2d ser., **17**, 139.
Mikesell, A. H., Hoag, A. A., and Hall, J. S.	1951	*J. Opt. Soc. America*, **41**, 689.
Nettleblad, F.	1953	*Lund Obs. Medd.*, Vol. **2**, No. 130.
Protheroe, W. M.	1955	*Contr. Perkins Obs.* (Delaware, Ohio), No. II-4.
Rösch, J.	1955	*Ciel et terre*, **71**, 205.
Schwarzschild, M.	1959	*Ap. J.*, **130**, 345.
Sisson, G. M.	1957	*Nature*, **179**, 937.

CHAPTER 10

Astronomical Seeing and Observatory Site Selection

A. B. MEINEL

Director, Kitt Peak National Observatory

I. ASTRONOMICAL SEEING

1.1. INTRODUCTION

THE effects of the terrestrial atmosphere on an incoming beam of starlight are twofold: (1) time fluctuations in the *intensity* of the wave front arriving at a given point at the receiver aperture and (2) time fluctuations in the *direction* of the wave front. The former effect is usually termed *scintillation* and the latter *seeing* although "seeing" is sometimes used to cover both phenomena.

The cause of astronomical seeing is the presence of irregularities in the index of refraction in the atmosphere, chiefly from *thermal* inhomogeneities. Additional sources are the variation in the content of water vapor and other minor constituents, such as ozone in the region above the stratosphere.

Thermal inhomogeneities can arise in many ways, depending on the region of the atmosphere under consideration. At ground level, seeing effects can be produced by radiation cooling or by heating of the terrestrial surface and structures. Turbulence effects due to wind shear and eddies around obstructions also produce adiabatic thermal fluctuations, but numerically these effects are minute, as follows from Schlieren studies in wind tunnels. It is only when the interchange energy becomes large, as when the velocity of sound is approached, that the adiabatic effects become large enough to affect the passage of a wave front noticeably.

In the intermediate layers of the atmosphere, the principal thermal effects arise from the passage of large-scale meteorological systems. Since thermal differences as large as 15° C may be present, the arrival of a frontal system aloft can disrupt the homogeneity of the atmosphere even though the lower atmosphere is still undisturbed. The ordinary frontal systems are important in higher latitudes, while in lower latitudes the jet stream is a major source of thermal imbalance.

At extreme elevations, there exist large thermal differences within narrow ranges of height due to changes in chemical and ionic composition. Furthermore, high-velocity turbulence is present in these zones. Nonetheless, since the density of the air is less than 10^{-4} that of sea level, the effect on the wave front is small.

The net effect on astronomical observations of variations in the index of refraction in the atmosphere depends on the height above the observer at which the disturbance is located. Inhomogeneities *close* to the observer will produce only deviations in the *direction* of arrival of elements of the wave front. Disturbances in the wave front caused *far* from the observer also lead to variations of *intensity* along the wave front at the telescope. As a consequence, the image of a star in a small telescope may both move about in the field of view and vary in apparent brightness. It is therefore possible to have poor seeing but no scintillation, but it is not possible to have good seeing with strong scintillation. Scintillation measures, which are easily made, are therefore an inadequate substitute for seeing measures.

Scintillation is closely related to the shadow-band structure observed by placing the eye at the focus of a telescope. Scintillation depends on telescope aperture, since the observed stellar brightness depends on the fluctuating average of the bright and dark regions of the shadow pattern within the telescope beam.

The shadow-band pattern usually shows rapid change and gives the impression of flowing past the aperture. The band patterns are usually most conspicuous in poor seeing; but poor seeing can occur in the absence of a distinct pattern.

The bright and dark patterns of the knife-edge analysis at a telescope (measuring displaced wave fronts) made when shadow bands (and scintillation) are present are usually unrelated to the latter. This shows that *seeing and scintillation usually do not originate in the same layer of the atmosphere.*

1.2. Quantitative Seeing Studies

Mikesell, Hoag, and Hall (1951) in a basic paper determined the frequency spectrum of stellar scintillation. Nights of both good and bad seeing were used, and observations were made at Washington, D.C., and Flagstaff, Arizona. Representative scintillation spectra are shown in Figure 1. The authors consistently found that, when the seeing is good, the high-frequency components of scintillation are missing and the low-frequency components are much less pronounced than they are under bad seeing conditions. They also derived the dependence of scintillation on zenith distance (Fig. 1, *c*), showing the well-known fact that stars near the horizon scintillate more slowly and with greater amplitude than do stars near the zenith and with telescope aperture (Fig. 1, *d*), showing a decrease of scintillation roughly proportional to the inverse telescope

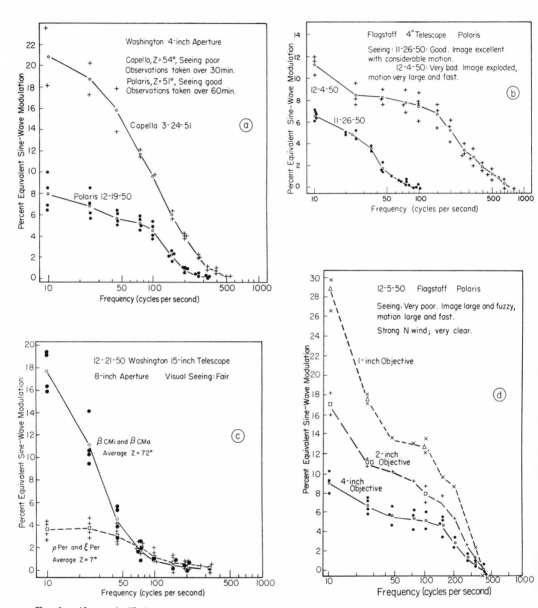

FIG. 1.—*Above:* scintillation spectra obtained with good and bad seeing, both at Washington and at Flagstaff. *Below, left:* scintillation spectra showing increase of scintillation with zenith distance; *right:* variation of scintillation spectra with aperture of telescope; open points represent means. (After Mikesell, Hoag, and Hall 1951.)

diameter. The color dependence of scintillation was found to be slight, and there was no evidence of dependence on the plane of polarization.

It has been found that the seeing phenomenon cannot be interpreted as due to a single disturbed layer as thin as, say, 10 cm. Statistical methods, allowing for thick disturbing layers, have been more successful. Reference is made here to the work of Little (1951), Chandrasekhar (1952), and particularly Keller (1953).

The image profile at the focal plane of the telescope was found to be a generalized Gaussian curve. Figure 2 shows typical seeing profiles observed in the McDonald 82-inch telescope under moderately good seeing. The curves are

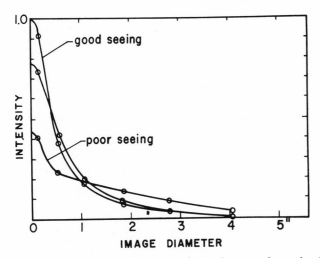

Fig. 2.—Observed radial intensity distributions for star images under good and poor seeing, as measured at the McDonald 82-inch telescope.

Gaussian near their cores, but the wings depend on conditions. As the seeing changes from good to bad, as, for example, from zenith to horizon, the image core may not appreciably alter its shape, the principal change being the growth of the wings at the expense of the central intensity. In bad seeing, none of the core is left, and the image is diffuse.

The simplest model representing this observed profile is made by dividing the aperture of the telescope into round cells whose size distribution is related to the spectrum of atmospheric turbulence. If we combine the cells having small relative phase shifts and again those having large relative phase shifts, we obtain a profile whose central core is caused by the first group and thus by the diameter of the telescope and whose wing profile is determined by the weighted Airy disk of the individual cells. Thus the profile depends on a spectrum of the element sizes.

This model predicts that the image in a telescope of large aperture will have a sharper core than in a smaller telescope but that intensity in the wing will have nearly the same angular distribution for all apertures, being dependent only upon the turbulence spectrum.

1.3. Seeing, Limiting Magnitude, and Telescope Size

Under theoretically perfect seeing, the energy density at the center of the stellar image varies as the fourth power of the aperture (since the total energy varies as the square and the image area as the inverse square). In the presence of a small seeing disturbance, the energy-density law (which determines the limiting photographic magnitude) will decrease with a lower power, until for very poor seeing, where the elements are small and phase-shift spread becomes

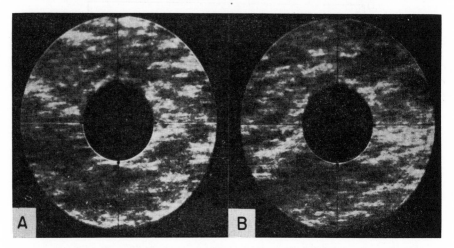

Fig. 3.—Knife-edge photograph of the 200-inch mirror, showing seeing disturbance along the path through the atmosphere.

statistically large, the energy density will depend on the square of the aperture, and the limiting magnitude will be independent of the aperture. Since, however, for equal discrimination against the sky background, the exposure time will vary as the inverse square of the aperture (other factors being constant), a large aperture will allow the use of more contrasty plates or lead to larger electron counts, facilitating discrimination against the background sky proportional to the first power of the telescopic aperture for equal exposure times.

The spectrum of atmospheric turbulence, as found in knife-edge photographs of a large mirror (Fig. 3), shows that the frequency of occurrence with size diminishes rapidly above 20–30 cm. The precise frequency function for an actual aperture has never been derived, but under average seeing conditions the most frequent size element appears to be about 10 cm. Under excellent conditions an 82-inch aperture may be free of detectable cell structure for brief instants.

1.4. COLOR EFFECTS IN SEEING

Differences of opinion exist on the question of color terms in seeing. With large telescopes, color effects in knife-edge tests are sometimes pronounced, especially in bad seeing; the colors may be present either in the shadow-band patterns flowing across the aperture or in the knife-edge pattern. Normally, however, there are no visible color effects. The origin of these colors has been ascribed to either physical-optical or geometrical-optical effects. Measurement of images taken by the writer on longer exposures with the 82-inch telescope, ranging by a factor of 2 in wave length, show no color variations. If the color terms were proportional to the wave length of light, a detectable effect would have been present.

Since these observations did not show the color variation predicted by Keller (1953), the writer has attempted to discover a possible error in the basic assumptions. The phase shift at a point on the disturbed wave front is dependent on the wave length, being only half at 8000 A of that at 4000 A. In this manner the phase-shift autocorrelation function appears to be dependent on the wave length in such a manner as to yield a correlation function independent of color in the image plane of the telescope.

1.5. EXPERIMENTAL LOCATION OF SEEING DISTURBANCES

A simple method proposed for determining the level at which seeing effects occur consists of racking out the eyepiece until the turbulence pattern becomes distinct or unified in motion. Control experiments in the laboratory by Rösch and others have shown that this technique does not give correct results.

An improved version has recently been suggested by I. S. Bowen (private communication) in that a double star of about one-millimeter separation is used in the focal plane of a large telescope. The following description of the method is taken from an unpublished memorandum by Dr. Bowen.

Two knife edges are used, the first cutting one component from the left, and the second, the other component from the right. In this manner the out-of-focus images of the stars become complementary to each other, i.e., one image is bright in areas where the deflection in the turbulent layer has been in one direction while the other image is dark in these regions but bright in areas where the deflection is in the opposite direction. As one recedes from the focus, the out-of-focus images increase in size and finally overlap. When the focal plane that is conjugate to the disturbing layer is reached, the light spots of one stellar image fill in the dark spots of the overlapping part of the other image and the turbulence pattern suddenly disappears. In practice, this disappearance is never quite complete because of inequalities in the magnitudes of the two stars or because of slight errors in adjustment of the knife edges so that the two images are not exactly complementary.

In carrying out a test of this method a slit from a stellar spectrograph was mounted at the Cassegrain focus of the 60-inch telescope. One star of the pair was brought to such a position that its light is half cut off by one jaw of the slit by using the guide motions of the telescope. The other jaw was then moved in to cut off half of the other star, using the slit-width adjusting screw of the slit. The out-of-focus images were then observed with a hand magnifier and the distance measured from the knife edges to the plane where the pattern disappears or is of minimum contrast.

A check on this procedure may be obtained by comparing the appearance of the superimposed out-of-focus star images when the two images are complementary to the appearance when they are additive, that is, when the images are formed with the knife edges cutting off the same side of both stars. In the additive case the prominence of the pattern increases at the conjugate focus of the disturbing layer, since the two patterns are then in phase in the overlapping section of the images. This test can be made by mounting a loop of small wire on the movable jaw of the spectrograph slit extending a short distance beyond the jaw and having a section parallel to the jaw. As before, one star is adjusted with respect to the fixed jaw. The wire is then moved forward until it cuts off the same half of the second star image as the fixed jaw to give the additive case or may be moved to cut off the opposite half for the complementary case.

Observations were first made with the above equipment mounted at the Cassegrain focus of the 60-inch telescope (focal length 24 meters) on the night of December 30, 1957. The overlapped patterns were observed out to a distance of about 60 cm behind the knife edges but no disappearance could be noted. This corresponds to a coverage of distances to the disturbing layers down to about 1000 meters. For the observations on the two following nights a field lens of 8 cm focus was placed near the knife edges. This made it possible to study the overlapping out-of-focus patterns in planes that were conjugate to layers in the atmosphere down to that of the 60-inch mirror. Definite disappearance was found at layers corresponding to distances from the main mirror to the disturbing layer of 100 ± 100 meters. From this it was evident that most of the disturbance to the seeing came from layers within 200 meters of the telescope. This was qualitatively confirmed by the observation that when the additive arrangement was used, or when the magnifier was focused at other points than that at which the complementary patterns disappeared, the turbulence pattern was seen to move from a direction slightly south of east. This was the same direction as that of the surface winds, as indicated by the wind vane on the top of the 60-inch dome. At the same time high-level winds as indicated by the motion of thin cirrus clouds, easily visible in the moonlight, were from the southwest. The pattern was at all times a smooth flow pattern that showed no effect from the outlines of the telescope or dome structures, thus indicating that the disturbance came from outside the dome.

Since earlier observers had found disturbances coming from high levels, the original equipment was designed for the use of double stars having a maximum separation of about 70^{m}. For the more precise location of these close-in turbulent layers it is evident that provision must be made for the use of stars with much wider separations up to 20 or 30 minutes of arc.

Recent balloon ascents, both manned and unmanned, have added information on high-altitude seeing effects. Seeing and scintillation greatly diminish upward in the first 20,000 feet (6 km) above the earth and are negligible above 50,000 feet (15 km). It has been found, however, that a light-source on a balloon observed from the ground does not begin to scintillate until high altitudes are reached.

PLATE I.—The 16-inch test telescope used in the selection of the Kitt Peak National Observatory Site

1.6. EFFECTS OF MOIST AIR

Water vapor has a greater effect on seeing than would be estimated from the index of refraction of moist air, owing to its high opacity for infrared radiation. This "greenhouse" effect of moist air is well known but has not been allowed for in treatments of the seeing problem.

At night, moist-air masses lose their heat by radiation to space. As a consequence of resulting temperature inequalities, the seeing in humid air tends to be inferior to that in dry air. If the entire lower atmosphere is nearly saturated, however, as in the tropics, the temperature differences will be small, and the seeing may be excellent in spite of high humidity.

1.7. DOME SEEING

Local seeing effects by man-made disturbances may ruin an otherwise good site. During the day the observatory dome can trap considerable heat; and the long relaxation time can result in significant heat dissipation during the night. If the shutters are exposed to the afternoon sunlight, the effects of the warm air caused thereby can be readily observed. Radiation cooling may also be observed, when the skin temperature of the shutters falls below the ambient temperature. The latter effect is more likely to occur with painted than with aluminum domes. White paint, particularly oil-based titanium dioxide–pigmented paint, is bad, since it is a black body in the infrared. In daytime this paints absorbs little in the visible region, while it reradiates well in the infrared. Thus it remains close to the ambient temperature in daytime; but at night the infrared radiation losses cause rapid cooling. Titantium white is therefore excellent for solar telescope structures but poor for stellar telescopes. Aluminum coats are neutral, showing high reflectivity in the visible wave lengths, and low emissivity in the infrared. As a consequence, an aluminum finish will heat 5°–10° F during the day but remain close to the ambient temperature at night.

Other causes of poor seeing are heat sources, in and below the dome. Even the emission by the human body (about 25 watts under quiescent conditions) is sufficient to ruin the seeing if the observer stands directly below the aperture of the telescope; this may occur at the Newtonian or prime-focus positions. The increased use of electric power by auxiliary equipment, reaching several thousand watts for multichannel photometers, is also a threat to good seeing.

While such local heat sources may be placed away from the telescope, the combined output will normally leave the open dome at the top, spoiling the seeing near the zenith. To correct this, several observatories have installed ventilation, to reverse the air flow by pulling in outside air at the shutter and exhausting the dome air at the opposite side at a lower level.

2. OBSERVATORY SITE SELECTION

2.1. Introduction

The first consideration in the location of an observatory is obviously the expected average annual number of clear nights. However, the quality of the images is very important. The site-selection problem is discussed here on the basis of experiences gathered in connection with the Kitt Peak National Observatory. Plate I shows the 16-inch telescope used in the later phases of the test program.

Systematic changes in seeing with latitude and longitude appear to be smaller than the variations between the best and the poorest seeing at any one site. Records for many years are therefore needed to yield a significant average. The jet stream shows an annual variation in latitude from 15° to 60°, while polar frontal systems range from 20° to 80°. The two principal sources of thermal inhomogeneity in the free atmosphere thus cover almost the entire globe, though the frequency of disturbances varies regionally.

The principal factors in the location of an observatory are therefore the general meteorological conditions and local seeing contributions.

2.2. Seeing

2.21. *Measurement of seeing, photoelectric.*—Reliable measurement of seeing under field conditions is difficult. By diffraction-ring criteria the seeing in a small telescope (4–6 inches) is good most of the time, and this needs to be supplemented by measurements of the image motion. Such measurements are difficult in a single small telescope, owing to vibrations due to the wind. The National Observatory project attempted to circumvent the problems of visual estimates by recording the image properties photoelectrically.

The site telescopes used were Cassegrain catadioptric systems of 6-inch aperture and 216 inches in focal length (Fig. 4). With the optical axis pointed at the apparent north celestial pole, the instrument was designed to give the image of Polaris just outside the primary mirror. The diurnal rotation of the earth then caused the image to travel around the mirror.

The image profile of Polaris was assessed by means of a reticle placed around the primary mirror. This reticle had occulting bars photographically reproduced on a glass plate. The width of these bars varied in steps of two, from $\frac{1}{2}$ second of arc to 8 seconds; a clear and a dark space, each 20 seconds of arc wide, separated the cycles.

The eccentric position of Polaris resulted in significant aberrations. The optical system was designed to show zero coma at the distance of Polaris, but this made it necessary to accept astigmatism. The resulting image shape is shown in Figure 5. The width of the image for the sagittal focal position is small enough, however, to detect seeing disks as good as $\frac{1}{2}$ second of arc.

In theory, the reticle system adopted was expected to give much detailed

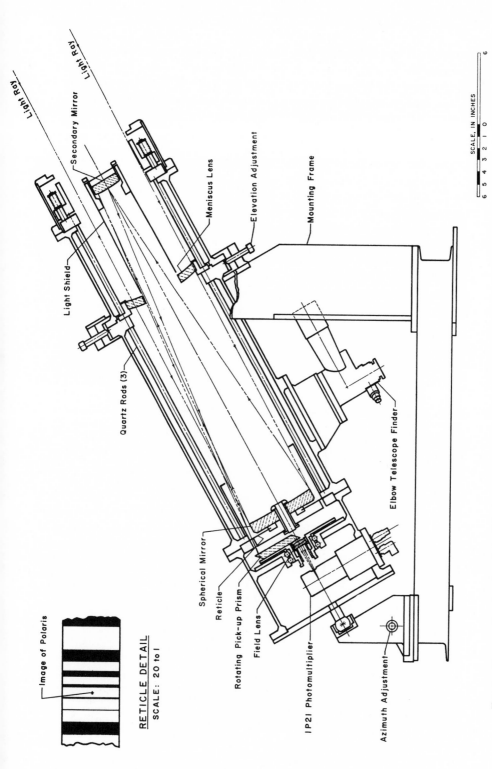

Image of Polaris

Light Ray

Light Ray

Secondary Mirror

Light Shield

Meniscus Lens

Elevation Adjustment

Quartz Rods (3)

Mounting Frame

RETICLE DETAIL
SCALE: 20 to 1

Spherical Mirror

Reticle

Rotating Pick-up Prism

Field Lens

Elbow Telescope Finder

IP21 Photomultiplier

Azimuth Adjustment

SCALE, IN INCHES
6 5 4 3 2 1 0 6

Fig. 4.—Cross-section drawing of the Polaris seeing monitor. The image of Polaris is formed outside the periphery of the primary mirror

information; but in practice it was necessary to select one reticle size and an assumed intensity distribution, in order to get synoptic results. For simplicity, the intensity distribution across the image was assumed to be Gaussian.

The image formed by this telescope is determined by five effects: (1) physical-optical; (2) geometrical-optical; (3) instrumental malalignments; (4) light-scattering; and (5) seeing disturbances. The geometry of the aperture determines a particular diffraction pattern. The geometrical aberrations of the telescope, such as natural astigmatism, coma, and defocusing, affect the "perfect-condition" image. In addition, the image is affected by the scattering of light for small angles due to reflections at two aluminized surfaces. Finally, we have the modification of the image profile due to seeing disturbances that both spread the image and cause it to move about. The visual appearance of the image and the type of intensity distribution that it yields with a line-element analyzer are shown in Figure 5. While the pattern is not precisely Gaussian, the approximation is not bad.

The Polaris telescope amplifier circuit integrated the light entering the tube

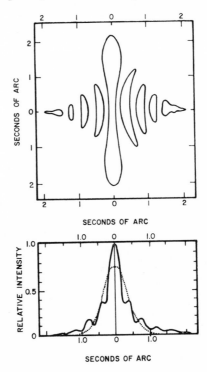

FIG. 5.—*Above:* visual appearance of the diffraction image of the Polaris telescope. The principal image is astigmatic because of the extreme field angle of the telescope. The high secondary maxima in the diffraction pattern are caused by the large central obstruction of the Cassegrain secondary, while the asymmetry in intensity of the diffraction maxima is caused by a small amount of coma. *Below:* the integrated intensity profile.

around each occultation wire over an interval of 1 second. During 1 second of time the diurnal motion of Polaris moved the image $\frac{1}{4}$ second of arc. The interval of integration is, therefore, great enough to include the effects of rapid image jumping. If the integration time were short, then the record would only give a measure of blur of the image. Under conditions of good seeing, the chief effect observable in a 6-inch telescope is image tremor. Only for poor seeing is the disk noticeably fuzzy. The atmospheric parcel integrated is 6 inches wide and of length determined by the wind velocity. For an average wind of 10 mph, the integration is effectively over an aperture 6 × 200 inches. The seeing-disk profile recorded by the Polaris telescope is therefore equivalent to one obtained

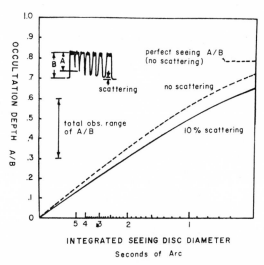

FIG. 6.—Occultation depth for a 1".05 reticle as a function of the integrated seeing-disk diameter parameter σ.

with a much larger telescope. This is confirmed by noting that a Polaris disk of 3 seconds of arc corresponded to a visual resolution of binary stars 1 second of arc apart.

The reduction of the Polaris record using the 1-second-of-arc reticle is made by measuring the effective σ, assuming a value of 0".8 for σ_0 for the undisturbed image. If the real value of σ_0 is 0".7 or 0".9, the result is only a shift of the zero point. The contribution of the seeing to the image is therefore measurable, assuming its distribution, as well as the intrinsic image, to be Gaussian.

On the basis of Gaussian distributions we have determined a calibration-curve for the occultation depth A/B (cf. Fig. 6). If the optical system did not have scattered light, we would theoretically obtain the upper curve. The amount of scattered light is difficult to estimate. According to our assumptions about the light-distribution, the excess in the image wings is considered "scattered light." In addition, we have the small-angle scattering by the aluminum reflecting surfaces and dust on the transmission surface. A value of 10 per cent scattering is selected to arrive at the (A/B) function shown in Figure 6. If the true value is greater, the actual seeing is better than indicated by Figure 6.

The results for the seeing on Kitt Peak obtained on the 150-night test run are shown in Figure 7. The distribution of image sizes indicates that this site is characterized by poor seeing being infrequent.

2.22. *Measurement of seeing, visual.*—The completely automatic Polaris telescopes proved only moderately successful under the primitive field conditions. The Polaris instruments were supplemented in the final year of the survey by 16-inch Cassegrain equatorial telescopes used visually. These instruments had an aperture large enough to be sensitive to seeing but required manned stations, and the determinations of seeing were often handicapped by wind shake and other problems.

A uniform visual seeing scale was achieved by comparing the appearance of a 2-second-of-arc binary star with the chart shown in Figure 8. The adopted

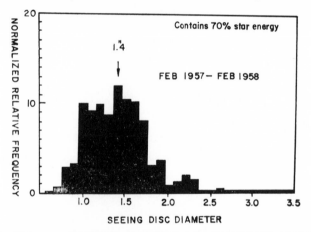

FIG. 7.—Histogram of the distribution of image sizes for 150 nights on Kitt Peak

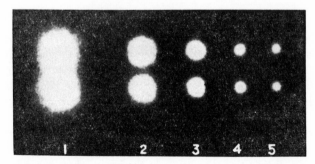

FIG. 8.—Visual seeing scale for a 16-inch Cassegrain telescope utilizing a binary star of equal magnitudes and 2ʺ0 separation.

scale is as follows: Seeing 5, $\frac{1}{4}''$ or better; 4, $\frac{1}{2}''$ or better; 3, $1''$ or better; 2, $2''$ or better; 1, $4''$ or better; 0, larger than $4''$.

The use of this scale succeeded in standardizing the observations by different observers. The results for the two principal sites are shown in Figure 9. Compared with the spread of conditions on each site, the difference is small. Other equipment might, of course, have been used: but no really satisfactory automatic recording method is known to the author. If the observer is limited to a single small-aperture telescope, the moon might be used, with the undulations of the limb particularly useful. Even if the seeing is so good that no corrugations travel along the limb, the eye responds to minute motions in the averted

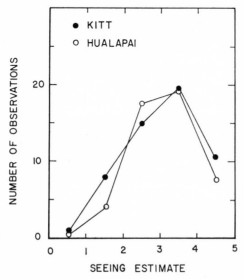

FIG. 9.—Distributions for Kitt Peak and Hualapai of visual seeing estimates, using the 16-inch Cassegrain telescopes.

field of vision of the extended object. This feeling of unsteadiness on the face of the moon provides a sensitive test of good seeing. Unfortunately for synoptic testing, the moon is not always available.

2.23. *Measurement of seeing, photographic.*—A simple instrument proposed for quantitative measures is shown in Figure 10. The small aperture is divided into two beams that cut the atmosphere at separations up to several feet. The alignment of the mirrors must be such as to make the images lie conveniently close together in the focal plane. A moving film will then record the paths of these images. Wind shake is largely removed, since both images move together. The seeing will be measured by changes in the relative positions of the two images.

2.24. *Ground effects on seeing measures.*—Any seeing test made near the ground appears to be of questionable value for the performance of a large telescope which will operate 20 or 40 feet above the ground. Height effects have been reported for the 48-inch Schmidt and the 200-inch telescope at Palomar. At the 48-inch or lower telescope, the seeing will deteriorate some time before the disturbing layer reaches the 200-inch telescope.

During the National Observatory site survey an attempt was made to place the Polaris telescopes above the ground effects. Towers 10 feet and 60 feet high were constructed. Each tower had triple walls; in each case the inner one carried the telescope, while the two outer towers were covered with a corrugated aluminum skin to provide both wind and thermal shielding. The requirements necessary to hold a tower fixed in space to angular tolerances of tenths of a second of arc proved beyond the possibilities of economic engineering practice, and consequently the high towers were of little value except under calm conditions. While it does not appear practicable to use towers to conduct automatic seeing surveys, the validity of results taken at ground level is open to question. Visual observations from towers appear indicated.

2.25. *Microthermal seeing.*—The key to a good site, other than climatic factors, is local seeing. Thermal differences are the principal causes of poor seeing,

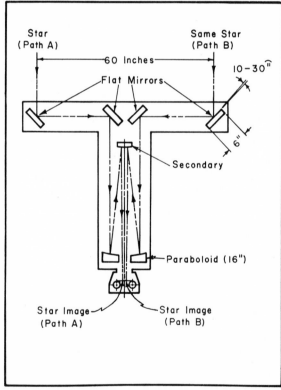

Fig. 10.—Schematic arrangement for the measurement of seeing, using photographs of the images of the same star, observed through two air paths. Wind affects both images similarly.

and these can be measured more easily than seeing itself. Simple towers equipped with high-speed thermal detectors have proved successful for such measurements.

In a clear and dry atmosphere the ground temperature at night drops rapidly. In level areas at high elevations, the nightly drop may be 10°–15°. The cold air drains into low pockets and forms local inversions. A strong inversion is the characteristic calm condition in the low areas of the plateau forest in northern Arizona during most of the year.

On windy nights the inversion layer is not present. This does not mean that the ground does not chill on such nights, since the radiation losses do not depend on wind. The absence of the inversion must be due to mixing of the chilled air with surrounding air; this will lead to microthermal fluctuations and poor seeing. This may be noticeable even on a peak, though much less so than at lower levels. Our tests indeed show that, among sites having the same absolute elevation, those with the smaller differential heights will have the larger microthermal fluctuations and the poorer seeing.

The seasonal distribution of microthermal fluctuations for Kitt Peak (Fig. 11) shows that the fluctuations are largest in July and August. It is during these months that heavy afternoon showers occur, leaving the surface of the mountain damp. It is assumed that during these months the large infrared emissivity of the moist foliage and ground increases radiation cooling.

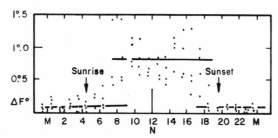

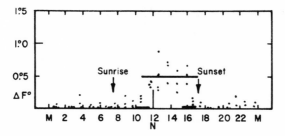

Fig. 11.—Observed microthermal fluctuations at 60 feet above the ground on Kitt Peak. The values plotted are the extreme range of temperature during a 3-minute time interval with a detector having a response time of 1–2 seconds.

2.3. Climate

2.31. *Climatological site factors.*—The existence of large observatories along the Pacific Coast has made it important to assess sites that are climatologically out of phase. The coastal region of Southern California has no doubt one of the best astronomical climates anywhere; but the phenomenal population growth and consequent pollution of the air and sky glow from the great cities present problems of increasing severity. Our survey would point to the coastal mountains of Baja California as most suitable for astronomical observation. It is indeed unfortunate that this region is so inaccessible.

2.32. *Dendroclimatology.*—It is not without danger to base the selection of an observatory site on recently acquired data alone. The climate of the southwestern United States has not been typical in the last three decades, during which time the area has received subnormal rainfall comparable only to the drought of the thirteenth century. This is shown by the many vanished lakes on the Arizona plateau, notably in the Williams-Flagstaff-Hever arc. The year 1958–1959 has been one of "unprecedented cloudiness and rainfall" but may actually be more typical than the recent decades. There are two main sources of information on this question—weather bureau records and, for longer intervals, dendroclimatic data.

The weather bureau records have been gathered chiefly in inhabited areas, in varying degrees of completeness, since the turn of the century. Information of astronomical interest is not easily extracted from them. Cloud records are the least extensive and the least reliable. Rainfall amounts clearly depend on the number of summer showers on the gauging station which account for 50–60 per cent of the annual total, so that the correlation between two stations only a mile apart is often surprisingly low.

The abundant records obtained by the late Dr. E. Schulman, of the Laboratory of Tree Ring Research at the University of Arizona, offer important new information. Measurement of the annual tree-ring size of drought-sensitive species shows variations which must be related to the climate. Ring growth is not a simple function of rainfall, however, but of the general subsoil moisture. The latter depends not directly on the rate of precipitation, since a heavy summer shower and its immediate runoff will contribute little to subsoil moisture compared with a day-long winter drizzle; but it will depend on the evaporation rate. This in turn depends largely on the percentage of *cloudiness*. Actually, the subsoil moisture as indicated by the tree-ring growth may be a better indicator of astronomical conditions than local weather records.

Tree-ring studies offer the possibility of examining the climate of a given area for at least a millennium. While the most numerous and precise chronologies are for the last 800 years, for the California desert region there are enough records of still-living trees to carry the information back to 2000 B.C. The 46-year drought in the thirteenth century, discovered by Douglass (1936), explained the disruption of the civilization of the early Arizona Indians. This severe drought is now matched by the drought which started in 1920 and which is now possibly ending. A graph of the records, averaged over the species used and over the Gila River drainage area, is shown in Figure 12. The limited applicability of surveys lasting a few years to following decades is apparent.

A quotation from Schulman's *Dendroclimatic Changes in Semi-arid America* will illustrate the need for local tree records:

In Southern Arizona the rainfall chronology parallels, on the whole, that in the main catchment areas of the Colorado River in Colorado (Rockies) and Utah (Wasatch). Yet some years and intervals are decidedly different. For example, the wetness of 1932–33 in Southern Arizona is not found farther north in such degree, even in the nearby Verde River basin (south of Flagstaff), a northern tributary of the Gila; also, the 1920s average near normal (i.e., wetter) in the Verde, whereas in Southern Arizona this decade averaged well below normal.

At present it is not possible to derive from these same species the absolute rainfall, since the sensitive trees grow near the natural-selection limits. The rainfall can be estimated, however, from the general tree-species population distributions.

Dendroclimatic studies indicate that there has been *no detectable secular climatic change in the southwestern United States during the last 4000 years.* The pattern of drought and heavy rainfall, moreover, shows *no periodic tendencies,* and the frequency spectrum of duration of drought or heavy rainfall shows *no terms longer than one century.* The evaluation of the long-range performance of a test site therefore requires one to establish the relation of the test years with respect to the centennial average.

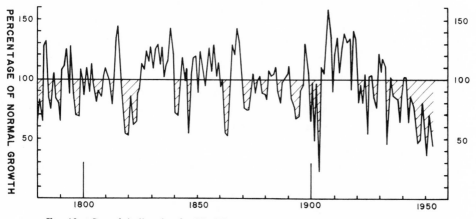

Fig. 12.—Growth indices for the Gila River Basin, period 1780–1950, indicating long-term variations in the climate, as reflected by tree-ring growth. Mixed species, 142 trees; includes central Arizona (south of Flagstaff), southern Arizona, western New Mexico, and northern edge of Sonora.

2.4. Atmospheric Effects

2.41. *Atmospheric circulation.*—The large-scale circulation of the atmosphere has an important bearing on site conditions. The movement of high- and low-pressure systems is accompanied by wind patterns, not to mention precipitation. The wind velocity is an important factor at an observatory. In the first place, strong wind is a handicap in operating a telescope, and frequent strong winds are a powerful psychological deterrent. Second, strong wind produces local pollution from either agricultural areas or the barren desert.

In the southwestern United States strong winds are produced by the passage of low-pressure systems over the Pacific Coast barrier ranges. The usual path of a winter storm has the low-pressure system moving over northern Nevada. This causes strong winds in the Colorado River Basin, with a maximum near Las Vegas, Nevada. The large distance of Kitt Peak from the Colorado River Basin and its southerly position mean that, of the southwestern sites, it will be least affected by the passage of these storms.

During the summer the atmospheric circulation pattern in Arizona is significantly influenced by the Bermuda High. This high, extending aloft far westward over the heated continent, causes Gulf of Mexico air to flow westward into northern Mexico and then curve northward into the southwestern United States. In winter westerly flow predominates and no moist Gulf air reaches the Southwest.

The intense heating of the desert region around Yuma also plays a role in the summer air flow by producing a semipermanent "thermal low" there that aids in drawing in the moist recurving Gulf air. In the Kitt Peak region summer thunderstorms forming in the Gulf air are common in July and August, but are less frequent in September and relatively rare in June when the "monsoon" flow is not yet established.

2.42. *Thermal profiles.*—The diurnal temperature range has importance in the selection of an observatory site. First of all, temperature changes during the night should be small, in order to preserve the mirror figure. Second, the diurnal range should be small, to prevent overheating the dome in the daytime.

Measurements at several heights are necessary. During the daytime the temperature at ground level may rise 10°–30°. The free-air temperature, i.e., 30–60 feet above the terrain, normally does not show such a striking temperature rise. Mountain summits have been found to show very low diurnal temperature ranges and stable night temperatures. An elevation difference of a thousand feet or more is often enough to insure good thermal stability. Small rises on plateaus generally show large temperature drops during the night.

2.43. *Vapor trails and cirrus.*—Condensation trails from aircraft constitute a real nuisance in the southwestern United States. Actually "contrail" formation does not show as marked a geographic variation as casual observation might indicate. The apparent frequency of contrails in the Southwest is due in part to the high frequency of otherwise clear skies.

The upper-air condition during the passage of a high-pressure system shows a progression from stable to unstable conditions. During the stable phase high-altitude aircraft produce only temporary vapor trails. As saturation is approached, the vapor trails become stable contrails. Often the contrail acts as a catalyst and causes large areas of the sky to be covered with cirrostratus. Although contrails precede the natural influx of cirrus formations, several nights of otherwise photometric skies may be lost.

The problem of contrails is likely to increase in the future. One may reduce it by selecting a site on the southwest border of the country. The northern Arizona sites lie along the heavily traveled transcontinental air routes, with their increasing numbers of jet flights. Kitt Peak, to the south of this, stands relatively clear of such interference. However, freedom from local contrail formation does not mean freedom from the cirrostratus resulting from contrails elsewhere. Cirrus clouds are rather stable; contrails formed over the heavily traveled skies over Southern California and the approaches can affect Arizona sites, even the southern ones.

2.44. *Jet stream.*—The mean position of the winter jet stream is across the tip of lower California. Secondary flows occur in winter across the United States, but the principal jet stream is almost entirely in Mexico. During the summer, the mean position of the jet stream is along the Canadian border. As a consequence, during the fall and spring the jet stream crosses the United States frequently.

The jet stream has cirrus associated with it. The belt of "fair-weather" cirrus is 50–500 miles wide and principally on the southern side of the jet stream. Clear weather generally lies on the northern side of the jet stream.

2.45. *Air pollution.*—The distribution of pollutants depends chiefly on the low-level air trajectories. A pall of smog due to the large copper smelters in central and eastern Arizona is often visible at Kitt Peak along the northern horizon. Since the prevailing low-level air flow is from the south, the region of Kitt Peak, is kept free. Smoke from forest fires in Southern California shows a similar pattern; it drifts into Arizona in the belt between Phoenix and Las Vegas.

Dust may form in nearby agricultural areas but will usually be carried away along low-level trajectories and not affect the higher elevations.

2.46. *Haze.*—Daytime heating of the earth's surface produces a convective zone in the atmosphere. The depth of this zone depends on the actual and the adiabatic lapse rates. In early morning the atmosphere is usually stable or superstable when an inversion layer of cold air rests on the desert floor.

In winter, radiation-caused inversions are comparatively strong and the ground heating weak, so that convective mixing during the day is delayed or even absent. The convective layer is then usually 2000–4000 feet deep over the Arizona desert and 1000–2000 feet deep over snow-covered uplands.

In summer, the inversion layer due to radiative cooling is weak or absent and the ground heating more intense and of longer duration, so that the convective layer in mid-afternoon can reach from 10,000 to 20,000 feet in depth. In both summer and winter the depth of the convective zone is clearly indicated by a sharp upper boundary of haze or cloud elements.

The natural haze represented by the convective layer is weak or strong, depending principally on the humidity. A very hazy day (visibility less than 15 miles) shows no significant difference in the number of condensation nuclei from a very clear day (visibility more than 100 miles); the principal difference is the high relative humidity on hazy days.

One may question whether the depth of the haze layer is less over an isolated mountain than over an extended plateau of the same altitude. The author has made observations on this question over the southwestern United States principally from the air. From a distance the haze layer appears to bulge upward over an extended plateau, but not by as much as the elevation difference. Visibility downward is better over the plateau, which is not surprising, since the desert floor is viewed through more atmosphere. The scattering within the deeper layer over the desert also lowers the apparent contrast of the desert terrain.

Quantitative data on the haze level were collected visually. Conspicuous landmarks were selected at ranges of about 60 miles distance. Several months of observations showed that there was little systematic difference between plateaus and isolated mountains of the same heights. To the unaided eye, the sky at Kitt Peak appeared whiter than on the plateau, but this must be an optical illusion caused by the ocean of air below the horizon at Kitt Peak and the tree-limited horizon on the plateau.

2.47. *Sky darkness.*—In the absence of artificial lights, the brightness of the night sky depends on the albedo of the earth and the luminance arising from the airglow and scattered starlight. The airglow is composed of line emissions, molecular bands, and a continuum. At times the lines and bands are enhanced by factors up to 10^3 by auroral activity. The integrated flux of the normal airglow is relatively constant, although the intensities of certain of the forbidden atomic lines vary by factors of 5–10. The green line λ 5577 shows such variations (Roach 1960), and this is noticed even visually. Recent studies by Roach of both the line emission and the integrated emission show that, in the absence of auroral activity, there is no appreciable latitude effect over the region of the site tests. The probability of auroral enhancement of sky light is higher for the northern sites.

The effect of ground albedo can be large. Snow-covered ground will have an albedo of 0.6–0.7 against the normal value of 0.1–0.3. The high albedo of snow reduces the exposure time required for airglow spectra and, by the same token, is a disadvantage for observations of very faint stars. This factor favors southerly sites.

2.48. *City effects.*—The chief effect of a city is the sky glow, though in some cases also the production of smog. At Kitt Peak the sky glow from Tucson is appreciable on the northeast horizon only. The glow can be traced spectroscopically to about 10° altitude. Most of the city itself is hidden from view by the Tucson Mountains, west of the city. At present, the city's growth potential is limited by the availability of water and is directed eastward because of the Tucson Mountains. For the foreseeable future there appears to be no serious threat to the astronomical conditions on Kitt Peak.

REFERENCES

CHANDRASEKHAR, S.	1952	*M.N.*, **112**, 475–483.
DOUGLASS, A. E.	1936	Carnegie Inst. Wash. Publ. 289, Part III.
GARDINER, A. J., GIF- FORD, F., JR., MITCH- ELL, R. E., GICLAS, H. L., JOHNSON, H. L., and WILSON, A. G.	1957	Final Report, Contract AF 19(604)-953, Lowell Observatory, AFCRC.
KELLER, G.	1953	*A.J.*, **58**, 113–125.
LITTLE, C. G.	1951	*M.N.*, **111**, 289–302.
MIKESELL, A. H., HOAG A. A., and HALL, J. S.	1951	*J. Opt. Soc. America*, **41**, 689–695.
ROACH, F. E.	1960	*J. Geophys. Res.* **65**, 1495–97.

CHAPTER 11

Radio Telescopes

J. G. BOLTON
California Institute of Technology

1. INTRODUCTION

THIS chapter is intended primarily as a guide to radio telescopes already in use or in construction, for radio observations of stars and galaxies. Radio instruments for solar work have been described by Wild (1953) in a companion volume, and instrumentation for meteor studies has been discussed by Lovell and Clegg (1952). Here we are concerned only with the antenna section of the radio telescope, its astronomical requirements, and the methods adopted to meet those requirements. An adequate description of the physical principles of both antenna and receiver which comprise a complete radio installation has been given by Pawsey and Bracewell (1955).

A casual glance through the illustrations in this chapter will show the enormous diversity among the structures that constitute radio telescopes. This diversity is due to two reasons—the tremendous range of the radio spectrum over which astronomical observations are possible and the fundamentally low resolving power of the radio instruments.

Radio observations of astronomical interest are made in the wave-length range from 1 cm to 15 meters. At the long-wave-length end of the spectrum, a limit to observation is imposed by absorption of extra-terrestrial signals in the ionized layers of the upper atmosphere and at the short-wave-length end partly by instrumentation and partly by absorption in the lower atmosphere. Radio telescopes fall into two broad classes—arrays and reflectors. A radio reflector is the analogue of an optical reflector; the energy is concentrated at the focus, where it is picked up by a "feed" for amplification in a radio receiver. In arrays the energy from a large number of individual collecting elements is added together via a network of cables or transmission lines connected to the receiver input. In either case, the receiver receives the integrated energy collected by the telescope over a solid angle determined by the aperture of the telescope

ᴀᴛᴇ I.—The original Mills Cross near Sydney, Australia. This antenna has a pencil beam about 50′ between half-power
s and operates at a wave length of 3.7 meters.

PLATE IIa.—The Dipole elements in part of the north-south arm of the Mills Cross

PLATE IIb.—One of the remotely operated phase changers between two sections of transmission lines

PLATE III.—General view of the Christiansen Cross, showing one arm of reflectors, the twin-wire feeders and phase changers (*under covers*)

PLATE IV.—The multielement interferometer at Nançay, France

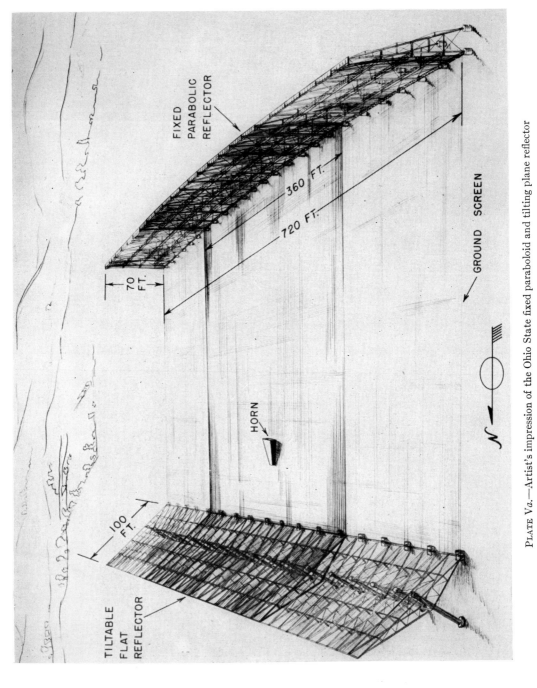

PLATE Va.—Artist's impression of the Ohio State fixed paraboloid and tilting plane reflector

PLATE V*b*.—Scale model of the Ohio State telescope used at a wave length of 1 cm. for solar observations

PLATE V*c*.—Air view of Ohio State University 360-ft. standing parabola radio telescope showing completed parabola and tiltable flat reflector. In this view, taken late in 1959, the telescope is complete except for installation of conducting ground plane and feed system at the prime focus.

PLATE XIII.—The Naval Research Laboratory 84-foot reflector at Riverside, Maryland, U.S.A. (U.S. Navy photograph

PLATE XII.—The 60-foot reflector of Harvard College Observatory

PLATE XI.—The 250-foot reflector at Jodrell Bank, England

PLATE X.—The 83-foot reflector at Stockert Mountain, Germany

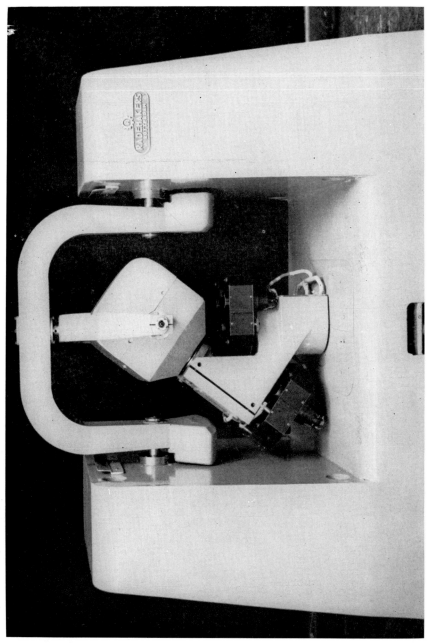

PLATE IX. —The co-ordinate converter used with the Netherlands 83-foot reflector

PLATE VIII.—The 83-foot reflector at Dwingeloo, Netherlands

PLATE VII.—The 50-foot reflector of the United States Naval Research Laboratory. (U.S. Navy photograph.)

PLATE VI.—Fixed section of the Cambridge 160-Mc/s aperture synthesis interferometer

PLATE XIV.—The Howard E. Tatel 85-foot radio telescope of the National Radio Observatory at Greenbank, West Virginia.

PLATE XV.—One of the two 90-foot telescopes of the California Institute of Technology in the Owens Valley, Californ

and the wave length. The telescope has a reception sensitivity pattern whose half-power points in a given direction are virtually determined by wave length/ aperture. The sensitivity pattern can be computed on standard diffraction theory. Generally, the "illumination" or effective use of the aperture is tapered to the edges, in order to avoid undue sensitivity in the secondary diffraction side lobes. In arrays such tapering is usually achieved by attenuating the amplitude of the signal received from outer elements, in reflectors by a suitable choice of feed.

2. INTERFEROMETERS

2.1. GENERAL PRINCIPLES

In the early days of radio astronomy, almost all observations on radio stars were made with interferometers. Nowadays, for many purposes, large arrays and reflectors have replaced the interferometer; however, some forms of inter-

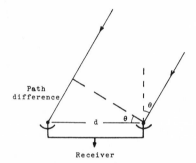

FIG. 1.—The simple two-element interferometer

ferometer are still used for positional work, and interferometers are necessary for the measurement of small angular diameters. It is planned to use the largest steerable reflector in existence—the 250-foot at Manchester—as one element of an interferometer for angular size work. The two steerable reflectors, 90 feet in diameter, under construction for the California Institute of Technology will also be used for the determination of angular diameters at centimeter and decimeter wave lengths. A limited discussion of interferometry deserves a place in this chapter both because of its historical importance in radio astronomy and for its part in the development of techniques that have been carried over into the design of certain arrays.

The simple interferometer consists of two antennae spaced some distance apart, connected by lengths of cable to a central receiver. The path difference of the antennae in the rays from a source is $d \sin \theta$, and the phase difference $(2\pi/\lambda)d \sin \theta$ (Fig. 1). Interference minima occur where

$$\frac{2\pi}{\lambda} d \sin \theta = 2n\pi ,$$

and maxima where

$$\frac{2\pi}{\lambda} d \sin \theta = \frac{2n+1}{2} \pi \qquad (n = 0, 1, 2, \text{etc}) .$$

A sinusoidal pattern whose envelope is due to the sensitivity pattern of one of the individual antennae is recorded as a source passes through the fringe system. Provided that the interferometer is correctly collimated—i.e., the antennae are on a level east-west base line and the receiver is connected to the electrical center of the cable—the right ascension of a source can be found from the time of occurrence of the central maximum. The declination can be determined from a knowledge of the wave length, the separation of the antennae, and the fringe period. A complete account of the simple method and the determination of experimental errors has been given by Mills and Thomas (1951) and an account of refinements of the simple technique by Smith (1952).

The angular diameter of a radio star is determined from observations over a wide range of antenna spacings. As the base line of the interferometer is increased and the angular separation of the fringes approaches the size of the source, various sections of the source occur in different parts of a fringe, and thus the amplitude of the fringe, or the fringe visibility, gradually diminishes. For a source whose brightness distribution is that of a uniform strip perpendicular to the antenna base line, the visibility is zero for a fringe separation equal to that of the strip. In nature, more complex brightness distributions occur; these can be determined from the variation of fringe visibility and phase with antenna base line. The radio method is a complete analogue of Michelson's method of measuring stellar diameters, although the physical separations of the antennae are very much greater than those of Michelson's mirrors. In order to measure angular diameters of a minute of arc or less at meter wave lengths, base lines of the order of tens of miles are required. Here radio links instead of cables are used to transmit the received signals to a central station. For complete details of these techniques, the reader is referred to a paper by Mills (1953).

2.2. PHASE SWITCHING AND ELIMINATION OF BACKGROUND

The initial observations of radio stars were made with antennae and receiving equipment such that the angular size of the star was small compared with the resolving power of the antenna and the signal from the star was small compared with the total signal. Use of interference techniques made possible both the separation of a small signal from the background and the recognition of a discrete object. Figure 2, *a*, illustrates the types of observation made with a single antenna fixed in space; the effect of a bright radio star is barely discernible as a slight bulge in the total signal variation with time. In Figure 2, *b*, a representation of the same observation made with a two-element interferometer, the bright star becomes clearly visible, as does a fainter object not distinguishable in *a*. Such a receiving system, in which the background signal occurs in the recorded output, is known as a *total-power receiver*. In order to see fainter stars, the output must be further amplified and/or antenna elements of higher collecting area, and thus resolving power, used. In either case, the slope of the background is increased to an undesirable extent. The best solution to the problem of background elimination was provided by Ryle (1952), who devised the *phase-switching* technique. Here the receiver is alternately connected to two points, a quarter wave length apart, on the antenna interconnecting cable. This has the effect of switching the interference fringes through half a fringe width (Fig. 3). The output of the receiver is fed into a synchronous detector, and only the difference in receiver output in the two switched positions is recorded. Neither the receiver noise nor the background galactic noise appears in the recorded output (Fig. 2, *c*). Phase switching can be achieved at various stages in a superheterodyne receiver, either in the radio-frequency stages, the

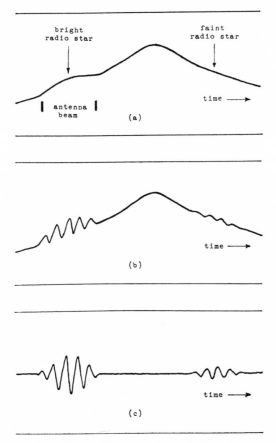

FIG. 2.—*a*) Radio star and general background of galactic radiation as seen with a fixed antenna and a total-power receiver. *b*) The same observation with a two-element interferometer and a total-power receiver. *c*) The same observation as 2, *b* but with phase-switching.

local oscillator stages, or the intermediate-frequency stages. The last two alter-
natives require two mixers but are generally preferred, as the effects of the
phase switch are not reflected into the antennae and any transients produced
by the switches are subject to less amplification.

2.3. Fringe Swinging

Fringe swinging or rotation can also be achieved by introducing continuous
phase changes in either radio-frequency, intermediate-frequency, or oscillator
stages and has been used for a variety of purposes. It was first employed by
Payne-Scott and Little (1951) in a fast interferometer for the determination of

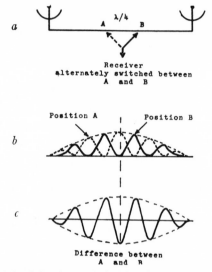

Fig. 3.—The principle of the phase-switched interferometer. *a*) Alternate connections between antenna and receiver. *b*) Spatial fringe patterns with receiver connected to *A* and *B*.
c) Difference between patterns with two alternate connections. Receiver noise and galactic
background noise are same for both connections and thus do not appear in the difference
recorded at the receiver output.

position of rapidly changing solar disturbances. Bolton, Westfold, Stanley, and
Slee (1953) used a slow fringe rotation for the study of sources of large angular
extent. In this case the natural rate of transit of the fringe system by the source
due to the earth's rotation had to be increased to avoid complications due to
changes in orientation of the object.

A further need for fringe rotation arises in work with long-base-line interferometers. Depending on the ratio of the signal from a star to other background
and system noise, detection of the signal requires a finite time of observation or
output time constant. Detection of an interference pattern becomes difficult,
therefore, when the angular separation of the fringes becomes so small that the
star passes through a fringe in a time comparable with the necessary time constant. Observations can still be made if the fringe system is caused to move

from east to west at a rate slightly higher or lower than that of the star. Such a system has been used by Hanbury Brown (unpublished).

2.4. DOUBLE INTERFEROMETERS

Two systems have been used in which two-dimensional interference patterns were produced by two interferometer systems mutually at right angles. Both systems were such that the fringe separations in the two dimensions were quite different. Bolton, Westfold, Stanley, and Slee (1953) used two fairly closely spaced antennae along a cliff edge as a phase-switched interferometer in combination with the Lloyd's mirror interference system due to the sea. The angu-

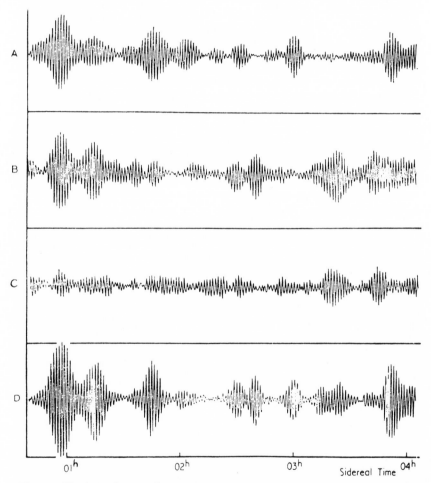

FIG. 4.—"Confusion" in interferometry. A typical set of records on adjacent declinations obtained with the large interferometer at Cambridge. The pattern of greatest amplitude (*extreme left*) is due to a radio star about one hundred times fainter than the brightest known (Cass-A). (Ryle and Hewish 1955.)

lar separation of the sea interference fringes was much smaller than the fringes due to the other system. This permitted the discrimination of objects intermediate in size between the fringe separations of the two interference patterns.

Ryle and Hewish (1955) used a similar system consisting of four antennae which were directly connected in pairs (either north-south or east-west), followed by a phase-switching interconnection of the pairs. The east-west separation was considerably greater than the north-south separation. The system was used with the east-west pairs directly connected for the detection of large-diameter sources and with the north-south pairs directly connected to improve the discrimination in declination when the instrument was used for a survey of the distribution of radio stars.

2.5. CONFUSION IN INTERFEROMETRY

The true or usable resolving power of an interferometer is a complex thing. An interferometer possesses a primary resolving power due to the individual antenna element and a secondary resolving power which depends on the separation of the two elements. The secondary resolving power is properly realized only in the study of objects which can be considered sufficiently isolated. Reasonable isolation may occur for a variety of reasons, as, for instance, in the case of an object which is several orders of magnitude brighter than any other within the primary beam of the individual antenna (e.g., the sun at decimeter wave lengths). Alternatively, an object may be virtually isolated because it is the only one in the primary beam of an interferometer that has an angular size smaller than the fringe separation.

Under circumstances in which isolation is not complete, the output of an interferometer is a sinusoidal pattern due to the sum of the effects of a large number of objects within the primary beam. In such a case, "confusion" is said to exist. An example of confusion is shown in Figure 4, which is a reproduction of patterns of adjacent regions as seen by the large Cambridge interferometer. From records such as these it is impossible to sort out the effects due to all the faint objects contributing to the pattern, and, even in the case of relatively bright objects, confusion may cause errors in the positions deduced from the complex patterns.

This situation has led to a trend away from simple interferometers for such work as the statistics of radio-star distribution and toward the construction of large arrays.

3. LARGE ARRAYS

3.1. AIM OF ARRAYS

In building large optical telescopes, the main aim is to achieve a large collecting surface. Little gain results from the high resolving power because of atmospheric scintillation. In the centimeter- and decimeter-wave-length region of the radio spectrum, advantage can be taken of both the resolving power and the collecting area of large antennae except in the case of certain solar observations

where the area is unnecessary. However, in the meter-wave-length region, receiver sensitivities and radio-star luminosities are such that, with quite small
antennae, more objects can be detected than can be resolved by the instrument.
Both the sensitivity of the whole receiving system and the resolving power of
the antenna vary directly as the area of the antenna, if the antenna is of a conventional type. For a normal isotropic distribution of radio stars, the distance to
which stars are detectable varies as the square root of the sensitivity, the number detectable as the volume of space out to that distance and hence as the $\frac{3}{2}$
power of the sensitivity or area. The number discernible, however, depends
directly on the resolving power and thus on the area. This means that, as the
area of the antenna is increased, the number of stars detectable increases faster
than the number discernible. Thus great advantage can be taken of antennae
designed so that a higher resolving power is obtained than the physical area
would suggest.

3.2. The Mills Cross

Ryle (1952) first pointed out that an effective gain in resolving power can be
obtained with an interferometer consisting of two dissimilar primary antennae
—one, say, with a narrow beam in the east-west direction and the other with a
narrow beam in the north-south direction. No interference can result in directions where the sensitivity pattern of either antenna is zero. In the actual case
of a phase-switched interferometer considered by Ryle, the resulting power-
sensitivity diagram of the interferometer is due to the product of the voltage-
sensitivity patterns of the two elements. The next logical step was made by Mills
and Little (1953), who proposed that if the two elements had a common electrical and physical center (virtually an interferometer of zero spacing), a pencil-
beam antenna would result. Such an antenna is now known as a *Mills Cross*,
and a number have been built, and several others are projected. The original
cross, built for a wave length of 3.7 meters, is shown in Plate I. It consists of
two arms, each of 250 elements fed from transmission lines. The east-west arm
has a fan-shaped beam about $\frac{1}{2}°$ wide in the north-south direction and some 60°
wide in the east-west. Similarly, the north-south arm has a fan beam narrow
in the east-west direction. Phase switching between the two arms produces an
effective beam given by the product of the voltage-sensitivity patterns (shaded
cone in Fig. 5). The direction of the east-west fan beam and hence the altitude
of the pencil beam can be altered by changing the relative phases of the elements
in the north-south arm. Plug-in tapping points are provided at tenth wave-
length intervals along the transmission line for this purpose. Changing the
beam direction involves moving the tap of each of the 250 elements and takes
over an hour. Small direction changes of ± 20 and ± 40 minutes can be made
by changing the phase of some ten separate groups of elements with remotely
operated phase changers between these groups. Plate II*a* shows the construction of the dipole elements in part of the north-south arm, and Plate II*b* shows

one of the remotely operated phase changers between two sections of the transmission line.

For general survey purposes at relatively low sensitivity, the cross is operated
with the beam in each of five close positions for a period of the order of 10
seconds. A typical record from this type of operation is shown in Figure 6, *a*,
and the reduced data gained by plotting each fifth point in Figure 6, *b*. Figure
6, *c*, shows a typical record obtained without the beam switching.

The Mills Cross achieves a resolving power equivalent to an antenna of dimensions equal to a square array whose sides are the length of the arms but
whose collecting area is only the physical area of the arms. A price, however,
has to be paid for this low-cost resolving power. This price appears principally

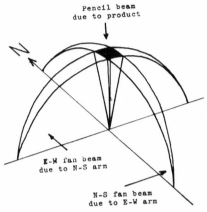

Fig. 5.—The principle of the Mills Cross. The east-west fan beam is produced by the north-
south array and vice versa. The pencil beam indicated by the blacked-in cone is formed by the
product of the two fan beams.

in the side lobes of the array. In a normal array where the full aperture is filled
or in a reflector, the power-sensitivity pattern results from squaring values in
the voltage diffraction pattern, whereas in the cross the power-sensitivity pattern is given by the product of the values in the voltage diffraction patterns
of the two arms. Thus a side lobe of the complete array, which has a relative
voltage level of 0.1 in the pattern of the east-west arm, has a relative power
level of 0.1 when it coincides with the main beam of the north-south arm. A
thermodynamic argument may be used to show that the average value of the
product pattern over the complete solid angle must be zero; in other words,
the main pencil beam and the side lobes in the same or positive sense must
be balanced by the negative side lobes. While tapering of the feed of the individual arms can reduce the positive side lobes to a significant extent, the negative side lobes must remain. The best that can be done is to design for an
extremely slow amplitude response over the side lobes.

The Mills Cross is an extremely effective antenna, in that it achieves high

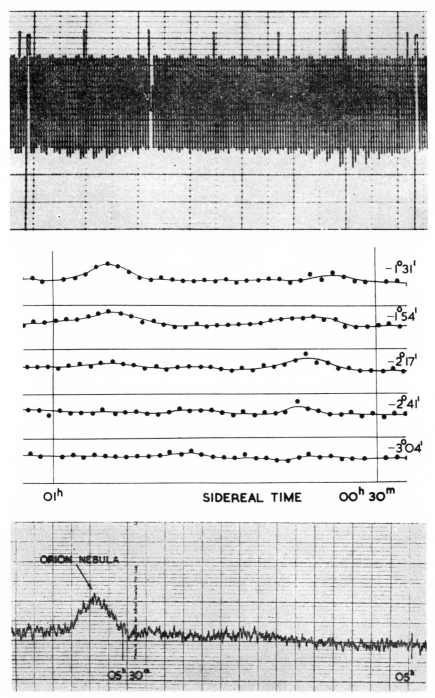

SIDEREAL TIME   OO^h 30^m

FIG. 6.—*a*) Typical observation with the Mills Cross in which the beam position is switched between five positions 20′ apart. *b*) Reconstruction of the observations for each of the five beam positions. *c*) Typical observation with the beam in the fixed position.

resolving power at relatively low cost. In its original form it has several disadvantages: (i) it is a fixed-frequency array—only a very small variation can be
made in the operating frequency in order to avoid, say, terrestrial interference;
(ii) the collinear feed and large number of elements make it inherently narrow-
banded; (iii) considerable labor is involved in changing the beam position.

3.3. THE CHRISTIANSEN CROSS

This antenna represents a development of the Mills Cross principle for the
decimeter-wave-length range and is intended primarily for solar observations.
However, minor modifications would permit its use for measurements on radio
stars; it would be particularly useful for the determination of brightness distribution on objects larger than 3 minutes of arc. The resolving power achieved in
the Christiansen Cross is an order of magnitude higher than that in the 85
Mc/s Mills Cross, and it can be fairly easily steered in both co-ordinates.

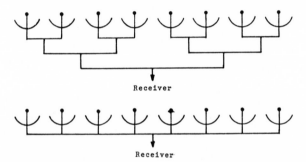

FIG. 7.—a) A collinear feed system as used in the Mills Cross. This gives different feed
lengths from each element to the receiver and thus restricts the band width of the array even
for a wave front normal to the array. b) A branching feed system as used in the Christiansen
Cross and the Nançay multielement interferometer. For a wave front normal to the array there
is no band-width restriction on the receiver.

The individual elements of the cross are parabolic reflectors, 20 feet in
diameter, mounted on rather simple equatorial mountings. There are thirty-
two reflectors in each arm of the cross, and the reflectors are all driven together
by an ingenious system of cables and ratchets. The motive power for tracking
the sun during the day is provided by the potential energy stored in a large
concrete block which is elevated during the night by a small electric motor.
A general view of the array is shown in Plate III.

The thirty-two reflectors in each arm are electrically connected by a branching feeder system (Fig. 7), so that the electrical path length from each reflector
to the center of the array is the same. This system involves considerably higher
losses of power than in the collinear system as used by Mills, but it permits a
much wider receiver band width and a change of basic operating frequency if
required. Remotely operated phase shifters are provided between adjacent
antennae in the north-south arm, in order to change the beam position in alti-

tude or declination. These phase shifters can be seen in Plate III under the
covers between each reflector. Also visible are the twin-wire feeders and the
control wires.

The array is at present used at a wave length of 20 cm; thus the beam width
of the individual reflectors is of the order of $2\frac{1}{2}°$. The antennae are spaced 400
feet apart, making the total arm length 1240 feet. Each arm produces a series
of knife-edge beams about 3 minutes wide separated by 1°. The combination
of the two arms thus gives rise to a series of pencil beams at the intersections
of the two series of knife-edge beams (Fig. 8).

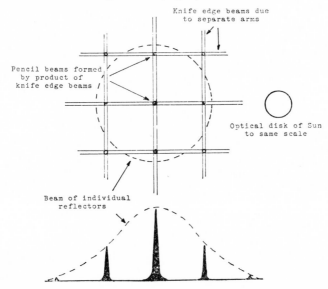

Fig. 8.—Illustration of the production of multiple pencil beams in the Christiansen Cross
and their relation to the envelope pattern or pattern of the individual reflectors.

In making solar observations, the normal procedure is to let the sun drift
through one of the pencil beams and then change the phasing in the north-
south arm so that an adjacent strip on the sun is scanned. For observations
near the zenith, a band width of several megacycles per second can be used.
For observations well away from the zenith, the band width has to be reduced
so that no deterioration of the antenna beam results from different path lengths
from a source to different parts of the array.

3.4. The Nançay Multielement Interferometer

As pointed out in the last section, the use of a branching feeder network to
interconnect the elements in the arms of a cross has the advantage of permitting
the use of wider receiver band widths. This is offset by the disadvantage of a
much greater loss in the feeder system. This loss can be eliminated if preamplifiers are used near the individual elements or groups of elements. The principal

difficulty with preamplifiers lies in their lack of reliability, particularly in regard to the stability of the phase change through the amplifier. This problem has been successfully tackled by Blum, Boischot, and Ginat at Nançay, France (1956), in the construction of a grating or multielement interferometer similar to the original Christiansen multielement interferometer (Christiansen and Warburton, 1953) or one arm of the Christiansen Cross. The Nançay array consists of thirty-two 16-foot reflectors, spaced 165 feet apart along a 1-mile base line (see Pl. IV). The frequency at present in use is 170 Mc/s, and the band width is 7 Mc/s. The antennae are connected in pairs at sixteen preamplifiers contained in temperature-controlled inclosures. These preamplifiers are connected in turn to a single receiver through a branching feeder network consisting of special air-cored coaxial cables, which are buried several feet underground to minimize variations in temperature which would change the electrical lengths. It is estimated that the variations in electrical length from the various antennae to the receiver are less than one-tenth of a wave length.

The beam pattern of the Nançay grating consists of a series of knife-edges of $3'.8$ separated by $2°$, within the envelope pattern of the individual elements (beam width to half-power $\sim25°$). The reflectors are mounted so that they can be moved only in altitude; thus observations are limited to near the meridian.

The instrument has so far been used mainly for solar observations, but the sensitivity is such that about fifty radio stars can be detected. Observations of about ten have been made; typical records of the radio stars Cygnus A and Hydra A are shown in Figure 9.

3.5. THE OHIO STATE TELESCOPE

A limited but very useful amount of work has been done by compromise antennae consisting of fixed reflectors with feed masts that can be tilted to direct the beam. Of particular note are the 250-foot fixed reflector in Manchester, operated in the wave length of 2–7 meters, and the 80-foot reflector in Sydney, operated in the range 20–75 cm. Such reflectors are of considerable value for the investigation of limited regions of the sky which pass close to the reflector axis. For a focal ratio of 0.5 the efficiency of the antenna is little affected with off-axis angles equivalent to something of the order of 7 beam widths; however, beyond this, performance deteriorates rapidly, and coma effects become very serious.

A new approach to this type of instrument has been made by Kraus and Nash (1955), who are constructing a fixed paraboloid combined with a tiltable plane reflector for changing altitude or declination (see Pl. Va). A 12-foot scale model (Pl. Vb), operating at a wave length of 1 cm, has been successfully tested on the sun. Incoming radiation within a narrow beam is deflected by the plane reflector to the parabolic reflector and thence to the feed horn at the focus. A limited amount of steering in azimuth can be achieved by changing the position

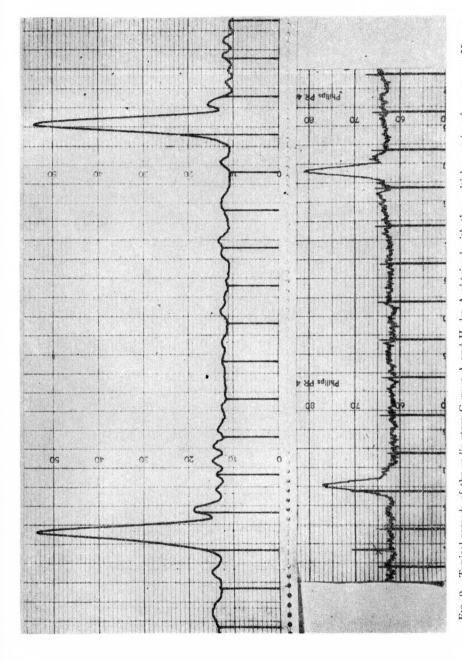

FIG. 9.—Typical records of the radio stars Cygnus A and Hydra A obtained with the multielement interferometer at Nançay, France.

of this feed horn. The reflecting plane is sufficiently large to permit 100 per cent use of the full aperture of the paraboloid between declinations $\pm 40°$ (70 per cent of the sky). Vertical polarization is used; the ground between the horn feed and the fixed reflector has to be covered with reflecting mesh to act as an image plane.

The Ohio design represents a considerable improvement on the original fixed reflector and tilting mast. The coverage in declination is much greater, and there are no coma difficulties associated with changes in tilt angle. The surface accuracy of the plane and standing reflectors has to be greater than in the case of a steerable reflector, as two reflections are involved. Even so, difficulties in obtaining the necessary accuracy are probably fewer than those involved in maintaining the figure of a fully steerable reflector, and monitoring is very much simpler. As the feed horn and reflector are firmly secured to the ground, no changes can occur in their relative positions. This telescope provides high resolving power at a fairly low cost; its principal use will probably be to work on spectra of radio stars at wave lengths longer than 40 cm, and possibly in the statistics of the distribution of radio stars. A view of the completed 360-foot parabola is found in Plate Vc.

3.6. APERTURE SYNTHESIS

The history of radio astronomy at the meter wave lengths is also the history of the struggle for ever increasing resolving power. The development of the Mills Cross represents one phase of this struggle, and undoubtedly there is more to be gained by the construction of larger and more refined crosses. Larger crosses involve either narrower band widths or larger feeder losses, depending on the type of feed. The problem of off-axis band-width restrictions becomes more important. The solution of these problems in terms of preamplifiers, bulk phase correctors, etc., means that the complexity, maintenance difficulties, and initial costs begin to increase far faster than the resolving power, as in the case of large steerable reflectors.

A new approach to the problem of large arrays has recently been made by Ryle (1957) and the Cambridge Radio Astronomy group in what they term "aperture synthesis." The fundamental principles are not new; in an early paper on the radiation from sunspots, McCready, Pawsey, and Payne-Scott (1947) pointed out that the one-dimensional brightness distribution across a source could be obtained from Fourier synthesis of measurements from a series of interferometer observations at many different spacings. Such a procedure has been followed in the determination of the brightness distributions of a number of effectively isolated radio sources. The more general problem of the analysis of a continuous complex distribution in two dimensions has been discussed from both the theoretical and the practical standpoint by a number of writers. However, the manual processing and reduction of the data posed such an impossibly laborious program that no action along these lines had been taken until the present Cambridge attempt. Here it is proposed to use the university's high-speed electronic digital computer EDSAC to process the data.

Two instruments using the aperture-synthesis principle are under construction at the new Mullard Radio Astronomy Observatory. One, operating at a frequency of 25 Mc/s, will produce a pencil beam in a manner equivalent to the Mills Cross, and the other, operating at a frequency of 160 Mc/s, will produce the equivalent of an interferometer consisting of two large square apertures. Each instrument is made up of a fixed rectangular aperture aligned east-west and a small movable section which will be used over a range of positions along a north-south line, as in Figure 10. A view of the fixed section of the 160 Mc/s instrument is shown in Plate VI.

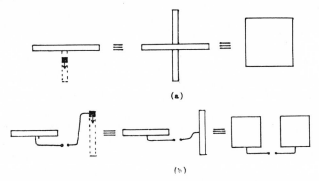

(a)

(b)

Fig. 10.—a) Aperture synthesis of a Mills Cross or its equivalent filled-aperture antenna b) Aperture synthesis of an interferometric cross or its equivalent.

In making observations with the aperture-synthesis system, both the movable and the fixed antennae are set for a particular declination. A series of phase-switched records is then made, with the movable antenna occupying, in turn, the various locations along the north-south line. The envelope pattern of the combination of the two antennae is given by the product of the two separate voltage patterns. Processing in the computer gives a result, as seen by a synthesized antenna beam, formed by the product of the voltage pattern of the fixed antenna and the equivalent of an antenna covering all the positions occupied by the movable section. The position of the synthesized beam within the envelope pattern can be varied by introducing phase corrections into the computer. Thus the time necessary to observe a given range in declination is the same as that required with the equivalent Mills Cross, and the observation can be accomplished without the labor involved in changing the beam direction of the cross.

Amplitude and phase relations have to be carefully preserved between individual observations for any given declination setting. It should be possible to provide sufficient calibration against purely instrumental variations, but ionospheric scintillation and refraction effects may prove troublesome. The net result of minor variations produced by either source would be to give a synthesized beam somewhat larger than the theoretical expectation.

4. STEERABLE REFLECTORS

4.1. NECESSITY OF STEERABLE REFLECTORS

The most desirable form of radio telescope is the steerable reflector. Such a telescope has none of the restriction of an array, such as limited frequency, band width, or difficulty of position changing. For wave lengths below 50 cm, it is almost a necessity, for stellar and galactic investigations require collecting area, as well as resolving power, and in many cases tracking of an object or region is desirable. With the ever increasing sensitivity of receivers in the microwave range due to improvements in conventional receivers and new advances, such as the traveling-wave tube and the maser, it is likely that much routine work, such as the determination of position or brightness distribution of radio stars, will in the future be carried out with large reflectors working in the microwave range rather than arrays and interferometers in the meter-wave-length range. This is certainly the trend in the United States; here it is probably stimulated by three factors: first, the relative freedom from terrestrial interference at the shorter wave length; second, the advances in specialized receiving tubes; and, third, the relatively greater financial resources. There is no doubt that a large reflector for the centimeter-wave-length range is more expensive than a large array for the meter-wave-length range; however, the higher initial cost is probably offset by a longer working life and greater versatility.

A number of the larger reflectors that are in operation, under construction, or about to be built are illustrated in the following pages. There is a great diversity in the forms which these telescopes and their mountings assume. Each one represents some compromise between electrical design, mechanical design, coverage, and financial resources. The designer of a radio telescope faces at least one problem that is not present in the case of an optical telescope, and that is the wind loading. Radio telescopes are much too large to be inclosed in protecting domes, and thus the same instrument that requires high precision in the surface and drive mechanism has to resist destructive loads due to high winds and, at times, ice.

4.2. DESIGN CRITERIA

The principal parameters under consideration in the design of a large reflector are as follows: (i) diameter, (ii) surface accuracy, (iii) focal ratio, (iv) type of mounting and coverage, (v) drive and tracking system.

Most of the requirements on these parameters are strongly interrelated. For example, it is usual to choose a certain diameter and a certain minimum wave length of operation. The wave length determines the nature of the surface and surface tolerances. The ratio of the minimum wave length to aperture determines the minimum beam width, which in turn determines the necessary drive accuracy and the tolerance on maintenance of the position of feed at the focus. This whole series is in turn affected by the maximum wind velocity at which it is desired to operate. Often the design of a particular instrument starts with a series of most desirable performance specifications which are relaxed one by one as the engineering difficulties or cost prevents their fulfilment. The main factors involved in performance specifications are as follows:

4.21. *Surface accuracy.*—The generally accepted tolerance on surface accuracy is plus or minus one-eighth of the minimum wave length. However, random variation up to plus or minus one-quarter wave length does not affect the beam shape, though there is some loss in forward gain and corresponding increase in side-lobe level.

Not all reflectors have solid surfaces. Depending on circumstances, open-wire mesh, metal strips, or expanded metal form suitable reflecting surfaces. A rough criterion for the permissible openings in such screens is that the length parallel to the electric vector should be less than a quarter of the minimum wave length. The use of an open-wire mesh is advantageous in reducing the wind load on the reflector and thereby reducing the cost of main gear drives and the mounting.

4.22. *Focal ratio and feed support.*—The range of focal ratios now in use is $0.25 < f/D < 0.5$. A deep reflector with the feed in the plane of the aperture has the advantage that it is mechanically strong and the feed supports are short and are less liable to sag. If the aperture of such a reflector is used efficiently, the side-lobe level is small, and there is less likelihood of interfering signals entering the feed directly. However, serious coma occurs for the feed off-axis, and the loss due to cross-polarization is greater than in an instrument of larger focal ratio. The maximum focal ratio now in use in 0.5. Ratios greater than this are unlikely to be used, owing to the complexity of efficient feed systems and structural problems associated in maintaining the position of feed support for all angles of tilt. Most reflectors now under construction have a compromise ratio of 0.4.

The two possible systems for feed support are either a central mast or a system of booms extending from a point beyond the focus to the near edge of the reflector framework. The latter may consist of a tripod, a quadrupod, or a bipod with tension cables in the plane at right angles to the bipod. Both systems, of course, introduce some shielding of the reflector and other effects. A central mast produces shielding of the center section of the reflector, and any distortion of the beam is probably symmetrical. For the non-central type, small side lobes may occur in the plane of the supports. The bipod or tripod is probably more suitable where it is essential to mount heavy receiving equipment really close to the focus. Supports made of dielectric material are used in some reflectors, but so much material is required for large telescopes that the effect on distortion of the beam is probably much the same as the equivalent support in metal.

4.23. *The mounting.*—This is by far the most controversial part in any radio-telescope design. Two types are used, the equatorial and altazimuth. In the latter, motion in equatorial co-ordinates is accomplished by means of an analogue computer or slave. Owing to the size of radio reflectors, in an equatorial mounting with full-sky coverage some cantilevering of the axes is required. Thus a double system of counterweights is needed, and a uniform wind load on the mirror throws a large moment on the right-ascension gears. Undoubtedly, for telescopes with full-sky coverage the structural and mechanical engineering for the equatorial is more complex and costly than for the altazimuth. However, the difference is somewhat offset by the additional cost and complexity of the co-ordinate converter and electrical engineering in the altazimuth. For star tracking, the equatorial system requires only one constant-speed motor; the altazimuth needs the co-ordinate converter system and two motors whose speed is constantly varying. The altazimuth drive system has a dead zone of about 10° near the zenith. The final choice of mounting for a telescope depends perhaps a little on the proposed scientific program, but mainly on the personal inclinations of the designer.

The remainder of this chapter is devoted to brief descriptions of the various large reflectors now in operation or construction and some of the designs for future construction.

4.3. THE NAVAL RESEARCH LABORATORY 50-FOOT REFLECTOR

Diameter—50 feet
Focal ratio—0.5
Surface—solid aluminum
Surface accuracy—±0.03 inch
Feed support—central mast
Beam width at minimum operating wave length—3.2 at $\lambda = 8$ mm.
Mounting—altazimuth
Tracking accuracy—±1.'5
Slewing rate—2° per minute
Maximum operating wind—20 mph
Maximum safe wind in stowed position—in excess of 100 mph
Weight of reflector—30 tons
Total weight of telescope—90 tons
Designer—Ned L. Ashton
Principal contractor—Collins Radio Corporation

This reflector, completed in 1951, was the first of the large steerable reflectors to be built and has a more accurate surface than any built since or yet contemplated. The ratio of minimum operating wave length to aperture, and therefore the minimum beam width, is smaller than any other large reflector. The method adopted in the construction of the reflector is unique; the surface was machined from a series of thirty bolted aluminum castings. These were unbolted for shipment and then reassembled at the site. The main ring truss

supporting the reflector is also made of aluminum; thus, in turn, is connected
to the trunnions and roller bearings which provide the altitude axis. A system
of parallel linkages is used to transform the standard altitude drive of the twin
5-inch gun mounts to the reflector altitude axis. The 5-inch gun mount serves
as a stable base and provides the motion in azimuth. The output of a co-ordinate
converter is transmitted to the mounting from a remote observing position by
selsyns which transmit instructions to a hydraulic servo system. The reflector
is shown in Plate VII. For further technical information the reader is referred
to an article by Sees (1957).

Much valuable work has been done with this instrument, particularly in pio-
neer observations of the radio stars at wave lengths of 3 and 10 cm and in absorption of the continuous spectrum of the radio stars at 21 cm by the interstellar
atomic hydrogen.

4.4. THE NETHERLANDS 83-FOOT REFLECTOR

Diameter—83 feet (25 meters)
Focal ratio—0.5
Surface—square mesh with $\frac{3}{4} \times \frac{3}{4}$-inch openings
Surface accuracy—0.4 inch
Feed support—central mast
Beam width at minimum operating wave length—20' at 10 cm.
Mounting—altazimuth
Tracking accuracy—3'
Slewing rate—20° per minute in azimuth, 5° per minute in altitude
Maximum operating wind—25 mph
Maximum safe wind in stowed position—80 mph
Weight of reflector—18 tons
Total weight of telescope (excluding foundations)—127 tons
Designer—B. G. Hooghoudt and Werkspoor N. V.
Contractors—Werkspoor N. V.

The Netherlands 25-meter reflector (Pl. VIII) has been in operation since
1955 and has been used principally for work on 21-cm line radiation from our
own and other neighboring galaxies. The reflector is of unusual but simple design; it consists of six main trusses, forming in plan a six-pointed star with a
number of subsidiary trusses, again forming triangles and hexagons (see Fig.
11). The surface consists of 1464 facets of flat mesh in supporting frameworks.
The deviation from the required paraboloidal shape due to the individual flat
facets is less than $\frac{1}{8}$ inch. Sets of four facets forming triangles are attached to the
trusswork by means of adjusting screws, about two hundred, so that any deformation in the trusswork due to time can be corrected. This feature has been
followed in several other reflectors, for example, the California Institute of
Technology 90-foot reflectors and in the proposed Associated Universities 140-
foot and Australian 230-foot reflectors, but in most others has been omitted.

The difference in design philosophy on this point appears to be one of whether the designer attempts to make use of the shear strength of the skin or not. If he does, then it is difficult to incorporate surface adjustment. In those reflectors where skin adjustment is provided, the engineers have decided that the main trusswork may suffer some deformation due, for example, to aging or the relief of built-in stresses under very high wind loads. As far as initial cost is concerned, the additional material involved in providing adjustment is probably offset by a reduction in tolerance on the assembly of the trusswork.

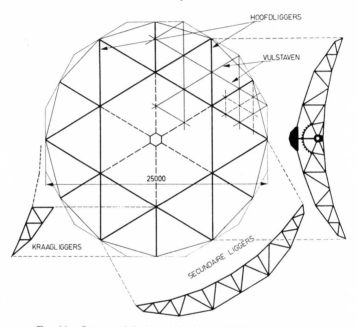

FIG. 11.—Structural design of the 83-foot Netherlands reflector

The feed support in the Netherlands reflector is a single-tube central mast supported by guys. The tube is hinged near the vertex of the reflector, and thus the feed end of the mast can be lowered to near ground level for servicing and alterations.

The co-ordinate converter, illustrated in Plate IX, is similar to that used on the Naval Research Laboratory 50-foot reflector. The converter is situated in the equipment cabin, which rotates about the azimuth axis with the reflector. The over-all pointing error is distributed evenly between the converter (about $0°.02$), the transmission and main gearing ($0°.03$), and deformation in the reflector and feed ($0°.02$). However, random deviations in tracking on a fixed point over an hour or so are an order of magnitude less.

For more detailed information on the Netherlands reflector, the reader is referred to a series of articles by Hooghoudt (1957) and others.

4.5. The German 83-Foot Reflector

Diameter—83 feet
Focal ratio—0.5
Surface—punched aluminum sheet
Surface accuracy—± 0.2 inch
Feed support—central mast
Beam width at minimum operating wave length—20′ at 10 cm.
Mounting—altazimuth
Tracking accuracy—2′
Slewing rate—20° per minute
Maximum operating wind—30 mph
Maximum safe wind in stowed position—100 mph
Weight of reflector—20 tons
Total weight of telescope, including building structure—1200 tons
Designer—Dipl. Ing. Mohr, Cologne
Contractors—Metallwerk Friedrichshafen

The German 25-meter reflector is of fairly conventional design. The basic structure consists of three ring girders and twelve radial trusses, stiffened by interconnecting diagonal members. The entire structure is made of aluminum alloy, apart from the inner ring, which is of steel. This use of two materials of different expansion coefficients is somewhat unique. The surface is punched sheet aluminum with holes 1 cm in diameter, secured to the radial trusses and radial purlins.

The drive gears for both axes are 10 feet in diameter, and special attention has been paid to the machining of the gears. Provision is made for very accurate adjustment of both azimuth and altitude axes; in fact, the azimuth axis can be adjusted to within 2 seconds of arc.

An unusual feature of the telescope is the large concrete building which serves as both the mounting base and the laboratory. Precautions have been taken to avoid angular shifts due to higher temperatures on one side of the building. The telescope is now being used for a program of 21-cm. observations. It is illustrated in Plate X. For a full description see Pederzani (1957).

4.6. The Jodrell Bank 250-Foot Reflector

Diameter—250 feet
Focal ratio—0.25
Surface—solid steel
Surface accuracy—± 1 inch to a radius of 75 feet
Feed support—central mast
Beam width at minimum operating wave length—27′ at 50 cm for whole reflector;
about 15′ at 21 cm for central section
Mounting—altazimuth
Tracking accuracy—12′
Slewing rate—22° per minute in azimuth and altitude

Maximum operating wind—30 mph
Maximum safe wind in stowed position—90 mph
Weight of reflector—700 tons
Total weight of telescope (excluding foundations)—2000 tons
Designer—H. C. Husband
Contractors—English Steel Corporation

The 250-foot reflector at Jodrell Bank (Pl. XI) was one of the first large reflectors conceived and took some seven years to design and build. Originally it was planned to operate at a minimum wave length of 1 meter, with a coarse open-wire mesh as the reflecting surface. The discovery of the 21-cm line in 1951 caused a radical change in the performance specifications and a virtual redesign. It is anticipated that the center section, possibly out to 75-foot radius, will be sufficiently accurate to permit observation at this wave length. The telescope was designed for both radio and radar astronomy, so that a wide variety of tracking rates and motions had to be provided. One of the initial specifications required that the reflector could be completely inverted for work on the feed system. This involved a design in which the reflector was supported from the outer edges; hence the surface is a membrane supported at the rim by an extremely heavy ring truss.

The telescope is mounted on a double circular rail track, 350 feet in diameter. Two towers, 170 feet high, supporting the altitude trunnions, ride on twelve bogies on this track. The towers are joined at the base by a heavy girder system supported on a central pivot which defines the azimuth axis. Driving in azimuth is accomplished through four of the twelve bogies on the rail track and in altitude via two 27-foot racks at the top of the towers.

Support for the reflecting surface is formed by sixteen main radial girders joining the main ring truss to a central hub. Ring purlins at intervals of 3 feet are attached to the main and subsidiary girders. Onto the ring purlins are welded some seven thousand individual steel sheets. The sheets, which are $\frac{1}{12}$ inch thick and measure about 3 feet square, are seam-welded to provide both good electrical conductivity and shear strength. No provision is made for surface adjustments.

The feed is supported on a 50-foot steel tube inside a central mast. With the reflector inverted, the 50-foot tube can be lowered to the ground and replaced with a further tube and feed assembly. Receiving equipment can be placed in a variety of positions. One location is in a small laboratory hung from beneath the reflector; others in the cabins at the top of the towers and another in a main control building some 500 feet from the telescope. In this building are housed the drive controls and analogue computers for conversion of celestial into alt-azimuth co-ordinates and galactic into celestial co-ordinates. A wide range of tracking and automatic scanning motions can be selected in any of the co-ordinate systems.

It is doubtful whether steerable reflectors larger than the Jodrell Bank reflector will be built for some considerable time. This telescope was designed at a time when receiving techniques were such that the main emphasis was on observation in the meter-wave-length range. The steady improvement in receiver techniques at much shorter wave lengths means that the same resolving power and sensitivity can be gained from smaller instruments of higher surface and pointing accuracy.

4.7. The George R. Agassiz 60-Foot Reflector (Harvard)

Diameter—60 feet
Focal ratio—0.42
Surface—$\frac{3}{8} \times \frac{3}{4}$-inch expanded aluminum
Surface accuracy—$\pm \frac{1}{8}$ inch
Feed support—tripod
Beam width at minimum operating wave length—25′ at 10 cm
Mounting—equatorial
Tracking accuracy—$\pm 2'$
Slewing rate—15° per minute
Maximum operating wind—30 mph
Maximum safe wind in stowed position—120 mph
Weight of reflector—4 tons
Total weight of telescope (excluding foundations)—52 tons
Designers—D. S. Kennedy & Co.
Contractors—D. S. Kennedy & Co.

The Harvard 60-foot telescope (Pl. XII) consists of a commercial 60-foot reflector on a specially designed equatorial mounting. It was the first reflector of this order of size to be mounted equatorially. Similar reflectors are used for both scatter communication and radar purposes, often in remote areas. This latter use strongly influenced the design requirements, in that the reflector had to be broken down into small sections for easy transport and handling. The individual pie-shaped sections consist of a framework of aluminum tubes and castings, onto which is welded a series of circular purlins and finally a skin of expanded aluminum. Accurate machining and fitting of the castings insures high accuracy of the reflector when it is finally bolted together at the site. No provision is made for surface adjustment.

The feed-support system consists of a tripod of three Fiberglas spars joined together at a ring in the focal plane. The use of Fiberglas is unique in this and some other telescopes built by the same company.

The declination and right-ascension gears and drive mechanism are housed in a compact unit at the top of a skew-cone steel tower. This use of rather small but accurate drive gears and short axes has been followed in the California Institute of Technology 90-foot design; however, much larger-diameter gears and longer axes are used in other designs. Such gears and axes can theoretically achieve better definition of the axes and drive accuracy, but they involve greater cantilevering of the declination axis and reflector. This in turn produces greater movements due to wind loading on the hour-angle gears and polar-axis bearings and supports.

A similar telescope, but 84 feet in diameter, has been built by the same company for the Naval Research Laboratory at Riverside, Maryland (Pl. XIII). The larger diameter was achieved by some strengthening of the basic 60-foot reflector and the addition of an outer ring section. The focal ratio of the larger reflector is consequently reduced to about 0.3. An instrument similar to this was built for the Dominion Observatory at a site near the Okanagan Valley in British Columbia. It was completed in 1959.

4.8. THE CARNEGIE INSTITUTION OF WASHINGTON 85-FOOT REFLECTOR

Diameter—85 feet
Focal ratio—0.42
Surface accuracy—$\pm\frac{1}{8}$ inch (3 mm)
Feed support—tripod or bipod
Beam width at minimum operating wave length—7' at 3 cm
Mounting—equatorial
Coverage declination—140° from north pole to southern horizon; hour angle ± 6 hours for all declinations except where restricted by southern horizon
Tracking accuracy—30''
Slewing rate—20° per minute
Maximum operating wind—30 mph
Maximum safe wind in stowed position—120 mph (87 mph in any position)
Weight of reflector—30 tons
Total weight of telescope—183 tons
Designers—H. W. Tatel, Blaw-Knox Co.
Contractors—Blaw-Knox Co.

Two 85-foot reflectors of this design have been built, one for the University of Michigan and the other for the United States National Radio Observatory at Greenbank, West Virginia. The design principles are due to the late Dr. Howard Tatel, of the Carnegie Institution of Washington. The mounting is a cantilevered equatorial. Motion in declination is restricted by the mounting to between the north celestial pole and the southern horizon and in hour angle by the hour-angle gear to ±6 hours. A basic feature of the design is the very large hour-angle and declination drive gears, which give high driving accuracy for relatively low tooth accuracy and a low tooth loading during high winds. Nevertheless, wind loads in excess of 60 mph are not taken on the gear teeth but are transferred to a brake system.

Slewing rates of 20° per minute are provided by induction motors and scanning and tracking drives by a variable-speed drive with tachometer feedback.

The feed support consists of a tripod capable of bearing instrument loads of up to 1000 pounds. Axial and lateral adjustments of up to 4 inches are provided. The surface is solid, and adjustments of $\pm\frac{1}{2}$ inch can be made at attachment points to the framework. Adjustments are also provided for both polar and declination axes. Plate XIV shows the 85-foot telescope at Greenbank.

Both the Michigan and Associated Universities reflectors were completed by the end of 1958.

4.9. THE CALIFORNIA INSTITUTE OF TECHNOLOGY 90-FOOT REFLECTORS

Diameter—90 feet

Focal ratio—0.40

Surface—$\frac{3}{8} \times \frac{3}{4}$-inch expanded steel

Surface accuracy—$\pm \frac{1}{4}$ inch

Feed support—bipod

Beam width at minimum operating wave length—18′ at 10 cm

Mounting—equatorial

Coverage declination—north pole to southern horizon; hour angle $\pm$ 4 hours except where limited by southern horizon

Tracking accuracy—0.′5

Slewing rate—10° per minute

Maximum operating wind—20 mph

Maximum safe wind in stowed position—90 mph

Weight of reflector—40 tons

Total weight of telescope—165 tons

Designers—B. H. Rule and C. W. Jones

Contractors—Allison Steel Co., Phoenix, Arizona

Two reflectors, 90 feet in diameter, have been constructed. They are designed to operate either independently or together as an interferometer, the base line of which can be varied by moving the reflectors on a network of rail tracks. As the telescopes were built in country liable to large earth movements, the mobile mountings did not raise additional engineering problems, as full adjustments on leveling, etc., had to be provided.

The principal feature of the California Institute of Technology design is that the declination and polar axes intersect; thus a uniform wind load acting through the intersection of the axes transmits no load to the main gears. The center of gravity of the reflector is fairly close to the declination axis; thus only small counterweights are required, mainly to counterbalance the bipod feed-support system and instrument load at the focus. The price paid for these features is in the smaller coverage of the telescope, which is ± 4 hours over a range of declinations from $+90°$ north to $-50°$ south.

The reflectors consist of a basic tubular framework with a main ring girder and cantilevered radial trusses. This structure is entirely welded. Attached to the main framework are some 36 pie-shaped skin frames consisting of expanded steel on a framework of channel sections. The reflector can be brought into shape by means of three hundred adjusting screws, which have a range of 2 inches and are accessible from the front surface. Plate XV is a photograph of a model which shows the basic structural components.

Adjustments are provided to align the base towers, the polar axis, the declination axis, and the mesh and alignment of all gears.

The drive and control system in this telescope is unique: a single gear train and two-phase servo motor provide all speed ranges for each axis. For tracking, the actual right ascension of the telescope is obtained by comparing the actual hour angle and sidereal time. The difference between this and the desired right ascension gives an error signal, which is amplified in a magnetic amplifier controlling the servo motor. Slewing is achieved by applying fixed voltages to the magnetic amplifiers. The telescope can be equally well controlled by a photoelectric guider or on the signal from a radio star. The servo system should not produce any radio interference such as may well arise from the Ward Leonard system of some other instruments.

The first of these reflectors was completed in July, 1958, the second in September, 1958. The basic framework of the reflectors is strong enough to permit the future use of a solid surface or to extend the diameters to 120 feet with the existing expanded metal surface.

4.10. THE PROPOSED ASSOCIATED UNIVERSITIES' 140-FOOT REFLECTOR

Two telescopes, intermediate in size between the popular 80-foot size and the Jodrell Bank instrument, are at present on the drawing boards. These are the proposed 140-foot reflector for the Associated Universities in the United States and the proposed 230-foot reflector for the C.S.I.R.O.[1] Radiophysics Division in Australia. The following are the performance specifications for the A.U.I. 140-foot reflector:

> Diameter—140 feet
> Focal ratio—0.43
> Surface—solid aluminum
> Surface accuracy— $\pm \frac{1}{4}$ inch
> Feed support—quadrupod
> Beam width at minimum operating wave length—3′ at 3 cm
> Mounting—equatorial
> Coverage declination—full coverage for all declinations south of $23\frac{1}{2}°$ N;
> $\pm$ 8 hours for declination $23\frac{1}{2}°$–90° N
> Tracking accuracy— $\pm$ 20 minutes up to 16 mph over period of 1 hour
> Slewing rate—30° per minute
> Maximum operating wind—30 mph
> Maximum safe wind in stowed position—120 mph (80 mph in any position)
> Weight of reflector—250 tons
> Total weight of telescope (excluding foundation pillar)—1500 tons
> Designer—Ned L. Ashton

This telescope is to be constructed at a site near Greenbank, West Virginia, as part of a national radio observatory for the United States. The telescope is mounted on a huge hollow concrete pillar carried down to rock foundations;

[1] Commonwealth Scientific and Industrial Research Organization.

this pillar will contain adequate space for controls and electronic equipment. The polar axis is formed from a large steel shaft supported on two oil-pad bearings; this is the first use of such bearings in radio telescopes. The yoke supporting the roller bearings of the declination axis and a 45-foot-radius gear forming the hour-angle drive are rigidly attached to the upper end of the polar-axis shaft. The yoke and the declination-axis shaft are also of steel, but the reflector itself is entirely of aluminum. The basic framework for the reflector is a conventional structure of radial and ring trusses. The surface is composed of seventy-two pie-shaped sections of $\frac{1}{4}$-inch aluminum plate with suitable stiffening ribs; these are connected to the main trusses or secondary stringers through adjustable shoes.

Full adjustments are also provided for both the axes, the oil-pad bearings, and the mesh of the hour-angle and declination gear devices. No details are as yet settled on the form of the drives or position-indicating equipment.

4.11. THE PROPOSED AUSTRALIAN 230-FOOT REFLECTOR

Diameter—230 feet
Focal ratio—0.41
Surface—wire mesh, $\frac{1}{2} \times \frac{1}{2}$ inch
Surface accuracy— $\pm \frac{1}{2}$ to ± 1 inch, depending on zenith angle
Feed support—tripod with equipment cabin behind focus
Beam width at minimum operating wave length—6' at 10 cm
Mounting—altazimuth, restricted to zenith angles of less than 60°
Tracking accuracy— $\pm 1'$
Slewing rate—30° per minute
Maximum operating wind—20 mph
Maximum safe wind in stowed position—100 mph
Weight of reflector—330 tons
Total weight of telescope (excluding concrete in pier)—1200 tons
Designers—Freeman and Fox, London

The design for the 230-foot reflector is the result of a design study of large reflectors undertaken by Freeman and Fox to general specifications produced by the C.S.I.R.O. Radiophysics Laboratory. The designers were given the choice of altazimuth or equatorial and chose the altazimuth for its mechanical simplicity and lower cost. The lower cost appears to have been due to the adoption of a very simple but accurate co-ordinate converter. The designers were assisted by the unusually low coverage required in the specifications, i.e., coverage only for zenith angles less than 60°. It was felt that, in view of the large number of radio telescopes being built in the Northern Hemisphere, it was foolish to penalize the design by turning the reflector to the vertical position for observations of a part of the sky well covered by northern instruments.

The reflector framework consists of a central hub to which is attached the altitude axis and drive gears, from which are cantilevered twenty-four radial pipe trusses. The pipes decrease in diameter from the center outward. Over the

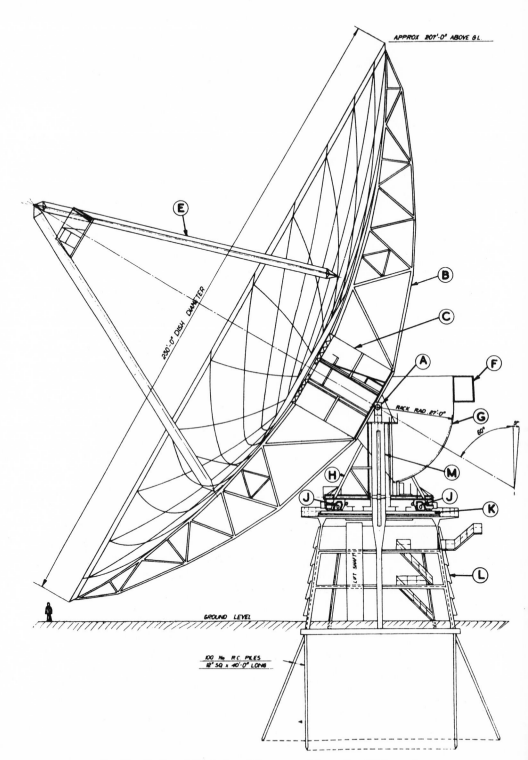

FIG. 12.—Outline of the design of the proposed Australian 230-foot reflector

top of the radial trusses run a system of 24 I-beam purlins in the form of equiangular spirals with a second set of ninety-six lighter members with the spiral in the opposite direction. These two sets of purlins cross at right angles; they provide support for the mesh and contribute about 30 per cent of the bending stiffness and almost all the shear and torsional stiffness of the reflector. To complete the structure, there are four stiffening rings which joint the bottom chords of the radial ribs to each other and the nodes of the spiral-member membrane.

The surface consists of about three thousand approximately square panels of rectangular wire mesh of size ranging from 2 to 5 feet. These panels are welded to light-steel channels supported off the purlins by adjustable studs.

Drive in altitude is to be accomplished through a 27-foot radius rack and pinion and in azimuth through a friction drive onto the azimuth rollers. Drive in equatorial co-ordinates is arranged through a master equatorial unit on a concrete pillar at the intersection of the altitude and azimuth axes. An optical comparison is made between the actual position of the antenna and the desired position set on the master equatorial from a remote-control panel. An error signal is obtained via a flat mirror on the master equatorial, a light-source, photocell, and autocollimator attached to the reflector. The error signal is used to drive a fairly conventional Ward Leonard system. Manual slewing with reference to a slave at the control panel to set the antenna within 1° of the required position is required before the error detector and servo system take control. The master equatorial can be driven at sidereal rate and various scanning rates superimposed. A drawing of the basic structure of the telescope is shown in Figure 12.

5. FUTURE RADIO TELESCOPES

It is difficult to make sure predictions on the most likely developments in radio telescopes. To date, there have been two distinct stages in radio astronomy. The first, covering perhaps the first five years after World War II, was a stage involving a wide range of observation and discovery, much of it with relatively small and crude antennae. In the second stage, still in progress, larger instruments, conceived in most cases for certain specific investigations, have been designed. Many of the large arrays, which can be constructed fairly fast, have been in operation for several years. A few of the large reflectors have been in operation for a year or more, but many more will be completed in the next year. Only the results of investigations with the present generation of telescopes can really define the needs in future instruments. Nevertheless, it is safe to say that there will be a demand for increased resolving power, and thus physical sizes will continue to increase.

While certain investigations require observations in definite regions of the radio spectrum, it is probable that greater use will be made of the higher frequencies for investigations such as the determination of position and angular size of the radio stars. The principal reason for this is the steady improvement in receiver sensitivity at the high frequencies due to such devices as the wideband traveling-wave amplifier and the maser. The disadvantage of a lower signal level is offset by the greater receiver band width, freedom from man-made interference, and more easily achieved primary resolving power.

The development of receiving devices in the millimeter and submillimeter range may well lead to the construction of relatively small, but highly accurate, steerable reflectors. Such telescopes would be of great value in investigation of planetary atmospheres and surfaces and in the study of emission and planetary nebulae in the regions of the galaxy inaccessible in the visual range.

At the very long wave lengths, where, for instance, studies of the radio stars can provide valuable information on the absorption due to tenuous interstellar ionized hydrogen, telescopes of the Mills Cross type will very probably be employed. If experience proves that Ryle's aperture-synthesis idea is successful in practice, this will greatly reduce such difficulties as the narrow off-axis band width and maneuverability of the cross.

Application of the cross principle may very well be extended into the 30-cm to 1-meter range for radio-star investigations. G. J. Stanley has recently proposed to the author that the individual elements of such an array should be helixes. The helical antenna has the advantage that the phase between individual elements can be changed by rotation; at the same time, it is broad-banded and has a considerably larger effective area than the dipole and reflector. At these wave lengths, feeder and transmission-line losses are serious; so preamplifiers would be required, each one serving a number of elements. The pencil beam of such an array could be directed or tracked very simply by mechanical rotation of the helixes.

Steerable reflectors in the range of 500 feet in diameter are already being discussed by some workers in the field, but the engineering and financial difficulties are enormous. For some purposes, fixed low-cost reflectors of this size may well be constructed at various latitudes for specific purposes. For instance, a 500-foot reflector would have sufficient resolving power at 21 cm to permit study of the hydrogen-line radiation from the individual spiral arms of M31. Location of a fixed reflector with a range in declination (from feed tilt) of 3° or 4° at latitudes of 41° would be extremely valuable for such a study.

6. TABLES OF MAJOR RADIO TELESCOPES

TABLE 1

Major Radio Telescopes Excluding Steerable Reflectors

Location	Controlling Organization	Type and Aperture	Wave Length of Operation	Status
Washington, D.C., U.S.A.	Carnegie Institution of Washington	Mills Cross, 1500 feet	14 meters	In operation (completed 1954)
Sydney, Australia	Radiophysics Laboratory, C.S.I.R.O.	Mills Cross, 3500 feet	10 meters	In operation (completed 1957)
Cambridge, England	Cambridge University	Synthesized Cross, 3200 feet	8 meters	In operation (completed 1958)
Sydney, Australia	Radiophysics Laboratory, C.S.I.R.O.	Mills Cross, 1500 feet	3.5 meters	In operation (completed 1952)
Cambridge, England	Cambridge University	Four-element interferometer; 4 elements 320×40 feet	3.7 and 1.7 meters	Completed 1951; now being dismantled
Cambridge, England	Cambridge University	Synthesized interferometer, 1500 feet	1.7 meters	In operation (completed 1958)
Manchester, England	Manchester University	Fixed paraboloid, 220 feet	1.7–10 meters	In operation (completed 1949)
Nançay, France	Paris Observatory	Multielement interferometer, 5000 feet	1.6 meters	In operation (completed 1956)
Columbus, Ohio, U.S.A.	Ohio State University	Helix array, 160×22 feet	1–1.5 meters	In operation (completed 1952)
Washington, D.C., U.S.A.	Carnegie Institution of Washington	Linear array, 3000 feet	1 meter	In operation (completed 1959)
Serpukhov (near Moscow), U.S.S.R.	Lebedev Institute	Mills Cross 3200 feet	1 meter	Under construction (to be completed 1962)
Danville, Ill., U.S.A.	University of Illinois	Fixed paraboloid cylinder, 400×600 feet	49.1 cm. (611 Mc/s)	In operation (completed 1962)
Columbus, Ohio, U.S.A.	Ohio State University	Fixed paraboloid and tilting plane, 70×700 feet	40 cm–4 meters	Under construction (half to be completed in 1960)
Sydney, Australia	Radiophysics Laboratory, C.S.I.R.O.	Cross,* 1240 feet	20 cm	In operation (completed 1957)
Palo Alto, California, U.S.A.	Stanford University	Cross,* 350 feet	10 cm	In operation (completed 1959)
Pulkova, U.S.S.R.	Pulkova Observatory	Sliced paraboloid, 350×10 feet	10 cm	In operation (completed 1958)
Ottawa, Canada	National Research Council	Compound interferometer*	10 cm	In operation (first stage completed 1951, additions since)

* Principally intended for solar observation.

TABLE 2

MAJOR RADIO TELESCOPES OF THE STEERABLE REFLECTOR TYPE

Location	Controlling Organization	Diameter (Feet)	Type of Mounting	Status
Jodrell Bank, England............	Manchester University	250	Altazimuth	In operation (completed 1957)
Sydney, Australia...............	Radiophysics Laboratory, C.S.I.R.O.	230	Altazimuth	Under construction (to be completed 1961)
Greenbank, West Virginia, U.S.A.........	National Science Foundation through Associated Universities	140	Equatorial	Construction (to be completed 1962)
Owens Valley, California, U.S.A...........	California Institute of Technology	Two 90	Equatorial	In operation (completed 1958)
Ann Arbor, Michigan, U.S.A...........	Michigan University	85	Equatorial	In operation (completed 1959)
Okanagan Valley, British Columbia, Canada.....	Dominion Observatory	84	Equatorial	In operation (completed 1959)
Riverside, Maryland, U.S.A............	U.S. Naval Research Laboratory	84	Equatorial	In operation (completed 1957)
Greenbank, West Virginia, U.S.A............	National Science Foundation through Associated Universities	84	Equatorial	In operation (completed 1959)
Malvern, England.............	Royal Radar Establishment	Two 83	Altazimuth	In operation (completed 1960)
Dwingeloo, Netherlands.........	Leiden Observatory	83	Altazimuth	In operation (completed 1955)
Stockert Mountain (near Bonn), Germany.	Bonn University	83	Altazimuth	In operation (completed 1956)
Serpukhov (near Moscow), U.S.S.R.......	Lebedev Institute	72	Altazimuth	In operation (completed 1959)
Cambridge, Massachusetts, U.S.A.......	Harvard Observatory	60	Equatorial	In operation (completed 1956)
Washington, D.C., U.S.A...........	Carnegie Institution of Washington	60	Equatorial	Completed 1960
Washington, D.C., U.S.A...........	U.S. Naval Research Laboratory	50	Altazimuth	In operation (completed 1951)

REFERENCES

Many of the telescopes mentioned in this chapter have been described in detail in the January, 1958, issue of the *Proceedings of the Institute of Radio Engineers*. This issue also contains many articles devoted to instrumentation and analysis.

BOLTON, J. G., WESTFOLD, K. C., STANLEY, G. J., and SLEE, O. B.   1953   *Australian J. Phys.*, 6, 434.

BLUM, E. J., BOISCHOT, A., and GINAT, N.   1956   *C.R., Acad. Sci., Paris* 244, 1326.

CHRISTIANSEN, W. N., and WARBURTON, J. A.   1953   *Australian J. Phys.*, 6, 190.

HOOGHOUDT, B. G.   1957   *Ingenieur*, No. 3.

KRAUS, J. D., and NASH, R. T.   1955   *Ohio State U. Radio Obs. Rep.*, No. 5.

LOVELL, A. C. B., and CLEGG, J. A.   1952   *Radio Astronomy* (London: Chapman & Hall).

McCREADY, L. L., PAWSEY, J. L., and PAYNE-SCOTT, R.   1947   *Proc. R. Soc. London, A*, 190, 357.

MILLS, B. Y.   1953   *Australian J. Phys.*, 6, 452.

MILLS, B. Y., and LITTLE, A. G.   1953   *Australian J. Phys.*, 6, 272.

MILLS, B. Y., and THOMAS, R. N.   1951   *Australian J. Sci. Res. A*, 4, 158.

PAWSEY, J. L., and BRACEWELL, R. N.   1955   *Radio Astronomy* (Oxford: Clarendon Press).

PAYNE-SCOTT, R., and LITTLE, A. G.   1951   *Australian J. Sci. Res. A*, 2, 214.

PEDERZANI, T.   1957   *Elec. Engineering*, 76, 196.

RYLE, M.   1952   *Proc. R. Soc. London, A*, 211, 351.
                1957   *Nature*, 180, 110.

RYLE, M., and HEWISH, A.   1955   *Mem. R.A.S.*, 67, 97.

SEES, J. EDWIN   1957   *N.R.L. Report.*

SMITH, F. G.   1952   *M.N.*, 112, 497.

WILD, J. P.   1953   *The Sun* (Chicago: University of Chicago Press), p. 676.

CHAPTER 12

Radio-Astronomy Radiometers and Their Calibration

FRANK D. DRAKE

National Radio Astronomy Observatory, Green Bank, West Virginia

1. INTRODUCTION

THE function of the radio-astronomy radiometer is to measure accurately the radio power collected by the antenna in the desired frequency band. This could be done by conventional radio receivers, if it were not that the receiver output power due to cosmic radiation would be far less, in most cases, than the noise power created by the receiver itself. Since both the cosmic power and the receiver noise power have random noise wave forms, a device is needed which can separate accurately a very small random noise power from a much larger one. This difficult requirement is always met by surrounding a high-quality receiver with peripheral circuitry whose purpose is to remove the effects of internal receiver noise as much as possible. The resulting configuration is called a *radiometer*.

The radiometer performs many functions in addition to achieving its primary goal. It must select the band of frequencies to be observed and reject thoroughly all other bands of frequencies, especially those on which man-made interference may be expected. It must amplify the radio power provided by the antenna to a level consistent with the needs of its final recording device. These requirements are generally met by the high-quality conventional receiver. Finally, the recording device must provide measurements of the observed cosmic power level in a form convenient for analysis. In the past, moving-chart pen recorders have been almost universally used for this purpose, but at present most observatories are rapidly converting to digital methods of data presentation.

The terminology used with radiometers is quite standard throughout the radio-astronomy field and is thoroughly described in Pawsey and Bracewell

(1955). The *power*, P_{in}, collected by a radio telescope, when pointed at a radio source of sufficiently small angular size, is

$$P_{in} = \frac{SAB}{2},$$
(1)

where S is the flux density of the radio source at the frequency observed, in watts m^{-2} (c/s)$^{-1}$; A is the effective collecting area of the antenna, which is usually less than the true geometric area of the antenna; B is the bandwidth over which the radiometer accepts power; and the factor of $\frac{1}{2}$ appears because a conventional feed arrangement accepts only one polarization, thus, at best, only half the energy impinging on the antenna, if the polarization of the source is random.

The *brightness temperature*, T_B, is defined by the relation

$$\frac{2kT_B}{\lambda^2} = \lim_{\Delta\Omega \to 0} \frac{\Delta S}{\Delta\Omega},$$
(2)

where λ is the wave length, k is the Boltzmann constant, $\Delta\Omega$ is an increment of solid angle, and ΔS is the flux density from $\Delta\Omega$. This definition is derived from the Rayleigh-Jeans approximation to Planck's law, which is almost always appropriate in radio astronomy. By this definition, the brightness temperature is the temperature that the increment of solid angle on the sky would require to give the observed flux density, from the solid-angle increment, assuming the sky to be a black body. Of course, since the sky is not a black body, the brightness temperature of any point on the sky varies with frequency.

The *antenna temperature*, T_A, is defined by the relation

$$T_A = \frac{P_{in}}{kB}.$$
(3)

This definition has its roots in the fact that the power radiated into a transmission line from a resistor, electrically matched to the line, is kBT, where in this case T is the temperature of the resistor. Thus the antenna temperature is the temperature to which a matched resistor would have to be raised to provide as much power as is provided by the antenna. Antenna temperatures may range from a few degrees at centimeter wave lengths to many millions of degrees at wave lengths of tens of meters. The change in antenna temperature as the faintest detectable radio sources pass through the beam of a radio telescope may be of the order of 0.1° K.

The *excess receiver noise temperature* is a measure of the noisiness of the receiver used in a radiometer. In general practice, the figure usually published is actually that for the entire radiometer rather than that of the receiver portion of the radiometer. In defining quantitatively the excess receiver noise temperature, we imagine that the receiver generates no noise within itself, and a matched resistor at a temperature of 290° K is connected across the receiver-input terminals. The excess receiver noise temperature then is the further increase in resistor temperature that would be required to produce the same noise level in the receiver output as is present when the true receiver is terminated at its input by a 290° K matched resistor.*

The excess receiver noise temperature, T_R, can be expressed mathematically in several ways. Assume that the receiver has a matched 290° K resistor at its input. Then

$$T_R = \frac{P}{kBG} - 290°\,\mathrm{K}, \tag{4}$$

where, in this case, P = the receiver noise power level at a point where the over-all receiver gain to that point is G. Or,

$$T_R = (F - 1)\,290°\,\mathrm{K}, \tag{5}$$

where F = the conventional receiver-noise figure (cf. Pawsey and Bracewell 1955).

For conventional receivers, T_R ranges from about 10,000° K at short centimeter wave lengths to about 200° K at meter wave lengths. As will be discussed, at present, maser amplifiers give values of T_R as low as 50° K over the entire microwave region, with values less than 10° K probably attainable.

At most radio-astronomy frequencies, T_R is measured with the arrangement of Figure 1. A gas-discharge noise source, generally an argon tube, is substituted for the antenna. The argon gas-discharge source simulates with great stability an antenna temperature, T_{ns}, of about 10,000° K. When the source is not conducting, the receiver sees the resistive termination beyond the tube only, which should be at a temperature of 290° K. The measurement is made by first noting the reading of the output meter when the noise source is turned off. The noise source is turned on, which increases the output noise level, and the attenuation of the variable attenuator is increased by a factor Y until the output meter reads as it did in the beginning. This method releases one from the need to know the characteristics of the receiver detector, which are usually non-linear and complicated. We then have

$$290 + T_R = \frac{T_{ns} + T_R}{Y},$$

* The value 290° is convenient and has been made standard by definition.

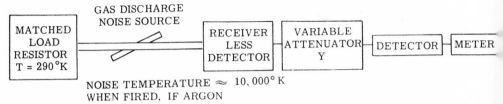

FIG. 1.—Experimental setup for the measurement of excess receiver noise temperature.

from which

$$T_R = \frac{T_{ns} - 290\,Y}{Y - 1}. \tag{6}$$

In an otherwise perfectly built receiver, the significance of T_R is that it determines the best sensitivity available from the system, or *the minimum detectable signal*. Since the concept of "minimum detectable signal" is so important in radio astronomy, it is discussed in detail in section 3.

2. STANDARD RADIOMETER CONFIGURATIONS

The four standard radiometer configurations described below include almost all the radiometers in use today.

2.1. THE DIRECT RADIOMETER

The direct radiometer is the most obvious radiometer design. A block diagram is shown in Figure 2. If the receiver output is linear in power, the power output will be given by

$$P_{\text{out}} = GkB\,(T_A + T_R), \tag{7}$$

where G is the over-all receiver gain. In the direct radiometer, an auxiliary circuit produces a stable direct-current (DC) reference power, whose value is adjusted to $GkBT_R$. This power and the receiver output power are inserted into a differencing circuit, from which emerges the difference between the two powers. This will be $GkBT_A$. Thus the constant component of receiver noise is eliminated, and only the noise power from the antenna and variations in receiver noise appear in the input to the data-recording device.

The great disadvantage in this arrangement is that G must be held highly constant. Because the ratio T_A/T_R is usually quite low, small changes in G have the same effect in P_{out} as quite large changes in T_A, as is readily seen from equation (7). Thus a small change in G can produce a spurious change in the final data which is equivalent to quite a large change in T_A.

As an example, with a receiver having $T_R = 1000°$ K, one might be trying to detect increments of antenna temperature $\Delta T_A = 0.1°$ K, which would not be masked by the noise fluctuations in most modern receivers. In such a case

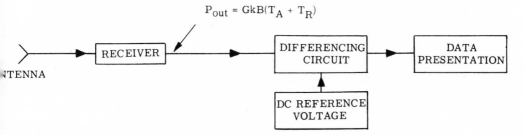

FIG. 2.—Block diagram of basic direct radiometer

the gain must not vary by more than one part in 10^4 if we are to avoid the observation of spurious signals caused by gain changes alone. Such high standards are difficult to meet in practice and generally require that extremely stable, expensive power supplies be used for the entire radiometer. Furthermore, it is usually necessary to hold the radiometer component temperatures within a very small range, possibly only 0.01° K, over periods as long as a day to achieve the required stability. A given variation in ambient temperature usually produces a much larger variation in the recorded ΔT_A in the direct radiometers used today.

2.2. THE DIRECT-CURRENT COMPARISON RADIOMETER

This is a variation of the direct radiometer used in 21-cm observations and was first proposed by Selove (1954). In this radiometer the final stages of the receiver are altered in the way shown in Figure 3. Filters are used to select two channels from the receiver band pass, one in the 21-cm band and the other outside the 21-cm band but closely adjacent to it. One band is called the "signal band," which we shall denote by the subscript h. The other is the "comparison band," to be denoted by subscript c. The latter is usually made much broader than the signal band, as this minimizes fluctuations due to noise. The receiver now has two outputs, at which

$$P_h = G_h k B_h \left(T_{Rh} + T_{A\,\text{cont}} + T_{21\text{-cm}} \right) , \quad \text{and} \quad P_c = G_c k B_c \left(T_{Rc} + T_{A\,\text{cont}} \right) .$$

Here $T_{A\,\text{cont}}$ is the antenna temperature due to continuous radiation, which we assume to be the same in both bands (this is because of the small percentage frequency separation between bands), and $T_{21\text{-cm}}$ is the antenna temperature due to 21-cm radiation. We now either tune the receiver so that neither band falls at 21-cm line frequencies or point the antenna at a part of the sky where $T_{21\text{-cm}} = 0$ and adjust G_h and/or G_c so that

$$G_h k B_h \left(T_{Rh} + T_{A\,\text{cont}} \right) = G_c k B_c \left(T_{Rc} + T_{A\,\text{cont}} \right) . \tag{8}$$

Now, when P_h and P_c are introduced into the differencing circuit, the only thing that emerges is $G_h k B_h T_{21\text{-cm}}$. Thus the receiver rejects the constant components of receiver noise and also continuous noise from the antenna.

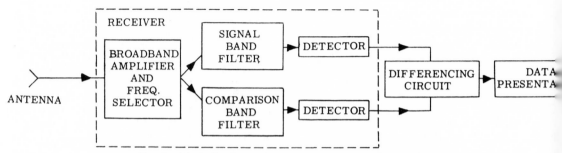

FIG. 3.—Block diagram of basic direct-current comparison radiometer

It is quite important to note, however, that the rejection of continuous noise may not be complete. From equation (8), if $T_{Rh} = T_{Rc}$,

$$G_h B = G_c B_c .$$

In such a case, no matter what the value of $T_{A\ cont}$ becomes as a result of discrete sources entering the antenna beam, etc., the total power in each band due to the continuous emission is the same and is eliminated completely in the differencing circuit. It is to be expected that $T_{Rc} = T_{Rh}$ because of the small percentage difference in the radio frequencies of the two bands. However, circuitry often causes a small difference between T_{Rh} or T_{Rc} (or between F_h and F_c), in which case

$$G_h B_h \neq G_c B_c$$

if equation (8) is to hold. In such an event, a change in $T_{A\ cont}$ will not cause an equal change in the power levels in the signal and comparison bands. There will then be a net output from the differencing circuit whenever there is a change in the continuous noise from the antenna. Thus the passage of a discrete radio source through the antenna beam, a change in the amount of radiation received by the antenna from the ground, etc., can cause a change in output which imitates a true 21-cm signal. This effect is sometimes called "total power pulling" and is often difficult to detect. It has been the cause of several spurious results in 21-cm radio astronomy.

In most 21-cm receivers, provisions are made to tune the received frequency slowly across the 21-cm frequency band. This is usually achieved by tuning the frequency of one of the local oscillators in the superheterodyne receiver. Tunable local oscillators are often unstable in frequency, which is undesirable. It is generally required that the local oscillator not wander more than a few kilocycles per second, equivalent to a few tenths of a kilometer a second in radial velocity. This often results in complex local oscillator designs employing such circuits as frequency multiplier and addition circuits.

Invariably there is incorporated in the 21-cm receiver a means of measuring the frequency being observed. The usual way of doing this is to generate a large number of calibration frequencies from a high-stability oscillator whose frequency is checked regularly against one of the standard-frequency radio transmissions. These calibration frequencies are then heterodyned with the local oscillator frequency or one of its subharmonics. Equality of the calibration and local oscillator-derived frequencies is easily noted when zero frequency audio beat notes occur in the mixture of frequencies. A simple calculation then determines the actual frequency being observed.

The DC comparison radiometer is quite effective, as it is very insensitive to changes in receiver gain. Its main weakness is toward changes in receiver gain that are not the same in both channels. This can result from a change in receiver ambient temperature, which will alter the dimensions in the tuned circuits of the receiver, shifting the resonant points and causing an over-all change in the shape of the receiver band pass. Ambient temperature changes usually make unequal changes in the gain–band-width products of the filters also. Therefore, it is necessary with these receivers to stabilize the ambient temperature to a very high degree. Since the electrical power levels in the electronic circuitry determine component temperatures, high-stability power supplies must again be used. Thus in the DC comparison radiometer, as in the direct radiometer, simplicity in design is purchased at the price of expensive power supplies and temperature-stabilizing devices.

2.3. THE DICKE RADIOMETER

A means of overcoming both the effect of receiver noise and some of the effect of gain variations was published by Dicke in 1946. The method used in the Dicke radiometer is to switch the receiver input periodically from the antenna to a resistive load, thereby causing the antenna output power to enter the receiver in pulses. The receiver output is fed to a device called a "phase-sensitive detector" or "synchronous detector." The synchronous detector responds only to pulses of power in phase with the switch and produces a DC output whose magnitude is proportional to the amplitude of the synchronous signal. Since the receiver noise is not pulsed, the synchronous detector does not respond to it. Receiver-gain variations should then affect only the measured amplitude of the cosmic signal. A short discussion of these devices is contained in MacRae (1948). The best up-to-date descriptions of these devices are in the advertising brochures of the commercial firms which manufacture them.

The block diagram of the Dicke radiometer is shown in Figure 4. It is evident that the input to the receiver will consist of a constant noise level plus a square pulsed noise signal whose peak-to-peak intensity is

$$kB \, (T_A - T_L) \, .$$

The receiver output is a large constant noise signal plus a square pulsed signal of peak-to-peak amplitude,

$$GkB \, (T_A - T_L) \, . \tag{9}$$

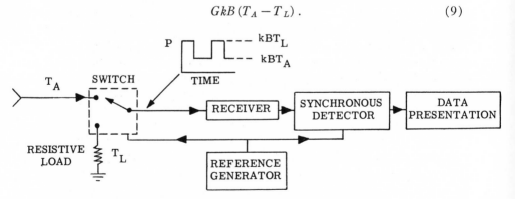

FIG. 4.—Block diagram of basic Dicke radiometer

The output of the synchronous detector to the data-presentation device is a DC voltage whose amplitude is proportional to $T_A - T_L$.

One should recognize that this radiometer does not eliminate the effect of fluctuations in the receiver noise. Since the receiver noise is random, it occasionally generates a series of pulses that are synchronized with the synchronous detector. This, of course, produces a wander in the output, and it can be shown that this wander is just as much as would occur with a direct radiometer of the same T_R and B. In fact, since the output fluctuations are the same as in the direct radiometer, but half the power received from the antenna is being rejected by the switch, the signal/noise ratio, or sensitivity, is actually a factor of 2 worse than with the direct radiometer. Furthermore, the radiometer is measuring the temperature of the load resistor just as much as the antenna temperature. Thus the temperature of the load resistor must not be allowed to vary more than a small fraction of the value of ΔT_A being searched for and should not vary more than the antenna temperature equivalent to the noise fluctuations in the output.

Gain variations can still have serious effects in the Dicke radiometer. Consider a radiometer operating at centimeter wave lengths, where T_A may be only a few degrees. If the load resistor is being operated near room temperature, $T_A - T_L$ will be of the order of 300° K. From relation (9), a 1 per cent change in gain, typical of radio receivers, may produce as much change in the radiometer output as a 3° K change in T_A. A Dicke radiometer which can theoretically detect 0.01° K., now possible, must have a gain stability of better than 1 part in 10^4 if theoretical sensitivity is to be achieved.

This places about as heavy a burden on the receiver as in the direct radiometer, but in this case there is another solution. If T_L can be made nearly the same as T_A, the problem will be eliminated. This was first tried by Ryle and Vonberg (1948), who replaced the load resistor with a diode noise source. The diode noise source generates an amount of noise which may be calculated directly from the current through the diode. Ryle and Vonberg used the radiometer in a servo loop in which the receiver output controlled the current through the diode noise source. The servo acted to make the radiometer output zero. Thus the radiometer continuously kept the noise temperature of the diode noise source the same as the antenna temperature. The antenna temperature was calculated from the diode current, and receiver gain variations caused no undesirable effects whatsoever. However, this technique is useful only at lower frequencies, where T_A is greater than ambient, because the noise source can never produce a noise temperature less than its physical temperature.

The Naval Research Laboratory radio-astronomy group (Mayer, McCullough, and Sloanaker 1958) have attacked this problem by replacing the load resistor with a small feed horn pointed at the sky. The horn should have about the same antenna temperature as the main antenna beam, since they are both observing about the same brightness temperature. This arrangement has been quite successful. A weakness which occasionally causes difficulty is the wide reception pattern of the small horn. This can result in pickup of radiation from the ground and can lead to the ready reception of any sources of radio inter-ference.

Another method of making T_A nearly equal to T_L at microwave frequencies was described by Drake and Ewen (1958). In this approach, called *noise compen-sation*, noise is deliberately added to the antenna power output to raise T_A to the value of T_L. The block diagram of a noise-compensated radiometer is shown in Figure 5. Noise from a gas-discharge tube is attenuated and injected into the transmission line from the antenna through a directional coupler. The variable attenuator is then adjusted until $T_A \approx T_L$, and the observations are made with no further attenuator adjustment. The addition of noise to the system will increase the noise fluctuations somewhat. However, in the applica-tion where this technique is widely used—namely, with traveling-wave tube radiometers—the increase in fluctuations is negligible.

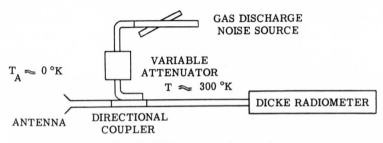

FIG. 5.—Noise compensation circuit

A practical problem in the Dicke radiometer is to obtain high-quality switches to place in front of the radiometer. The switch must provide good isolation between the load and the antenna and not attenuate the signal signifi-cantly. Furthermore, as the switched connection moves from load to antenna, the changing impedance presented to the receiver must not cause undesirable effects, such as electrical oscillation or large electrical transients. Either of these may produce spurious output signals or cut the receiver off so strongly that it does not recover to normal operation before the next switching transient occurs. Occasionally it is necessary to "gate" the receiver, or turn it off while the switching operation is occurring. At the present time, switches using Fara-day rotation in ferrite materials give best performance at wave lengths of about 10 cm and less, while, at longer wave lengths, mechanical switches and switches constructed from crystal diodes are to be preferred.

The most serious disadvantage of the Dicke radiometer is that it admits the signal power only half the time, so that half the energy gathered by the antenna is wasted. Nevertheless, the Dicke radiometer's strong defenses against electron-ic component instabilities have given it great popularity.

2.4. THE SWITCHED-FREQUENCY RADIOMETER

The switched-frequency radiometer is a variation of the Dicke radiometer used for 21-cm observations. A typical block diagram is shown in Figure 6. In this radiometer, instead of switching from antenna to a load, the radiometer switches the frequency it is receiving. In 21-cm work the received frequency is periodically switched from a 21-cm line signal frequency to a nearby comparison frequency outside the line. This is normally done by switching the first local oscillator frequency in the superheterodyne receiver used, as indicated in Figure 6. At the signal frequency, the receiver output power is

$$G_s kB \left(T_{Rs} + T_{A \, \mathrm{cont}} + T_{A \, 21\text{-cm}} \right),$$

while at the comparison frequency the output power is

$$G_c kB \left(T_{Rc} + T_{A \, \mathrm{cont}} \right).$$

If the receiver is operated properly, $G_c = G_s$, $T_{Rs} = T_{Rc}$, and a pulsed wave will leave the receiver output with intensity

$$GkBT_{A \, 21\text{-cm}}.$$

The output of the synchronous detector will be proportional only to the strength of the 21-cm line power from the antenna. Since the radiometer sees very nearly the same antenna temperature in both switch positions, the need to balance the input temperatures does not exist.

If $G_s \neq G_c$, total power pulling can occur, as with the DC comparison radiometer. This condition can come about if the antenna presents a different impedance on the two frequencies observed or if the mixer impedance changes as a result of the change in local oscillator frequency. The latter can quite easily happen if the local oscillator output power, and thus the mixer current, are different at the two local oscillator frequencies. The mixer is a non-linear device, and any change in the current through it will markedly change its impedance.

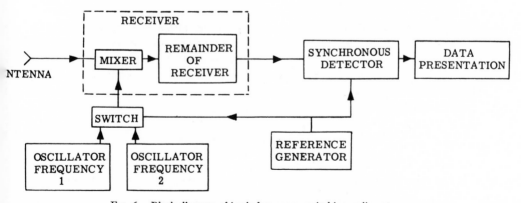

FIG. 6.—Block diagram of basic frequency-switching radiometer

To meet these requirements, it is necessary to equalize carefully the antenna impedance at all the frequencies to which the radiometer responds and to insure that the mixer current is the same at either switch position. This latter is best achieved by using an automatic gain control circuit in such a way that the mixer current is maintained constant. A discussion of these problems is given by Muller and Westerhout (1957).

As with the Dicke radiometer, the switching transients can cause spurious signals and must be thoroughly eliminated. In its basic form, this radiometer also rejects half the power captured by the antenna. However, since the antenna is connected to the receiver at all times, all the power from the antenna is available to the receiver. It is possible to take advantage of this by doubling some of the receiver circuitry and thus recover the information that would otherwise be lost. An example of a radiometer that does this will be shown later.

In fact, by adding large sets of duplicate circuitry, it is possible to make measurements at many frequencies within the 21-cm line simultaneously. Such arrangements are termed *multichannel* radiometers and are the basis of a new generation of 21-cm radiometers. Such receivers are possessed by the Carnegie Institution of Washington, Leiden Observatory, and the C.S.I.R.O.[1] radio-astronomy group at Sydney, Australia.

As was mentioned in the section on the DC comparison radiometer, these receivers usually have a means to vary slowly the frequency actually being observed, and they invariably incorporate a method of measuring accurately the observed frequency.

At the present time, almost all new 21-cm radiometers under development employ the switched-frequency configuration. This is simply because this type of radiometer has proved most resistant to the deleterious effects of component and voltage variation and, in particular, has shown the best stability during the process of changing the observed frequency.

3. RADIOMETER SENSITIVITY

3.1. INTRODUCTION

This section is devoted to a discussion of the limitations on radiometer sensitivity. Because the radiometer noise is a random series of voltages, there will always be a variation in the radiometer output due to this noise alone. Dicke (1946) first gave a theoretical discussion of the fluctuations in the Dicke radiometer and concluded that the r.m.s. output fluctuations due to noise, ΔT_n, would be given by

$$\Delta T_n = 0.70 \frac{T_S}{\sqrt{(Bt)}}, \tag{10}$$

where T_S is the over-all radiometer system noise, to be discussed later, and t is the time over which the radiometer output is averaged. This averaging is

[1] Commonwealth Scientific and Industrial Research Organization.

usually accomplished electrically in the radiometer. However, averaging time can be increased in the data-reduction process or by combining many duplicate observations.

The actual value of the coefficient in the equation for ΔT_n depends on the type of radiometer used, the type of detector in the receiver, and the shape of the band pass of the various receiver filters. In recent years, Goldstein (1955, 1957), Tucker (1957), Graham (1957), Strum (1958), and Blum (1959) have contributed to the analysis of this coefficient. However, no rigorous derivation of the coefficient exists, and the matter is somewhat controversial, However, it is known that relation (10) is a good approximation for almost all high-quality radiometers, and in practice a semiempirical relation for the r.m.s. fluctuations is employed:

$$\Delta T_n \approx \frac{T_S}{\sqrt{(Bt)}}. \tag{11}$$

In the older literature it was considered that a true signal of this magnitude could be distinguished from the radiometer noise. However, there are, of course, frequent excursions in a radiometer output due to noise that are much greater than the r.m.s. fluctuation. As a result, the general rule of thumb now used is that a signal is clearly detectable if it is somewhere between five and ten times greater than ΔT_n.

As can be seen from this formula, signals may be detected that are considerably weaker than the radiometer system noise. In a standard superheterodyne receiver operating near 21-cm wave lengths, for example, we may have $T_S = 1000°$ K, $B = 10$ Mc/s, and $t = 10$ seconds. Then ΔT_n is 0.1° K, giving a minimum detectable ΔT_A of the order of 0.5° K, which is 1 part in 2000 of the radiometer noise. In some of the traveling-wave tube radiometers now in use, $T_S = 2000°$ K, $B = 10^9$ c/s, and t may be 100 seconds. This gives a minimum detectable signal of the order of 0.04° K, which is only 1 part in 50,000 of the radiometer noise. It is because our radiometer techniques allow us to detect such low signal levels that radio astronomy as we know it is possible at all.

From relation (11) it is clearly desirable to make the bandwidth as wide as possible, keeping in mind the fact that broadening the bandwidth beyond a certain point acts to worsen the noise figure. Thus, except in 21-cm work, the bandwidth is always broadened to the point where further broadening will decrease the over-all sensitivity. In 21-cm work the bandwidth is set by the resolution in frequency, thus radial velocity, with which one wants to observe the line. At present, superheterodyne receivers can provide bandwidths of the order of 10 Mc/s on all but the lowest astronomical radio frequencies. Traveling-wave tube radiometers can produce bandwidths of about 15 per cent of the mean frequency of observation.

From equation (11), it is also desirable to increase the averaging time as much as possible. With most radiometers, the maximum averaging time is set by the maximum time over which the radiometer stability maintains nonrandom output fluctuations below the noise fluctuations from relation (11). This time is dependent on a host of factors, including electrical supply voltage variations, temperature variations, and quality of design and construction of the radiometer. It may range from minutes to hours. Changes in the radio-brightness temperature of the sky as an object is tracked can also limit averaging time. In any case, the maximum averaging time for a single observation is set by the time an object observed is above the horizon. By combining many observations of the same object, however, it is possible to build up an effective averaging time considerably in excess of the receiver instability time scale or the above-horizon time. In fact, it is usually desirable to combine a large number of quickly taken observations rather than to make one long observation, as this eliminates most thoroughly the effect of long-term radiometer instabilities. Furthermore, it minimizes the effect on the results of any spurious observations caused by interference, line voltage surges, and other rare events.

The parameter T_S, which affects ΔT_n most strongly, has been considered the same as T_R until recently. This was because the noise figures of available receivers were so high that the receiver noise was quite accurately the total noise of the system. However, the development of reactance amplifiers and masers has produced receivers with such low excess receiver-noise temperatures that the noise generated in other parts of the radiometer system becomes quite important. In the following sections, the various contributions to system noise in low-noise radiometers are discussed.

3.2. RADIOMETER SYSTEM NOISE

The radiometer system noise consists of the excess receiver noise plus several noise contributions radiated into the system. These latter sources of noise include cosmic noise, atmospheric radiation, radiation from the earth into the antenna, and radiation from antenna and radiometer components in front of the receiver in the system. Ewen (1959) and Strum (1958) have discussed these in detail.

Wherever an attenuating medium or device exists either in the antenna beam or in the circuitry before the first receiver stages, Kirchhoff's law states that noise will be radiated. This is, of course, exactly the phenomenon that plays a leading role in the theories of radiative transfer. Thus, if the power out of a passive device of temperature T_i is related to the power in by the equation

$$P_{\text{out}} = P_{\text{in}} \left(1 - \epsilon_i\right) . \tag{12}$$

then the noise temperature T_{ni} added to the system by the device is

$$T_{ni} = \epsilon_i T_i . \tag{13}$$

It should be remembered that if there are subsequent attenuating devices, this noise temperature, as seen by the radiometer, will be reduced by the amount of the subsequent attenuation.

3.3. Noise Radiation from Antenna and Radiometer Components

The antenna feed, the transmission line connecting antenna to radiometer, and components of the radiometer will all possess some attenuation. In the case of the feed, there may actually be no attenuating element but only an electrical mismatch to the transmission line. Some of the radiation incident on the feed that would be captured by a perfect feed is reflected, giving a loss equivalent to attenuation. The feed will still introduce noise into the system, not by radiating, but rather by reflecting back to the radiometer some of the thermal noise radiated by the radiometer down the transmission line toward the antenna. In such a case, relation (13) is modified to

$$T_{ni} = \epsilon_i T_j , \tag{14}$$

where T_j is the ambient temperature of the components radiating energy toward the feed. With well-designed and constructed feeds, ϵ_i is usually no greater than about 0.01, meaning that the feed will introduce only about 3° K of noise if T_j is near room temperature.

The attenuation of the transmission line between feed and radiometer is proportional to its length, and therefore the line must be made as short as possible. This calls for the mounting of the first radiometer amplifier stages near the antenna feed, which is generally done primarily to minimize signal attenuation.

Only radiometer components earlier than and including the first receiver stages usually need be considered when calculating over-all system noise. These may include calibrating devices such as directional couplers, switches, as in the Dicke radiometer, and circulators or isolators if a low-noise amplifier such as a maser is being employed. The attenuation in such devices is rapidly being decreased. At present they may contribute as much as 100° K of noise, but it is to be expected that this will decrease to less than 10° K in the near future. Part of this reduction may result from cooling the devices themselves to liquid nitrogen or liquid helium temperatures.

It should be remembered that there is a small attenuation when power is reflected in reflector-type antennae. The magnitude of this loss is not well known but appears to be a few per cent at most.

3.4. Atmospheric Radiation

The oxygen and water vapor of the atmosphere are weak attenuators of radio waves of all wave lengths. The attenuation due to oxygen varies only very slowly with wave length and is of the order of 2 per cent at the zenith in the microwave region. The influence of water vapor is significant only at frequencies of about 8000 Mc/s and higher. Above 10,000 Mc/s, water vapor may render the atmosphere nearly opaque, which obviously prevents all observations, as well as introducing about 290° K of noise into the system. The theoretical strength of the atmospheric attenuation has been given by Van Vleck (1951), and experimental studies by André, Kazes and Steinberg (1956) and

Westerhout (1958) have shown the theoretical analysis to be substantially correct, for our purposes here. Ewen (1959) has plotted the noise contribution to be expected from the atmosphere, based on the theoretical relations, and this is shown as part of Figure 7. It should be noted that the noise shown here is for a line of sight at the zenith; for other lines of sight, the increase in noise due to the increased air mass in the line of sight must be taken into account.

Extinction in the ionosphere will also contribute a small amount of noise,

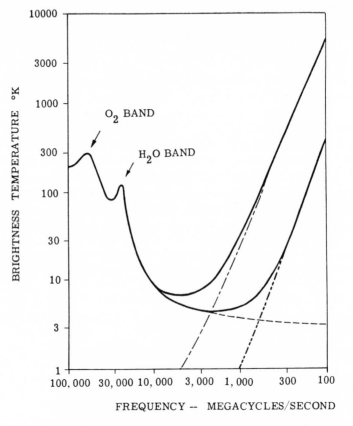

O$_2$ BAND

H$_2$O BAND

FREQUENCY -- MEGACYCLES/SECOND

— · · — · · — MINIMUM RADIO SKY BRIGHTNESS TEMPERATURE.

— · — · — MAXIMUM RADIO SKY BRIGHTNESS TEMPERATURE.

——————— TOTAL BRIGHTNESS TEMPERATURE OF SKY, AT ZENITH.

— — — — — BRIGHTNESS TEMPERATURE DUE TO ATMOSPHERIC
RADIATION (AT ZENITH).

FIG. 7.—Contributions of cosmic noise and atmospheric radiation to the brightness temperature of the sky, and total resultant brightness temperature as a function of frequency.

but this becomes appreciable only at lower frequencies, where other sources of noise are usually dominant anyway.

It should be mentioned that time variations in atmospheric extinction can be quite troublesome. This is not so much because they introduce increased noise fluctuations in the system but rather because the variations in the noise temperature appear directly at the radiometer output and may have the same appearance as true cosmic radiation.

The noise radiation from the atmosphere is reduced by the attenuation in the radiometer and antenna components.

3.5. Antenna Spillover and Minor Lobes

All antennae capture some small fraction of the radiation impinging on them from all directions. Since the earth radiates strongly, with a brightness temperature of about 290° K, the antenna will intercept some of this radiation. This will contribute to the noise level in the radiometer system. In the case of reflector antennae, radiation entering the feed horn directly, usually along paths close to the edge of the reflector, is termed *spillover* radiation. Radiation from directions outside the main beam, including the spillover radiation, is collectively called *minor-lobe radiation*. The noise contribution made by this minor-lobe radiation from the earth depends critically on the antenna and its feed and may be as low as a few degrees or may be an appreciable fraction of 300° K. This radiation is reduced by the attenuation in the antenna, transmission line, and radiometer components.

3.6. Cosmic Noise

At all frequencies and in all parts of the sky, there is a radio brightness temperature due to general galactic radiation and integrated extragalactic emission. The mean brightness temperature of the sky varies from nearly 0° K at centimeter wave lengths to millions of degrees at decameter wave lengths. Since the antenna temperature is simply a weighted mean of the radio brightness temperature over all solid angles, these brightness temperatures become approximately the noise added to the radiometer system due to cosmic radiation. It should also be noted that, if a discrete source is present in the radio telescope beam, the change in antenna temperature created by it is also added to the system noise.

The cosmic noise brightness temperatures set the lower limit on the value of T_S. A perfect radiometer and antenna located above the terrestrial atmosphere would have T_S = the radio sky temperature. The magnitude of the radio sky brightness temperatures has been included in Figure 7.

It is of interest that the combined effect of atmospheric attenuation and cosmic noise produces a "window" in which radiometer system noise may be very small. This is evident in Figure 7. The window extends from about 1000 to about 10,000 Mc/s.

3.7. SUMMARY

From the preceding sections, the radiometer system noise T_S to be used in the sensitivity equation (10) is

$$T_S = T_R + T_r\epsilon_r + T_t\epsilon_t (1 - \epsilon_r) + T_d\epsilon_d (1 - \epsilon_r)(1 - \epsilon_t)$$
$$+ T_s\epsilon_a (1 - \epsilon_r)(1 - \epsilon_t) + T_a (1 - \epsilon_r)(1 - \epsilon_t)(1 - \epsilon_d) \quad (15)$$
$$+ T_c (1 - \epsilon_r)(1 - \epsilon_t)(1 - \epsilon_d)(1 - \epsilon_a) + \Delta T_A ,$$

where the subscript r refers to the radiometer components prior to the first receiver stage; t refers to the antenna-radiometer transmission line; d refers to the antenna and feed; s refers to minor-lobe radiation; a refers to the atmosphere; and c refers to general cosmic noise. Except in the cases of T_R, T_S, T_c, and T_s, the temperatures T are the ambient temperatures of the entity concerned. The attenuations ϵ are defined by equation (12); T_s is the antenna temperature resulting from minor-lobe pickup of ground radiation; T_c is the weighted mean cosmic noise brightness temperature seen by the antenna; and ΔT_A is the increase in antenna temperature due to any discrete radio source that may be present in the antenna beam.

The value of T_S given in equation (15) is referred to the receiver input, as is customary. The value of ΔT_n computed from T_S will also refer to the receiver input. Whenever comparing a value of antenna temperature with ΔT_n to determine what the signal-to-noise ratio might be, the value of the antenna temperature at the antenna must be reduced in accordance with any attenuation between the antenna and the receiver. This gives the noise temperature increment due to the cosmic signal that the receiver will see. Alternately, one may obtain a correct signal-to-noise ratio by increasing T_S, thus ΔT_n, by the amount of attenuation between receiver and antenna and comparing the result directly with the actual antenna temperature. This latter approach is also common, but it is academic as to which is used, as long as the approach used is made clear.

As an example of what the various contributions to radiometer system noise may be in an advanced radiometer system, Giordmaine et al. (1959) have given the contribution of the various terms of the equation to the over-all system noise in a radiometer with a ruby maser. The contribution of each term is given in the accompanying table.

	°K
Receiver noise (of which 3° K is in the maser and 26° K is due to subsequent stages)	29
Radiometer components forward of receiver	20
Transmission line	10
Antenna (no estimate given, but probably negligible)	0
Minor-lobe pickup	20
Atmospheric radiation	6
Cosmic noise, 3-cm wave length	0
Total radiometer system noise	85

This is a very low system noise. One notes that no one portion of the system is producing a dominant contribution to the noise. It can be expected that future technological developments will reduce the noise contributions of the man-made components to such an extent that the atmospheric contribution is dominant. System noise temperatures of the order of 10° K should then be available.

4. LOW-NOISE AMPLIFIERS

Low-noise amplifiers are radio-frequency amplifiers that may be used in front of a conventional receiver to produce a system having very low-noise properties. At present, useful low-noise amplifiers are the product of solid-state research and are found in two categories: masers and parametric or reactance amplifiers. It should be noted that these amplifiers are not the basis of new radiometer systems but are used simply as building blocks in the radiometer types already discussed.

The solid-state maser was first proposed by Combrisson, Honig, and Townes (1956). Later, Bloembergen (1956) suggested a convenient way to achieve continuous amplification by using three energy levels in a paramagnetic substance. His method is the one now generally used. The principle of operation of a maser is to invert the spin energy level populations in the paramagnetic substance and thereby secure amplification because the rate of stimulated emission will exceed the absorption rate for photons whose frequency is that connecting the levels of inverted populations. The inverted level populations are achieved by applying a saturating radio-frequency field to the substance, which usually must be held in liquid helium temperature. For a detailed discussion of this device, the reader is referred to the papers of Bloembergen (1956), Giordmaine et al. (1959), Wittke (1957), and Heffner (1959).

The lower limit on the excessive receiver noise of a maser is $0.048f°$ K, where f is the frequency in kilomegacycles. Thus excess receiver noise temperatures of less than 1° K should be obtainable at all frequencies of radio-astronomy interest. Actual measurements of maser noise have suffered from the large amount of noise generated by the measuring apparatus itself, but McWhorter and Arams (1958) succeeded in showing that the noise of a solid-state maser was about 2° K. There is no doubt that the low theoretical noise levels can be approached closely. Bandwidths available with maser amplifiers may be quite large, with 25 Mc/s bandwidths already attainable.

In general, the gain stability of masers is worse than the stability of conventional radio receivers. This is a consequence of the highly regenerative nature of the device. Significant gain variations can be caused by a change in the output impedance presented to the maser, by a change in the field of the maser magnet, and by changes in the level of the liquid helium in the device. This last effect not only can be a result of changes in temperature in the maser but also can be due to reflections from the liquid helium surface. The standing wave pattern generated by these reflections will vary with time as the helium level changes, as noted by Giordmaine *et al.* (1959). A remedy for the problem is to fill the electrical transmission lines with polyfoam, which displaces the helium from this portion of the apparatus.

A solution to the gain stability problem now being attempted at several institutions is to send a pulsed "pilot" signal of constant pulse intensity through the device. The strength of this pilot signal in the output is measured by means of a synchronous detector controlled by the pilot signal pulsing device. The pilot signal output intensity is used to activate a servo loop controlling the amplifier gain in some fashion. The servo acts to maintain constant the pilot signal output amplitude and thus the amplifier gain.

Other practical difficulties encountered with masers include the inability to orient the devices at random without suffering serious disturbances in the liquid helium bath and loss of liquid helium. Finally, the devices are expensive to construct and operate, although the increasing general cost of operating a radio-astronomy facility is making the cost figure far less important. Because of the newness of practical maser systems and the small number of people capable of constructing them, the device has not yet seen wide use.

The reactance amplifier makes use of the ability of a non-linear reactor to produce amplification, when placed in a proper circuit. The non-linear reactor most commonly used is a semiconductor diode which acts as a non-linear capacitor. For the theory of operation of these devices, the reader is referred to Heffner (1959), Heffner and Wade (1958), and Bloom and Chang (1957). Noise temperatures is these devices have generally been of the order of 100° K and therefore are not competitive with a maser. However, Uenohara and Sharpless (1959) have measured excess noise temperatures of about 40° K in a reactance amplifier operating at 6 kmc/s. It would appear that technological improvements will make parametric amplifiers competitive with maser devices from a noise standpoint.

The parametric amplifier is especially appealing because it is much easier to operate than a maser and there is no liquid helium requirement at present. This latter advantage may disappear, however, as recent experiments, particularly those of Uenohara and Sharpless mentioned above, have shown that significant improvements in performance may be achieved through refrigeration. As with masers, parametric amplifiers have suffered from a serious lack of gain stability. This has prevented them from seeing much use in radio astronomy. However, this problem now appears solved, and much more extensive use can be foreseen.

5. DIGITAL DATA PRESENTATION

Digital data presentation is advantageous in radio astronomy for three reasons: (1) the need to measure tracings is eliminated, in turn removing the possibility of human error in the reduction process; (2) this same feature saves a large amount of personnel time; and (3) the observational data are produced directly in the proper form for high-speed reduction on electronic computers.

A digital data-presentation device must take the average of the radiometer output over the desired averaging time, and it must then present this average digitally. It is desirable that the digital presentation and preparation of the device for the next averaging period take as little time as possible, as this allows maximum utilization of telescope time. It is also desirable that the digital device print a digital record for inspection by the observer and also prepare a record of the data in a proper form, such as punched tape, punched cards, or magnetic tape, for direct insertion into an electronic computer. Commercial components now available make it possible to fulfil these two latter desires.

In Figures 8 and 9 are shown two digital data-presentation devices constructed by the staff of the National Radio Astronomy Observatory. The circuit of Figure 8 makes use of an extremely linear integrating circuit discussed by Gray (1948), produced when the input and output of a high-gain DC amplifier are connected by a large capacitor. This integrator computes the average radiometer output over the averaging period. Timing circuits are used with the integrator to control the time during which the integrator is connected to the radiometer, to trigger the digital voltmeter at the end of the integration period, and to discharge the integration capacitor after the digital reading is complete. The radiometer is also disconnected during the discharge process to prevent transients from being fed back into it. The integrating circuit used here is extremely stable and can suffer appreciable temperature and supply voltage changes without impaired performance. However, the somewhat complicated timing circuitry normally limits the available averaging times to a small number, unless special provisions are made.

The digital device of Figure 9 makes use of commercially available voltage-to-frequency converters. These are devices that generate an alternating current (AC) voltage whose frequency is strictly proportional to the voltages, usually slowly varying DC potentials, at their input. If the total number of AC alternations out of the device in a given period is counted, the sum will be a measure of the average input voltage to the device over the counting period. In this

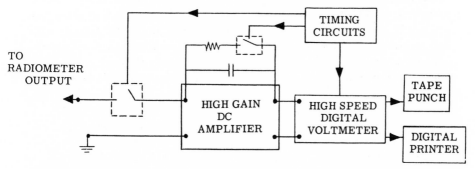

Fig. 8.—Block diagram of digital data-presentation system employing analogue integrator and digital voltmeter.

integrator, then, the voltage-to-frequency converter is connected to the radiometer output, and its output is counted over periods controlled by timing circuitry within the counter. Commercially available counters provide simple controls by which the length of the counting period can be made almost continuously adjustable. The counter causes the tape punch and data printer to print the count at the end of the counting period.

This device has the advantage of providing a wide range of averaging times. Furthermore, since it is entirely digital, extremely long averaging times can be used without having to consider problems of capacitor leakage. However, care must be taken to operate the voltage-to-frequency converter on the linear part of its characteristic. Also, it is usually possible to misadjust the voltage level out of the radiometer in such a way that the small variations in the performance of the voltage-to-frequency converter will cause variations in the final data that are as large as the effects of radiometer noise. This is to be avoided, of course, as it is equivalent to a great increase in radiometer noise.

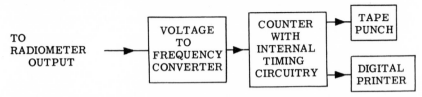

Fig. 9.—Block diagram of digital data-presentation circuit employing digital integration

6. RADIOMETER CALIBRATION

Radiometer calibration has been discussed in detail by Pawsey and Bracewell (1955). The most advantageous means of calibration at present is the circuit of Figure 10a. Simply by firing the gas-discharge tube, a noise signal of very stable intensity is inserted into the antenna transmission line through the directional coupler. If the strength of this noise signal has been calibrated in terms of equivalent antenna temperature, the deflection in the radiometer output due to the noise signal gives a calibration for the radiometer.

This circuit has many advantages. The use of a gas-discharge source insures that the calibration signal is of quite constant intensity. Tests of these tubes have indicated that the long-term variation in their noise temperatures is less than 0.25 per cent. A further advantage is that the calibration signal is obtained with a minimum of effort; one need only apply power to the gas-discharge tube. Since the calibration must often be done at an inaccessible point, such as the focus of a large reflector, this can be quite important, particularly when frequent radiometer calibrations are required. Finally, no changes in the radio-frequency (RF) circuit are required. One is thus protected from the usually unmeasurable errors introduced in the course of a calibration when changes in electrical impedance matching occur. Such changes in impedance are the inevitable result of rearrangements of RF circuitry.

A primary calibration of the calibration signal itself must always be made. This is generally accomplished by means of the circuit of Figure 10*b*, where the antenna is replaced by a dummy load, whose impedance is well matched to the radiometer. The load is immersed in a thermal bath whose temperature may be accurately controlled. The temperature of the thermal bath is then altered a small and carefully measured amount, and the resultant radiometer output deflection is compared with the deflection produced by the calibration noise signal.

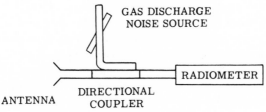

FIG. 10*a*.—Preferred radiometer calibration circuit

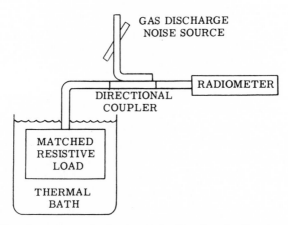

FIG. 10*b*.—Experimental setup for fundamental calibration of radiometer calibration noise source.

There is a danger in this method, in that the impedance of the dummy load may change as its temperature is changed, thus causing an erroneous calibration. It is therefore desirable to use a dummy load whose impedance is not temperature-sensitive or to alter the dummy-load temperature only very slightly in the course of a calibration. This problem can be particularly acute in the case of radiometers employing superheterodyne receivers. The dummy-load impedance is usually seen directly by the superheterodyne mixer, and the values of T_R and gain are quite sensitive to the impedance load on the mixer. Thus small changes in the dummy-load impedance may result in great apparent changes in the receiver-noise level. This problem is not important with traveling-wave tube receivers, since the performance of a traveling-wave tube is far less dependent on the impedance connected to its input.

The method of calibration described above is suitable only for the calibration of direct and Dicke radiometers. With DC comparison radiometers the usual procedure is to disconnect one channel, making the radiometer a direct radiometer, in turn allowing the use of the above method. Calibration of switched-frequency radiometers is quite difficult and must be accomplished by measuring the electrical characteristics of all the components in the radiometer. For details the reader is referred to Muller and Westerhout (1957).

It should be noted that the performance of the detectors in the radiometer receiver can strongly affect calibration. Ideally, these detectors should produce outputs that are linearly related to the power input to the detector. This is never the case. Thus, in the primary radiometer calibration, unless the change in the thermal-bath temperature gives exactly the same output deflection as the calibration signal, the non-linearity of the receiver detector must be taken into account. In any case, the detector characteristic, or "law," must be measured carefully if radiometer output deflections of different intensity from the calibration signal are to be calibrated accurately.

7. EXAMPLES OF ACTUAL RADIOMETER CIRCUITS

As actual working examples of the principles stated above, we discuss here two radiometers which have seen extensive use.

7.1. THE UNIVERSITY OF MICHIGAN–UNIVERSITY OF CALIFORNIA–N.R.A.O. 8000 MEGACYCLE PER SECOND RADIOMETER

Figure 11 gives the block diagram of this radiometer, which is a production model of the radiometer described by Drake and Ewen (1958). It is a Dicke radiometer using a ferrite switch and a tuned radio-frequency receiver rather than the usual superheterodyne receiver. This latter feature allows the use of traveling-wave tubes in the amplifying stages, which gives, in this case, a bandwidth of 10^9 c/s. Noise compensation is used to balance the load and antenna temperatures seen by the switch. There is also provision, through a directional coupler and wave-guide flap switch, to insert an amount of noise equivalent to about 1° K into the antenna line. This provides easy calibration of signal intensities.

The audio amplifier acts to amplify only the audio component in the detector output that is of the same frequency as the switching frequency. It eliminates other audio components, which can be the result only of receiver noise and may cause the synchronous detector to malfunction if not eliminated. The reference generator provides the switching-frequency power.

The over-all radiometer excess noise temperature in this case is about 5000° K, so that the other sources of noise will not increase the output fluctuations appreciably in this case. Despite the high noise temperature, the wide

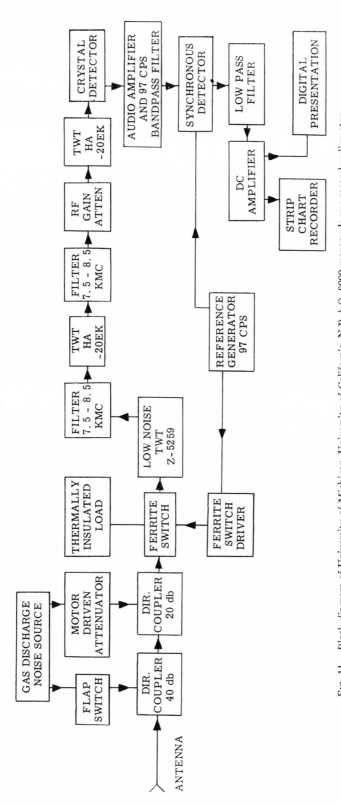

FIG. 11.—Block diagram of University of Michigan–University of California–N.R.A.O. 8000-megacycle-per-second radiometer

bandwidth allows ΔT_n to be of the order of $0.02°$ K, with averaging times of the order of 100 seconds.

7.2. THE LEIDEN OBSERVATORY 21-CM RADIOMETER

This radiometer has been described by Muller and Westerhout (1957) and is shown in Figure 12. It is a switched-frequency radiometer, incorporating a triple conversion superheterodyne receiver and containing extra circuits to save the power normally wasted in the fundamental switched-frequency system. It also has doubled circuitry after the second mixer, to allow simultaneous observations of two 21-cm line frequencies.

The first local oscillator frequency is generated by multiplying the output frequencies of one of two stable crystal oscillators. The switch chooses the crystal oscillator which is in use at any instant and thereby performs the frequency-switching function. Tuning of the received frequency is accomplished by varying the frequency of the second local oscillator. The dual intermediate frequency channels after the second mixer are arranged in such a way that, no matter which position the switch is in, one channel or the other is receiving the desired 21-cm frequency. Thus all the 21-cm radiation delivered by the antenna on the desired frequency is measured by the receiver. The outputs of the two channels are added before the signal is fed to the synchronous detector.

T_s is about $1500°$, $B = 37$ kc/sec, and $t = 54$ seconds, giving $\Delta T_n \approx 1.1°$ K. The bandwidth of 37 kc has been made small to allow adequate 21-cm line resolution.

It should be noted that the use of two channels will cause the output fluctuations to be greater than in a single channel by a factor of $\sqrt{2}$. Since the use of two channels has doubled the signal power available, the net improvement in radiometer sensitivity given by the two-channel operation is $2/\sqrt{2}$, or $\sqrt{2}$.

Circuitry designed to give frequency marks is included. The circuitry gives an output whenever the second local oscillator frequency is a multiple of 100 kc/sec or 10 kc/sec. This output is used to actuate pens on the chart recorder, so that the frequency of reception is marked at 10 kc/sec intervals.

A servo amplifier is used with the frequency multiplier of the first local oscillator to insure that the mixer current is the same in both switch positions. A suppressor is used with the first intermediate-frequency amplifier to turn off the amplifier and thus the entire radiometer while switching transients are in progress. Automatic gain controls are used with later intermediate-frequency stages to maintain radiometer gain constant and to keep the two channels in balance.

Finally, the dotted line incloses the portion of the circuitry that appears in duplicate. Frequencies in parentheses indicate where frequencies are different in the duplicate unit. This arrangement of frequencies causes the duplicate unit to receive 21-cm radiation at a frequency displaced by 500 kc/sec from the frequency of the first unit. The speed at which the radiometer may gather information is thereby nearly doubled.

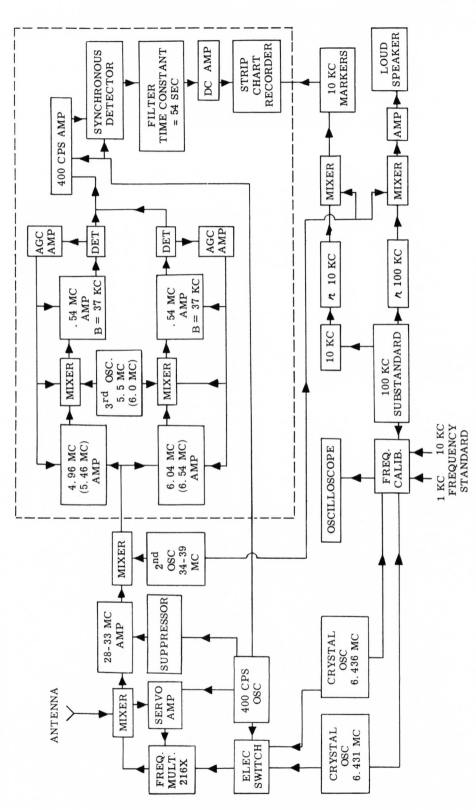

FIG. 12.—Block diagram of Leiden Observatory 21-cm radiometer

REFERENCES

ANDRÉ, P., KAZES, I., and
STEINBERG, J. L.   1956   *C.R.*, **242**, 2099.

BLOEMBERGEN, N.   1956   *Phys. Rev.*, **104**, 324.

BLOOM, S., and
CHANG, K. N.   1957   *R.E.C. Ref.*, **18**, 578.

BLUM, E. J.   1959   *Ann. d'ap.*, **22**, 140.

COMBRISSON, J., HONIG,
A., and TOWNES, C. H.   1956   *C.R.*, **242**, 2451.

DE LOACH, B. C., and
SHARPLESS, W. M.   1959   *Proc. I.R.E.*, **47**, 2115.

DICKE, R. H.   1946   *Rev. Sci. Instr.*, **17**, 268.

DRAKE, F. D., and
EWEN, H. I.   1958   *Proc. I.R.E.*, **46**, 53.

EWEN, H. I.   1959   *Microwave J.*, **2**, 41.

GIORDMAINE, J. A., ALSOP,
L. E., MAYER, C. H.,
and TOWNES, C. H.   1959   *Proc. I.R.E.*, **47**, 1062.

GOLDSTEIN, S. J., JR.   1955   *Proc. I.R.E.*, **43**, 1663.

———   1957   *Ibid.*, **45**, 366.

GRAHAM, M. H.   1957   *Proc. I.R.E.*, **45**, 366.

GRAY, J. W.   1948   In I. A. GREENWOOD, JR., J. V. HOLDAM, JR., and D. MACRAE, JR., *Electronic Instruments* ("Radiation Laboratory Series," Vol. 21 [New York: McGraw-Hill Book Co., Inc.]), p. 78.

HEFFNER, H.   1959   *Microwave J.*, **2**, 33.

HEFFNER, H., and
WADE, G.   1958   *J. Appl. Phys.*, **29**, 1321.

MAYER, C. H.,
MCCULLOUGH, T. P.,
and SLOANAKER, R. M.   1958   *Proc. I.R.E.*, **46**, 260.

MULLER, C. A., and
WESTERHOUT, G.   1957   *B.A.N.*, **13**, 151 (No. 425).

MACRAE, D., JR.   1948   In I. A. GREENWOOD, JR., J. V. HOLDAM, JR., and D. MACRAE, JR., *Electronic Instruments* ("Radiation Laboratory Series," Vol. 21 [New York: McGraw-Hill Book Co., Inc.]), p. 383.

MCWHORTER, A. C., and
ARAMS, F. R.   1958   *Proc. I.R.E.*, **46**, 913.

PAWSEY, J. L., and
BRACEWELL, R. N.   1955   *Radio Astronomy* (Oxford: Clarendon Press).

RYLE, M., and
VONBERG, D. D.   1948   *Proc. R. Soc. London, A*, **193**, 98.

SELOVE, W.   1954   *Rev. Sci. Instr.*, **25**, 120.

STRUM, P. D.   1958   *Proc. I.R.E.*, **46**, 43.

TUCKER, D. G.   1957   *Proc. I.R.E.*, **45**, 365.
UENOHARA, M., and
  SHARPLESS, W. M.   1959   *Proc. I.R.E.*, **47**, 2114.
VAN VLECK, J. H.   1951   In D. E. KERR, *Propagation of Short Radio Waves*
                                   ("Radiation Laboratory Series," Vol. 13 [New
                                   York: McGraw-Hill Book Co., Inc.]), p. 641.
WESTERHOUT, G.   1958   *B.A.N.*, **14**, 215 (No. 488).
WITTKE, J. P.   1957   *Proc. I.R.E.*, **45**, 291.

APPENDIX

(Solar Telescopes Excluded)

Optical telescopes of aperture diameters greater than 20 inches or 50 cm, currently in use for research, are listed in Table 1. A few telescopes that are expected to be completed soon after publication of this volume are included.

The order follows that of the list of observatories in the *American Ephemeris* for 1960 (pp. 434–448). The *Ephemeris* list is not complete, however, and additional institutions have been interpolated alphabetically according to their locations, except for stations, which have been placed with their parent institutions.

We wish to thank the staffs of well over one hundred observatories who have answered our questionnaires and thus assisted in this compilation. The data supplied were typed for planographing, photographed, and referred back for checking to the observatories which co-operated in the compilation of the table, before the table was printed; we hoped by this means to keep errors to a minimum.[1]

GERARD P. KUIPER

BARBARA M. MIDDLEHURST

---

[1] The second printing has allowed us to make minor corrections and a few additions, although a thorough revision has not been possible in the time available.

TABLE 1

ASTRONOMICAL OPTICAL TELESCOPES, APERTURE ≥ 20 INCHES OR 50 CM

(SOLAR TELESCOPES EXCLUDED)

OBSERVATORY	CO-ORD. Long. (h) Lat. (°)	ELEV. (m)	TYPE	APERTURE (inches)	APERTURE (cm)	OPTICS	FOCUS	F/	SCALE ("/mm)	ACCESSORIES	SINCE	NOTES
Abastumani Astrophysical Observatory, Mt. Konobili, Georgia, U.S.S.R.	- 2:51 +41.45	1600	Men	28 38	70 98	Cl Cl	Prime Cas	3 4	98 21	Pg Ob Pm Sp	1956	
Astrophysical Institute of the K.S.S.R. Academy of Sciences, Kamenskoje Plato, Alma-Ata, U.S.S.R.	- 5:08 +43:11	1450	Refl Mak	20 20 26.5	50 50 67	Cl Cl Cl	Cas Prime	24 2.4	17.2 173.4	Pe Sp Pg	1948 1950	
University Observatory, Ann Arbor, Michigan	+ 5:34 +42:17	282	Refl	37.5	95	Cl	Prime Cas	6 19	36 11.4	1 Pm Sp 2 Pm Sp Q Sp	1911	
Astrophysical Observatory of Padua University, Asiago, Italy	- 0:46 +45:52	1045	Refl	48	120	Cl	Newt Cas	5 15	34 11	Pg Pe Sp Mic	1942	
Astronomical Observatory, Belgrade, Yugoslavia	- 1:22 +44:48	253	Vis R	26	65	Cl		16	19.5	Pg Pe Mic	1929	
Leuschner Observatory, Berkeley, California, U.S.A.	+ 8:09 +37:52	94	Refl	20	51	Pyr	Newt Cas	4 16	101.5 25.4	Pg Pe Sp Mic	1956	
Sternwarte Berlin-Babelsberg, Berlin, Germany	- 0:52 +52:24	82	Vis R Refl Refl	26 28 21	65 70 52	Cl Cl	Cas Cas	16 22 20	20 14 20	Mic Pe Pe	1912 1957 1960	
Sternwarte Zimmerwald der Universität Bern, Kt. Bern, Switzerland	- 0:30 +46:53	900	Refl	24	62	Cl	Cas	25	13.5	Pe	1959	1

Observatory	Long.	Lat.		Type				Focus				Plates	Year	
Boyden Observatory, Bloemfontein, O.F.S., South Africa	− 1:46	−29:02	1387	Refl	60	152	Gl	Newt	5.3	26	Pg Pe Sp	1930	
				B-Schm	32 36	81 91	Gl Gl	Prime	3.7	68	Pg Sp	1950	
Bologna University Observatory, Loiano, Italy	− 0:45	+44:15	800	Refl	24	60	Gl	Prime	3.5	98	Pg Pe	1936	
National Observatory, Bosque Alegre Station, Argentina	+ 4:18	−31:36	1250	Refl	61	155	G	Newt Cas	5 21	27.5 6.6	Pg Sp	1942	
University Observatory, Brno, Czechoslovakia	− 1:06	+49:12	277	Refl	24	60	Gl	Newt	4.5	75	Pe	195?	
Goethe Link Observatory of Indiana University, Brooklyn, Indiana	+ 5:46	+39:33	300	Refl	36	91	Pyr	Prime Newt	5	45	Pg Pe Sp	1939	
Konkoly Observatory, Budapest-Szabadsághegy, Hungary	− 1:16	+47:30	470	Refl	24	61	Gl	Newt Cas	6 15	60 24	Pg Pe	1930	
Burakan Astrophysical Observatory, Burakan, Armenia, U.S.S.R.	− 2:57	+40:20	1480	Schm	21 21	53 53	Pyr Gl	Prime	3.4	114	Pg	1954	
University Observatory, Cambridge, England	0:00	+52:13	25	Refl	36	91	Pyr	Prime Cou Cou	4.5 18 30	50 12.5 7.5	Pg Pe Sp	1955	
Mount Stromlo Observatory, Canberra, Australia	− 9:56	−35:20	808	Refl	74	188	Pyr	Newt Cas Cou	5 18 31	22.6 6.3 3.6	Pg Sp Sp	1955	2
				Refl	50	127	Pyr	Greg	18	9	Pe	1954	
				Refl	30	75	Gl	Newt	4 18 12	68 15 26	Pg Pe Sp Pe Pg Pe	1930	3
				Refl	26	50	Pyr	Cas				1959	4
				Pg R	26	66	Gl	Cas	16.6	18.8		1953	
				Schm	20 26	50 66	Gl Pyr	Prime	3.5	120	Pg Ob Pm	1956	5

241

TABLE 1 - (Continued)

OBSERVATORY	CO-ORD Long. (h) / Lat. (°)	ELEV. (m)	TYPE	APERTURE (Inches)	(cm)	OPTICS	FOCUS	F/	SCALE ("/mm)	ACCESS-ORIES	SINCE	NOTES
Royal Observatory, Cape of Good Hope, South Africa	- 1:14 / -33:56	8	Pg R	24	61	Cl		11	30	Pg Pe	1901	
			Refl	40	102	Pyr	Prime / Cas	4.5 / 20	45 / 10.1	Pg Pe	1961	
Vatican Observatory, Castel Gandolfo, Italy	- 0:51 / +41:45	450	Refl	24	60	Cl	Newt / Cas	4 / 13.7	85 / 25	Pg Pe Ob Pm / Sp	1936	
			Schm	25 / 38.5	64 / 98			3.8	85	Pg Ob Pm	1959	
Leander McCormick Observatory, Charlottesville, Virginia, U.S.A.	+ 5:14 / +38:02	259	Vis R	26	66	Cl		15	20.8	Pg Pe	1883	
Jones Observatory, Chattanooga, Tennessee, U.S.A.	+ 5:40 / +35:01	750	Refl	20.5	52	Pyr	Cas	17.5	21		1936	6
Warner and Swasey Observatory, Cleveland, Ohio, U.S.A.	+ 5:26 / +41:32	247	Refl	36	91	Cl	Cas	14.4	16	Pe	1957	
Nassau Astronomical Station of Warner and Swasey Observatory, Ohio, U.S.A.	+ 5:24 / +41:34	410	Schm	24 / 36	61 / 91	Cl / Cl	Prime	3.5	96	2°,4° Ob Pm	1941	
Astronomical Observatory, Cluj, Roumania	- 1:34 / +46:46	412	Refl	20	50	Cl	Newt	5	81.9	Pg Pe	1933	
Observatory of the University of Copenhagen, Brorfelde, Tølløse, Denmark	- 0:48 / +55:38	91	Refl	20	50	Pyr	Cas	14	29	Pe	1958	7
Perkins Observatory, Delaware, Ohio, U.S.A.	+ 5:32 / +40:15	270	Refl	69	175	Cl	Newt / Cas	4.3 / 18	27.5 / 6.5	Pg Sp Pe	1932	8
			Refl	32	81	Pyr	Newt / Cas	4.7 / 16.5	54 / 15	Pg Pe	1958	

Observatory										Instruments	Year	Ref
Chamberlin Observatory, University of Denver, Denver, Colorado, U.S.A.	+ 7:00 +39:41	1644	Vis R Pg R	20 20	51 51	Gl Gl		16 11	24 27	Pg Pe Mic	1894	9
Dunsink Observatory, Dublin, Eire	+ 0:25 +53:23	86	Refl	28	71	Gl	Cou	4.3	67	Pe	1957	
Royal Observatory, Edinburgh, Scotland	+ 0:13 +55:55	146	Refl	36	91	Gl	Cas	18	13	Sp Pe	1928	
IRSAC Observatory, Elisabethville, Congo	- 1:50 -11:27	1500	Refl	38.5	98	Pyr	Prime Cas Cou	2 10 10	150 30 30	Fg Pe Sp	1960	10
			Schm	26.3 38.5	67 98	Q Pyr	Prime	3	150	Ob Pm	1960	10
Atmospheric Research Observatory, Arizona State College, Flagstaff, Arizona, U.S.A.	+ 7:27 +35:11	2105	Refl	24	61	Pyr Q	Newt Cas	4.5 25		Rocksalt Prism Monochrometer	1953	
U.S. Naval Observatory, Flagstaff Station, Flagstaff, Arizona, U.S.A.	+ 7:27 +35:11	2312	Refl	61.75	157	Q	Cas Newt	10	13.5	Pg Pe Sp Meinel Camera	1963	11,12
Lowell Observatory, Flagstaff, Arizona, U.S.A.	+ 7:27 +35:12	2210	Refl	42	107	Gl	Cas Cas Cas	33 23 15	5.9 8.4 12.8	Pg Pe Sp IT	1910	
			Vis R	24	61	Gl		16	21	Pg Pe Sp Mic	1896	
			Refl	20.8	53	Pyr	Cas	16	24	Pe	1953	
			Refl	24	61	Pyr	Cas Cas Cas	16 32 104	21 11 3.3	Pe Sp IT	1960	
McDonald Observatory, Fort Davis, Texas, U.S.A.	+ 6:56 +30:40	2081	Refl	82	208	Pyr	Prime Cas Cou	4.0 13.6 20.3	25.4 7.4 5	Pg Pe Sp Mic IR	1939	
			Refl	36	91	Pyr	Cas	13.6	16.8	Pe	1957	
Observatoire de Genève, Geneva, Switzerland	- 0:25 +46:12	406	Refl	40	100	Gl	Cas	3		Pe	1927	13

TABLE 1 - (Continued)

OBSERVATORY	CO-ORD. Long.(h) Lat.(°)	ELEV. (m)	TYPE	APERTURE (Inches)	(cm)	OPTICS	FOCUS	F/	SCALE ("/mm)	ACCESS-ORIES	SINCE	NOTES
Hamburg-Bergedorf Sternwarte, Hamburg, Germany	- 0:41 +53:29	40	Refl	40	100	Gl	Newt Cas	3 15	70 14	Pg Sp	1910	
			Refl	24	60	Gl	Newt	5	70	Pg Pe Sp	1935	
			Schm	32 48	80 120	Gl Gl		3	86	Pg Ob Pm	1955	14
			Vis R Pg R	24	60	Gl		15	23	Pg Pe Mic	1908	9
G. R. Agassiz Station, Harvard College Observatory, Cambridge, Massachusetts, U.S.A.	+ 4:46 +42:30	183	Refl	61	155	Gl	Newt Cas Cou	5.1 20	26 6	Pg Pe Sp	1934	
			Refl	24	61	Gl	Newt Cas	5.6 20.1	60 19	Pg Pe	1906	
			Schm	24 36	61 91		Prime	3.5	98	Pg	1941	
Landessternwarte, Heidelberg, Germany	- 0:35 +49:24	570	Refl	28	72	Gl	Cas	17.5	16.5	Pe	1906	
Helwan Observatory, Helwan, Egypt	- 2:05 +29:52	115	Refl	30	76	Gl	Newt	4.5	60	Pg Pe	1905	
			Refl	74	188	Gl	Newt Cas Cou	4.9 18 28.9		Pg Sp	1960	
Royal Greenwich Observatory, Herstmonceux, England	- 0:01 +50:52	47	Refl	36	91	Gl	Cas	15	15	Pg Sp	1934	
			Refl	30	76	Gl	Prime Cas	4.5 20	60 13.5	Pg Pe	1897 1957	
			Refl	20	51	Gl	Cas	16	25	Pe	1957	
			Vis R	28	71			12	24	Mic	1894	
			Pg R	26	66			10	30	Pg	1897	
Nizamiah Observatory, Osmania University, Hyderabad, India	- 5:14 +17:26	554	Refl	48	122	Pyr	Newt Cas Cou	4 15 30		Pe	1962	

Observatory	λ	φ	H (m)	Type	D (in)	D (cm)	Mirror	Focus	f/	Scale	Programme	Year	No.
Universitäts-Sternwarte, Astrophysikalisches Institut, Jena, Germany	− 0:46	+50:56	340	Refl / Refl	20 / 36	50 / 90	Gl	Newt / Cas	5 / 20	84 / 21	Pg Pe / Pg Pe	1958 / 1960	15
Union Observatory, Johannesburg, South Africa	− 1:52	−26:11	1806	Vis R	26.5	67	Gl	Cas	16	18.9	Pg Mic Int	1925	
Principal Astrophysical Observatory of the Ukr. S.S.R. Acad. of Sciences, Golossejevo, Kiev, U.S.S.R.	− 2:02	+50:22	150	Refl	28	71	Gl	Prime / Newt / Cas	4.5 / 4.5 / 15	66 / 66 / 20	Pg Pe / Sp	1959	
Astrophysical Observatory Kodaikanal, India	− 5:10	+10:14	2343	Refl	20	51	Gl	Newt / Cas	7 / 20	58 / 20	Sp	1905	
Kwasan Observatory, Kyoto University, Kyoto, Japan	+ 9:03	+34:59	234	Refl	24	60	Pyr	Newt / Cas	5.5 / 20	62.5 / 17.2	Pg	1960	
LaPlata Observatory, LaPlata, Argentina	+ 3:52	−34:54	17	Refl	33	84	Gl	Cas	18	13.7	Pg Pe Sp	1896	16
Observatoire Universitaire, Lausanne, Switzerland	− 0:29	+46:32	595	Refl	25	62.5	Gl	Newt / Cas	3.7 / 24	90 / 13.8	Pv Pg	1948	
Boscha Observatory, Lembang, Java, Indonesia	− 7:10	− 6:50	1300	Pg R / Vis R } Schm	23.6 / 20 / 28	60 / 51 / 71	Pyr Gl	Prime	17.9 / 2.5	19.3 / 19.2 / 163	Pg / Pg Mic	1928 / 1928	17
University Observatory, Liège (Cointe-Sclessin), Belgium	− 0:22	+50:37	127	Schm	24	60	Gl	Prime / Cas / Cou	3 / 3.75 / 13	113 / 92 / 26.4	Pg / 6° Ob Pm	1958	18
Lisbon Observatory Station, Alfeite, Portugal	+ 0:37	+38:40	45	Refl	20	50	Gl	Newt / Cas	6 / 18	68 / 22.5	Ob Pm / Pg / Sp	1957	19
Star Lane Observatory, Louisville, Kentucky, U.S.A.	+ 5:43	+38:08	143	Refl	20.3	51	Pyr	Newt / Cas	5	80	Pg	1950	
Washburn Observatory, University of Wisconsin, Madison, Wisconsin, U.S.A.	+ 5:58	+43:05	363	Refl	36	91	Pyr	Cas	13.7	16.5	Pe Sp Pg	1956	
National Observatory, Marseilles, France	− 0:22	+43:18	75	Refl	31.5	80	Gl	Newt	6	43	Mic	1864	

TABLE 1 - (Continued)

OBSERVATORY	CO-ORD. Long. (h) Lat. (°)	ELEV. (m)	TYPE	APERTURE (Inches)	APERTURE (cm)	OPTICS	FOCUS	F/	SCALE ("/mm)	ACCESS-ORIES	SINCE	NOTES
Observatorio Astronomica, Merate, Como, Italy	- 0:38 +45:42	325	Refl	40	102	Cl	Newt Cas	5	40	Pe Sp	1926	
			Vis R	20	50	Cl		14	29	Mic	1890	
			Refl	50	125	Cl	Newt Cas	5	32	Sp	1960	
Observatoire de Paris, Meudon, France	- 0:09 +48:48	162	Vis R Pg R	32.7 24.4	83 62	Cl Cl		20 25	12 13	Mic Pg	1893	20
			Refl	39	100	Cl	Newt	3	69	Sp Pe	1893	
			Refl	24	60	Cl	Cas	12	28	Sp Pe Pg	1949	
Observatoire du Pic du Midi, Bagnères de Bigorre, France	- 0:01 +42:56	2862	Vis R	24	60	Cl		30	11	Sp	1943	21
			Refl	24	60	Cl		3.5	98		1900	
Van Vleck Observatory, Middletown, Connecticut, U.S.A.	+ 4:51 +41:33	65	Pg R	20	51	Cl		16.6	24.5	Pg Pe Mic	1922	
London University Observatory, Mill Hill, England	+ 0:01 +51:37	77	Pg R	24	60	Cl		11.2	30		1939	
Sternberg Astronomical Institute, Moscow, U.S.S.R.	- 2:30 +55:42	190	Refl	28	71	Cl	Prime Newt Cas	4.5 4.5 15	60 60 18	Pg Sp	1957	
Sternberg Astronomical Institute, Southern Station, Crimea, U.S.S.R.	- 2:16 +44:43	600	Refl (Mak)	20 28	51 71	Cl Cl	Prime	4	100	Pg Sp 2 Ob Pm	1958	
			Refl	50	125	Cl	Prime Newt Cas	4 4 17	40 40 10	Pg Sp	1960	

Lick Observatory, Mount Hamilton, U.S.A.	+8:07 +37:20	1283	Refl	120	305	Pyr	Prime Cou	5	13.5	Pg Pe Sp	1959	
			Refl	36	91	Gl	Prime	5.8	38.6	Pg Pe Sp	1898	
			Vis R	36	91	Gl		19	11.7	Pg Pe Sp Mic	1888	
			Pg R	20	51	Gl		7.4	55.1	Pg	1940	
			Refl	22	56	Gl	Cas	11	34	Pe	1956	22
Palomar Observatory, Mount Palomar, California, U.S.A.	+7:47 +33:21	1706	Refl	200	508	Pyr	Prime Cas Cou	3.3 16 30	12.3 2.5 1.4	Pg Pe Sp / Pg / Sp	1948	
			Schm	48 72	122 183	Pyr Gl	Prime	2.5	67.5	Pg	1948	
			Refl	20	51	Pyr	Cas	12.7	32	Pg Pe	1951	
Mount Wilson Observatory, Pasadena, California, U.S.A.	+7:42 +34:13	1742	Refl	100	254	Gl	Newt Cas Cou	5 16 30	16.2 5 2.7	Pg Pe Sp / Pg / Sp	1917	
			Refl	60	152	Gl	Newt Cas	5 16	27 8.3	Pg Pe / Pg Sp	1908	
Purple Mountain Observatory, Academia Sinica, Nanking, China	-7:55 +32:04	267	Refl	24	60	Gl	Newt Cas	5 16.7	68 20	Pg Pe / Sp	1935	
Dyer Observatory, Nashville, Tennessee, U.S.A.	+5:47 +36:03	345	Refl	24 24	61 61	Pyr Gl	Newt Newt Cas	4.5 3.4 16	75 100 21	Pg Pe / Ob Pm TV	1953	23 24 25
Ondrejov Observatory, Czechoslovakia	-0:59 +49:55	528	Refl (Men)	25	63	Gl	Prime	1.4	230	Pg Pe	1959	
Flower and Cook Observatory, Philadelphia, Pennsylvania, U.S.A.	+5:01 +40:00	155	Refl	28	71	Pyr	Newt Cas Prime	5 15 5	58.3 19.5 58.3	Pe	1956	
Allegheny Observatory, Pittsburgh, Pennsylvania, U.S.A.	+5:20 +40:29	370	Pg R	30	76	Gl		18.5	14.6	Pg	1914	
			Refl	31	79	Gl	Cas	22	12	Sp	1906	

TABLE 1 - (Continued)

OBSERVATORY	CO-ORD. Long. (h) Lat. (°)	ELEV. (m)	TYPE	APERTURE (Inches)	(cm)	OPTICS	FOCUS	F/	SCALE ("/mm)	ACCESS-ORIES	SINCE	NOTES
Portage Lake Observatory, Dexter, Michigan, U.S.A.	+ 5:36 +42:24	321	Refl	24	61	Pyr	Cas	25 50 Inf	13 7 0	Sp Pe	1958	26
			Schm	24 36	61 91	Pyr Gl	Prime Newt	3.5 3.5	97	Pg Pe 4°,6° Ob Pm	1950	
Astrophysikalisches Observatorium, Potsdam, Germany	- 0:52 +52:23	107	Pg R Vis R	32 20	80 50	Gl Gl		15 25	16.9 16.4	Pg Sp Pg Mic	1899 1899	
			Schm	20 27	50 70	Gl Gl	Prime	3.4	120	Pg Ob Pm	1952	14
			Refl	28	72	Gl	Cas	32	9.2	Pe	1957	
Radcliffe Observatory, Pretoria, South Africa	- 1:53 -25:47	1542	Refl	74	188	Pyr	Newt Cas Cou	4.8 18 28	22.5 6.0 3.9	Pg Sp Pe Sp	1948	
University Observatory, Princeton, New Jersey, U.S.A.	+ 4:59 +40:20	43	Vis R	23	58	Gl					1882	
Brigham Young University Observatory, Provo, Utah, U.S.A.	+ 7:27 +40:15	1440	Refl	24	61	Pyr	Prime Newt Cas	3 4 15	111.3 84.6 22.6	Pg Pe	1959	
Astronomical Observatory of the Academy of Sciences, Pulkova, U.S.S.R.	- 2:01 +59:46	75	Vis R	26	65	Gl		16	20	Pg Mic	1957	
			Refl	20	50	Gl	Cou	13.5	30	Pg Pe Sp	1951	
			Refl	27.5	70	Met	Prime Cas Cou	3 12 29	100 25 10	Pg Sp	1960	
David Dunlap Observatory, Richmond Hill, Ontario, Canada	+ 5:17 +43:52	244	Refl	74	188	Pyr	Newt Cas	5 18	22.4	Pg Pe Sp Pe	1935	
Osservatorio Astronomico di Roma, Stazione di alta montagna sul Gran Sasso, L'Aquila, Italy	- 0:54 +42:27	2200	Schm	26 37	65 95	Pyr Gl	Prime	3	113.1	Pg Ob Pm	1959	

Observatory	Long. / Lat.		Type				Mounting				Year	
Observatoire de Haute Provence, Saint Michel l'Observatoire (Basses Alpes), France	- 0:23 +43:56	580	Refl Refl Refl	48 32 77	120 81 193	Gl Gl Gl	Newt Newt Cas Newt Cas Cou	6 6 15 5 15 30	29 43 17 21 7 3.5	Pg Pe Sp Pg Pe Sp Pg Pe Sp	1943 1932 1958	
Observatorio Astronomico Nacional, Universidad de Chile, Santiago, Chile	+ 4:42 -33:24	859	Refl Pg R	24 24	61 60	Gl Gl	Cas	16 18	22 18.2	Pe Pg Sp	1959 1956	
Simeis Branch of the Crimean Astrophysical Observatory, Simeis, U.S.S.R.	- 2:16 +44:24	350	Refl (Men)	25.5	65	Gl	Prime	1.4	230	Pg	1952	
Crimean Astrophysical Observatory, Nauchny, Crimea, U.S.S.R.	- 2:16 +44:44	570	Refl Refl Refl Refl (Men)	104 48 20 25.2	264 120 50 64	Pyr Gl Pyr Gl	Prime Cas Cou Nas Cas Cou Cas	3.8 16.4 40 15.7 20 13 1.4	20.1 4.8 2 5.1 8 15 232	Pg Sp. Sp Pe Sp Sp Sp Pe Pg	1960 1952 1950 1951	
Astronomicky ustav S.A.V., Skalnaté Pleso, Czechoslovakia	- 1:21 +49:11	1783	Refl	24	60	Gl	Newt Cas	5.5 32	60	Pg Pe Mic	1943	27
Stockholm Observatory, Saltsjöbaden, Sweden	- 1:13 +59:16	55	Pg R Vis R Refl Schm	24 20 40 26 40	60 50 100 65 100	Gl Gl Pyr Gl	Prime Newt Cas Prime	13.5 16.2 5 5 18 4.6	25 25 40 40 11 70	Pg Pe Mic Pg Sp Sp Pe Ob Pm	1931 1931 1960	13
Sproul Observatory, Swarthmore, Pennsylvania, U.S.A.	+ 5:01 +39:54	63	Vis R	24	61	Gl	Prime	18	18.9	Pg Mic	1911	

249

TABLE 1 – (Continued)

OBSERVATORY	CO-ORD. Long. (h) Lat. (°)	ELEV. (m)	TYPE	APERTURE (Inches)	APERTURE (cm)	OPTICS	FOCUS	F/	SCALE ("/mm)	ACCESS-ORIES	SINCE	NOTES
Observatorium der Deutschen, Akademie der Wissenschaften, Tautenburg, Thüringen, Germany	- 0:47 +50:59	330	Schm	54 80	137 203	Gl Gl	Prime Cas Cou	3 10 45	50 10 2.3	Pg Sp Pe Sp	1960	
Tokyo Astronomical Observatory, Mitaka, Tokyo-to, Japan	- 9:18 +35:40	59	Pg R Refl	26 36	65 90	Gl Pyr	Prime Cas	15 5 18	20 46 13	Pg Pe Sp Pg Pe	1930 1961	
Okayama Astrophysical Observatory, Kamogata, Okayama-ken, Japan	- 8:54 +34:34	370	Refl Refl	74 36	188 90	Pyr Pyr	Newt Cas Cou Cas	4.9 18 29 13	23 6 4 18	Pg Pe Sp Pe	1960 1960	28
Tonantzintla Observatory, Tonantzintla, Mexico	+ 6:33 +19:02	2193	Schm	26 32	66 81			3.2	95		1948	
Observatoire de Toulouse, Toulouse, France	- 0:06 +43:37	195	Refl	33	83	Gl	Newt	5.7	44	Pg Pe Sp	1895	
Osservatorio Astronomico, Trieste, Italy	- 0:55 +45:38	67	Refl	20	51	Gl	Newt	6	67	Pg Pe	1925	29
Kitt Peak Observatory, Tucson, Arizona, U.S.A.	+ 7:26 +31:57	2090	Refl Refl	36 84	91 213	Pyr Pyr	Cas Cas Cou	13.5 8 32	16 12 3	Pg Pe Sp Pg Pe Sp Pe Sp	1960 1961	
Steward Observatory, Tucson, Arizona, U.S.A.	+ 7:24 +32:11	757	Refl	36	91	Gl	Newt Cas Cou	5 15 36	45 15 6.1	Pg Pe Sp	1922	30
University of Arizona Catalina Station Tucson, Arizona, U. S. A.	+ 7:24 +32:30	2530 2560 2560	Refl Refl Refl	21.5 29 60	55 74 152.5	Pyr Pyr Pyr	Cas Cas Cas	16 16 16	24 17.5 8.1	Pe Pe Pe	1962 1962 1964	31 31 31,32
University Observatory, Turku, Finland	- 1:29 +60:27	28	Refl	20 24	50 60	Gl Gl		2	200	Pg	1934	33

Observatory	Longitude / Latitude		Type				Mounting			Detector	Year
Royal Observatory, Uccle, Belgium	- 0:17	+50:48	105	Schm	33 46	84 117	Gl Q	Prime Cas	2.5 10	98 17	Ob Pm Pg Pe Sp	1958
Kristaberg Observatory, Uppsala Observatory, Bro, Sweden	- 1:10	+59:30	20	Schm	40 54	100 135	Gl Pyr	Prime Prime	3	70	Pg Ob Pm	1962
Dominion Astrophysical Observatory, Victoria, B. C., Canada	+ 8:14	+48:31	229	Refl	73	185	Gl	Newt Cas	5 18	22 6	Pg Pe Sp	1918
				Refl	48	122	Pyr	Prime Cas Cou	4 18 30	42 9 6	Pg Pe Sp	1961
Universitäts-Sternwarte, Vienna, Austria	- 1:05		256	Vis R	26.5	67	Gl		15.7	19.5	Pe Mic	1878
U. S. Naval Observatory, Washington, D. C.	+ 5:08	+38:55	86	Vis R	26	66	Gl		15	21	Pg Pe Mic	1873
Yerkes Observatory, Williams Bay, Wisconsin, U.S.A.	+ 5:54	+42:34	334	Vis R	40	102	Gl	Newt	19	10.7	Pg Sp Mic	1897
				Refl	24	61	Gl		4	87	Pg Pe	1901

251

B-Schm	= Baker-Schmidt	Mak	= Maksutov	Pg	= Photographic
Cas	= Cassegrain	Men	= Meniscus	Pyr	= Pyrex
cou	= coudé	Met	= Metal	Q	= Quartz
Gl	= Glass	Mic	= Micrometer	Refl	= Reflector
Greg	= Gregorian	Nas	= Nasmyth	R	= Refractor
IT	= Image Tube	Newt.	= Newtonian	Schm	= Schmidt
Inf	= Infinite	Ob Pm	= Objective Prism	Sp	= Spectrograph
Int	= Interferometer	Pe	= Photoelectric	Vis	= Visual
IR	= Infrared				

NOTES

1 Schmidt (16", 24") attached to same mounting.
2 Redesigned Great Melbourne telescope, built 1868.
3 At Field Station.
4 Erected for Southern station of Yale, Columbia Observatories, previously in Johannesburg (since 1926).
5 Erected for Southern station of Uppsala Observatory.
6 Schmidt camera permanently attached to mounting.
7 Dall-Kirkham principle.
8 Moved to Anderson Mesa (7h26m, +3506') near Flagstaff, Arizona, at the end of 1960, in collaboration with the Lowell Observatory.
9 One tube. Visual and photographic objectives interchangeable.
10 Interchangeable optics in one mounting with the same primary mirror.
11 Cobain low-expansion glass, similar to Pyrex.
12 Erected first at Washington, D. C. in 1934.
13 Probably installed in Haute-Provence (France) in 1960.
14 Low-expansion glass.
15 This telescope can also be used with 24" Schmidt plate.
16 Modernized in 1952.
17 Pg R and Vis R in one tube. Combined mounting symmetric and reversible.
18 Mounting reversible.
19 Two secondary mirrors for Cassegrain and Coudé combinations.
20 Both telescopes on the same mounting.
21 Information taken from "Les Observatoires Astronomiques et les Astronomes" (Uccle, 1959).
22 Scale approximate.
23 Baker-Reflector-Corrector.
24 With Reflector-Corrector.
25 Closed circuit television and seeing compensator.
26 At McMath-Hulbert Observatory since 1940.
27 At Stará Dala from 1928.
28 Tokyo Astronomical Observatory Station.
29 Now dismounted, waiting for re-installation.
30 Moved to Kitt Peak, 1963.
31 UBVIRJKL photometry.
32 Date of completion estimated.
33 Anastigmat.

Subject Index